THE AQUATIC APE: FACT OR FICTION?

THE AQUATIC APE: FACT OR FICTION?

The First Scientific Evaluation of a Controversial Theory of Human Evolution

Edited by

Machteld Roede, Jan Wind,
John M. Patrick and Vernon Reynolds

SOUVENIR PRESS (E&A) LTD

First published 1991 by Souvenir Press (Educational & Academic) Ltd,
43 Great Russell Street, London WC1B 3PA
and simultaneously in Canada

ISBN 0 285 63033 4

Printed in Great Britain by
WBC Print Ltd, Bridgend, Mid Glamorgan

CONTENTS

List of Figures and Tables

FIGURES

TABLES

Preface

In Valkenburg, in the hilly southern part of the Netherlands, above limestone caves in which fossils like the Mosasaurus bear witness to a former marine environment, a conference, organised by the European Sociobiological Society and the Dutch Association of Physical Anthropology, was held in August 1987. Its aim was to evaluate the pros and cons of Sir Alister Hardy's daring idea about the Aquatic Ape, a presumed early ancestor of humans.

The number of fossil data relating to our evolutionary origins is increasing all the time; molecular studies further extend our understanding of hominid phylogeny. Hence the uncertainties and controversies surrounding reconstructed pictures of our early progenitors are decreasing. Though various interpretations of the fossil data exist, there is a growing consensus that about 5 million years ago there was a split of the lineages that finally led, on the one hand, to man, and on the other, to the chimpanzee. Humans are in various aspects so different from other mammals – including other primates – that, according to Darwinian theory, we could only have evolved when our earliest hominid ancestors occupied a specific niche, quite different from that of the other contemporary primates. Accordingly, there has been much discussion about our Miocene ancestors. Unfortunately, very few fossil data are available for that period, and so the dawn of mankind remains wrapped in mist.

Yet it is generally accepted that during that period the proto-hominids abandoned living in the trees and started to move, with the first steps of a primitive bipedalism, into a new environment. At the Valkenburg meeting the question of whether this was the savannah or, rather, an aquatic environment was raised.

Raymond Dart was among the first to suggest a transition from an arboreal into a savannah niche. The latter was the environment where later, about 3.5 million years ago, 'Lucy' (*Australopithecus afarensis*) and her australopithecine mates kindly left sufficient fossilised traces to enable us today to make statements about their morphological and physiological features, as well as about their behaviour. Dart's idea has been taken for granted ever since, and its acceptability has hardly ever been tested in the light of our knowledge of our physiological and motor development capabilities. Hitherto, possible scenarios for evolutionary paths have been proposed almost exclusively by experts on bones, few of whom are acquainted, for instance, with the specific demands on the bone–muscle apparatus involved in the specific skills and behaviours of a decreasingly quadrupedal creature, or with the special physiological demands posed by living in hot, open plains.

In accordance with the rule that the human mind is inclined to select from among new facts only those which fit into the pattern of concepts already shaped, and with our resistance to new, strongly deviating facts, the idea that hominid speciation was initiated during a (semi-)aquatic period has been ignored or played down. This occurred despite the fact that this new idea gave rise to various quite reasonable explanations, some more acceptable than those that have arisen from the Savannah Theory.

The aim of the present volume is to compare the traditional savannah scenario with the alternative aquatic one, and by so doing to attempt to reconstruct our very first hominid ancestors. Arguments both in favour of and against the savannah and the aquatic theories will be presented. One of the values of the present approach lies in the fact that in comparing the pros and cons, soft tissue such as fat and hair, and also tears, as well as skeletal structure, have been taken into account. Moreover, hypotheses have been tested in the light of current understanding of respiratory and other physiological processes, and particularly of behaviour. There is also a chapter on the underlying mechanism whereby an alternative idea such as the Aquatic Ape Theory tends to be rebuffed and rebuked.

This volume mainly offers the contributions presented at the Valkenburg meeting; but it is more than simply a collection of proceedings. The speakers were asked to write out their contributions, incorporating the discussions held during the conference. Other scientists were also asked to contribute, and it was decided to include presentations by young scientists as well as some by more senior scholars, all of quite diverse backgrounds.

The contents of the book are organised into three main parts. Part I starts with a survey of the history of Sir Alister Hardy's idea and an elaboration of the concept by Elaine Morgan. This is followed by a suggestion for the most likely place of origin of our presumed aquatic progenitors – the Danakil Alps – by Leon P. LaLumiere, an evaluation of the ecological wetlands conditions by Derek Ellis, and a survey of fossil material by Marc Verhaegen. Part II starts with a discussion by Graham Richards of why the Aquatic Ape Theory has encountered so much resistance. Then follow essays written from different angles, both protagonist and antagonist. Martin Pickford comments on the lack of geological and palaeontological evidence, and Alan Turner refers to the current debate in evolutionary biology about the significance of apparent adaptations. At particular points the debate concentrates on physiological characteristics such as thermoregulation in relation to water balance (Verhaegen), fat distribution (Caroline Pond), and hair pattern and hairlessness (Peter Wheeler, Paul Leyhausen). John Patrick and Erika Schagatay discuss respiratory adaptations for swimming and diving; Holger and Signe Preuschoft, and Joseph Ghesquiere and Helene Bunkens concentrate on buoyancy and locomotion. Jan Wind also discusses swimming, and provides evolutionary explanations of the human proneness to drowning. Shorter contributions cover comparisons of humans and apes (Karl-Erich Fichtelius) and of humans and sea mammals (Cornelis van Nie and Roede), and a proposal by Sarah B. M. Kraak that the Aquatic and Savannah Theories should be combined, while Schagatay offers some original speculations on breastfeeding, and suggests why the presumed aquatic niche was abandoned. Machteld Roede surveys the relations between man and the sea today. Part III comprises a concluding essay by Vernon Reynolds and an epilogue by the editors.

We wish our readers as much enjoyment and interest as we ourselves felt during the very stimulating meeting at Valkenburg, and while preparing this book.

October 1990
Machteld Roede, Jan Wind,
John Patrick and Vernon Reynolds

List of Contributors

Helene Bunkens, Institute of Physical Education, K.U. Leuven, Belgium

Derek Ellis, Department of Biology, University of Victoria, British Columbia, Canada

Karl-Erich Fichtelius, formerly of the Department of Histology, University of Uppsala, Sweden

Joseph Ghesquiere, Institute of Physical Education, K.U. Leuven, Belgium

Sarah B.M. Kraak, Biological Centre, State University of Groningen, The Netherlands

Leon P. LaLumiere, formerly at the Naval Research Laboratory, Washington D.C. Died 1988

Paul Leyhausen, Professor of Ethology (rtd.); formerly Head, Wuppertal Study Group, Max-Planck-Institute for Physiology of Behaviour

Elaine Morgan, author of three books on the Aquatic Ape Theory: *The Descent of Woman*, *The Aquatic Ape* and *The Scars of Evolution*

Cornelis J. van Nie, formerly of the Department of Anatomy and Biomechanics, Free University, Amsterdam, The Netherlands

John M. Patrick, Department of Physiology, Aga Khan Medical College, Karachi, Pakistan

Martin Pickford, Institut de Paléontologie, Paris, France

Caroline M. Pond, Department of Biology, The Open University, Milton Keynes, United Kingdom

Holger Preuschoft, Department of Functional Morphology, Anatomical Institute, Ruhr University, Bochum, Germany

Signe Preuschoft, Department of Comparative Physiology, State University of Utrecht, The Netherlands

Vernon Reynolds, Institute of Biological Anthropology, University of Oxford, United Kingdom

Graham Richards, Department of Psychology, Polytechnic of East London, United Kingdom

Machteld Roede, Department of Medical Philosophy and Health Ethics, State University of Limburg, Maastricht, The Netherlands

Erika Schagatay, Department of Animal Physiology, University of Lund, Sweden

Alan Turner, Hominid Palaeontology Research Group, Department of Human Anatomy and Cell Biology, University of Liverpool, United

Kingdom

Marc Verhaegen, author of several papers on the Aquatic Ape Theory; general practitioner in Putte, Belgium

Peter E. Wheeler, School of Natural Sciences, Liverpool Polytechnic, United Kingdom

Jan Wind, Department of Human Genetics, Free University, Amsterdam, and Gooi-Noord Hospital, Blaricum, The Netherlands

Part I

THE AQUATIC APE THEORY

1 The Origins of a Theory

Elaine Morgan

SUMMARY
The theory of a possible aquatic phase in human evolution was first presented in 1942 by Max Westenhöfer in Germany; it was also independently conceived by Alister Hardy in 1929 and published by him in 1960. This chapter quotes Hardy's reasons for delaying the publication, describes the reception accorded to his ideas, and outlines some subsequent developments.

THE BEGINNINGS

Alister Hardy first conceived the idea of a possible aquatic phase in human evolution in 1929 on reading the following passage from Wood Jones's *Man's Place Among the Mammals:*

> The peculiar relation of the skin to the underlying superficial fascia is a very real distinction, familiar enough to anyone who has repeatedly skinned both human subjects and any other members of the primates. The bed of subcutaneous fat adherent to the skin so conspicuous in man, is possibly related to his apparent hair reduction, though it is difficult to see why, if no other factor is invoked, there should be such a basal difference between man and the Chimpanzee.

Hardy's response was immediate. As a marine biologist, he was more familiar with the skinning of sea mammals than of either human or non-human primates. The phenomenon described by Wood Jones in connection with human bodies reminded him irresistibly of his own first-hand experience of the skin of various species of aquatic mammals in which a layer of subcutaneous fat is the norm. He wondered whether in man also it might initially have been an adaptation to a more aquatic way of life.

Other parallels between man and aquatic mammals soon sprang to his mind, such as the naked skin, the relatively streamlined silhouette of human beings compared with that of other primates, and the occasional incidence of interdigital webbing. He reasoned that for a primate which spent much of its time wading in water, an erect posture would become obligatory and, at the same time, easier to sustain without overbalancing. The precision hand-grip and the unusual arrangement of hair tracts on the human body (much debated at the time) could have been acquired in the same way.

He did not publish his ideas for over thirty years. His friends warned him that if he publicly advocated such a bizarre theory it would blight his career. They were probably right. At the end of his life he was refreshingly candid about his reasons for keeping silent: 'I wanted to get a good professorship; I wanted to be a Fellow of the Royal Society'. As it turned out, long before he was ready to publish, a version of the hypothesis appeared in print in Germany, as one passage in a book entitled *The Unique Road to Man* (Der Eigenweg des Menschen), written in 1942 by Max Westenhöfer, a professor at the University of Berlin.

Westenhöfer's account of the aquatic theory was that of a man who had not made up his mind about it. He made no claim to be the originator; neither did he credit anyone else with originating it. He seemed, rather, to assume that it had been around for some time and that his readers were likely to be familiar with it in general terms. It is quite conceivable, since Hardy spoke of his ideas to some of his friends and pupils in the interwar years, that speculation about it had already spread farther afield than Oxford, and had crossed to the Continent without being traceable to any particular source.

Westenhöfer searched the literature of primate anatomy for any reference to aquatic influence, and for species-specific features of human anatomy which remained unaccounted for. He made no attempt to identify the aquatic phase with any specific date, place or causative event. One of the papers, written by G. L. Sera in 1924, hypothesises a very early aquatic phase. Sera sought to account for some differences between Old World and New World primates by suggesting that the ancestors of the platyrrhines had undergone a period of aquatic development not shared by the catarrhines. Westenhöfer's general conclusion was that an aquatic experience at some time or other was a promising hypothesis worthy of further consideration.

Unfortunately, Westenhöfer's book was published in the middle of the Second World War. Europe had other things on its mind, and the usual channels for the exchange of scientific ideas were silted up. By the time they ran clear again, the heretical hypothesis had apparently been forgotten. Certainly Hardy knew nothing of Westenhöfer; he died in 1985 at the age of eighty-nine without ever learning that he had been forestalled. By 1960 he had achieved the aims he had set his sights on: the Oxford professorship and the FRS, and a high reputation as the author of authoritative works in his own field. He now felt able to lower his guard sufficiently to outline his theory to a local sub-aqua club that he had been invited to address. A version of his speech was communicated to the local press, and it appeared in garbled form under sensational headlines in the Sunday newspapers. Hardy published one article and one radio lecture to clarify what he had actually said and believed.

Since he was a man who inspired affection as well as respect, academic scholars adopted what they saw as the kindest and most British way of dealing with an embarrassing situation: they behaved as if he had not spoken or, at least, as if no one had happened to be listening at the time. Among many who were in all other respects his staunchest admirers this attitude never wavered, so that when he died his obituaries praised him for many things but conspired to ignore his aquatic 'indiscretion'. This has promulgated the myth in some quarters that Hardy had propounded the whole thing as an impish practical joke which some misguided people were naïve enough to take seriously. However, in the last year of his life he was interviewed about the subject on film* and he made it absolutely clear that he regarded his hypothesis as revolutionary, and significant, and entirely valid.

I first came across Hardy's theory on reading a brief reference to it in 1970 in Desmond Morris's book *The Naked Ape*, and vainly searched through books and journals on evolution for further information or commentary about it. Apparently for ten years it had been silently sinking into oblivion. I therefore wrote to Hardy saying that I intended to write a book about it. He knew nothing about me, and I did not conceal that I had no qualifications for entering the arena other than my conviction that he was right. So my letter came to him as, in his own words, 'a bit of a shock', since he had never relinquished the idea of one day writing at greater length on the subject himself.

However, he responded with characteristic generosity. On 26 October 1970, he wrote:

> Yes, of course you must go ahead and do so with my enthusiastic blessing. I hope it will be a great success. As it is turning out, it may well be the best arrangement from my point of view. You will be interesting – I hope and think exciting – the general public in the idea, and . . . preparing a wider public for my more zoological and anatomical treatment of the subject than I might otherwise expect. Press on with it as hard as you can, although I am in no hurry to publish quickly and my chapters are not written – just lots of notes.

I did not meet Hardy or discuss the contents of my book with him – or with any other scientist – until after it was published in 1972 under the title of *The Descent of Woman*. It featured some additional arguments which Hardy had not considered. Some of them – for example, the regression of the olfactory lobe and ventro-ventral copulation – had already occurred to Westenhöfer and were mentioned in his book (of which I knew nothing until Jürgen Hinrichs-Röhrig drew my attention

* *Water Babies*. Golden Dolphin Productions, 21–3 McLaren Street, New Sydney 2060, Australia.

to it in 1986). Other arguments, based on weeping and voluntary breath control, were new.

Whatever the book's merits or demerits, it performed one vital service: it attracted enough attention to ensure that the aquatic theory would this time have a greater chance of remaining on the agenda of evolutionary theorists. It was translated into ten languages and blew the spores of the idea all round the world; they germinated in the minds of the young and receptive and of many who were already convinced that there was something missing in the conventional scenario of the emergence of man.

THE HYPOTHETICAL AQUATIC MODE OF LIFE

For those interested in the history of this idea, the original documents are not always easy to retrieve. I therefore reprinted Hardy's papers on the subject in full in *The Aquatic Ape* (Morgan, 1982), and I append herewith a translation of the relevant passage from Westenhöfer's book.

> The postulation of an aquatic mode of life during an early stage of human evolution is a tenable hypothesis, for which further inquiry may produce additional supporting evidence.
>
> The shape of the human foot, broadening towards the front, could indicate a paludine habitat, especially when we note the observations of Mr O. Abel in his *Palaeobiology* (Stuttgart, 1912, pp. 229–30) where he discusses the secondary plantigradism of certain fossilised bog animals, for instance, Mesodon and Coryphodon, whose footprint shows a remarkable similarity to that of humans. For such a mammal, moreover, a move to an aquatic environment would mean that powerful teeth would become unnecessary due to the relative softness of the available food resources.
>
> The fact that man lacks hair – but probably was hairy at some earlier stage – suggests an analogy with the relative absence of hair in water mammals (whale, sea-cow, hippopotamus), especially since so far there is no other plausible explanation. Another indication is the subcutaneous layer of fat in humans; its capacity for expansion appears to predate human civilisation. The so-called Venus statuettes, dating back to the Stone Age, support this assumption. The hitherto unsolved problem concerning pigmentation in humans may be related to this problem; rather than loss of pigment in the white races, there may have been increased pigmentation in coloured ones, corresponding to the post-natal increase in pigmentation in children of all races.
>
> In his latest book *On the Significance of the Ear Muscle*, Mr B. Henneberg also proposes an aquatic mode of life in the prehuman primate. He assumes that this ancestral hominid featured a contractile

form of the ear muscle, with the anthelix (tragus and antitragus) differing in shape from that of *Homo*, and that this original form was subsequently lost during the transition to life on land. It is still easily possible to reproduce the original form in children by artificial means, and the original feature has in fact been observed in one living newborn baby. In his famous work *Physiology of Movement* [Philadelphia, 1949], Duchenne shows that electrical stimulation of the tragus and antitragus muscles in human beings is capable of closing the entrance of the ear, which is why he calls the two muscles 'constrictor conchae sup. and inf.'.

Man shares with the water mammals the regression of the olfactory organ, the bulbus and lobus olfactorius which, according to A. Kappera and Count Haller, is connected with a certain development in the conformation of the brain, not found in the macrosomatic animals.

As further evidence of an earlier aquatic way of living for man, one could also point to the existence of mucous glands in small benign tumours in the skin of man's back which the Prague pathologist Schickel has investigated and which, in the absence of any other possible explanation, with reference to fish and frogs, he has called atavistic. Such mucous glands have survived as the normal condition in the hippopotamus as a physiological adaptation to its aquatic environment, while in humans they appear under pathological conditions about which little is understood.

To this can be added the not particularly rare web-like skin formation on the hand and toes (seen also in *Potamogale*, the otter shrew), and the direction of the body hair towards the elbow on the lower arm in human beings and anthropoids, as well as in other apes and quadrupeds. The usual explanation, that the direction of the hairs functions as protection against rain when the arms are placed over the head, is too naïve to be correct. Apart from the fact that the head does not even get covered, the water then would be conducted forward from the elbow between the hairs of the upper arm and thereby directly to the skin of the armpit and chest, which would hardly be advantageous. Even if this direction of the hairs were peculiar to man, I would see it as not insignificant support for my aquatic hypothesis, since such a direction of the hairs on the lower arm during swimming (stretching the arms forward) would have been useful.

This summary should not be concluded without some reference to the ideas of the anthropologist, G. L. Sera, in Naples. He takes the view that the form and development of the Adam's apple, the shortness of the outer auditory passage, the form of the musculus glutaeocruralis (m. tenuisaimus), some characteristics of the female genitals, the formation of the kidneys, the form and development of the nasal cartilage, and the form of the ear muscle may constitute evidence of a possible aquatic phase in the evolution of the platyrrhine New World primates. And finally, I would point out that man's way of mating is also the standard method among water mammals such as beavers, cetaceans and sirenians.

The aquatic theory remains an open question. But such hypotheses, which at first sound so improbable, should at least serve as a stimulus to further research, on the principle that a good detective follows up the least promising clues as well as those which seem to point to a simple solution.

REFERENCES

Hardy, A., 1960, Was man more aquatic in the past? *New Scientist*, **7**, 642–5.
Morgan, E., 1972, *The Descent of Woman* (London: Souvenir Press).
Morgan, E., 1982, *The Aquatic Ape* (London: Souvenir Press).
Morris, D., 1967, *The Naked Ape* (London: Jonathan Cape).
Sera, G. L., 1938 *Archivo Zoologico Italiano*, Vol. 25.
Westenhöfer, M., 1942, *Der Eigenweg des Menschen* (Berlin: W. Mannstaede & Co.).
Wood Jones, F., 1929, *Man's Place Among the Mammals* (London: Edward Arnold).

2 Why a New Theory is Needed

Elaine Morgan

SUMMARY
Homo sapiens is the anomalous member of the primate order. The orthodox version of our evolutionary emergence on the savannah leaves too many unique features unaccounted for. The Aquatic Ape Theory (AAT) offers a unitary solution to a higher proportion of these anomalies than does any other hypothesis.

A SAVANNAH HABITAT?

Over a hundred years have passed since Darwin wrote *The Descent of Man*. During that time, despite intense research and speculation, the major questions – why man became bipedal, lost his body hair, learned to speak, developed a big brain – have come no nearer to solution. New hypotheses are regularly propounded, but none has yet commanded professional consensus or prompted the feeling that the search is now over. This record of failure has done little to weaken faith in the orthodox scenario – that is, that a move from the trees into a more open habitat was the ultimate and sufficient reason why hominids began to differ so radically from apes. A critique of this proposition is therefore an indispensable preliminary to advocacy of the Aquatic Ape Theory (AAT).

Other primates (baboons, patas monkeys, for instance) have made the transition to the savannah with minimal phenotypic or behavioural modification, and have flourished. There seems to be no inherent reason why the progenitors of hominids, faced by the same fairly simple problems of adaptation, could not have solved them just as economically. Instead, they resorted to a gradual but revolutionary restructuring of their methods of walking and running, breathing, regulating their temperature, and communicating with their fellows. The features distinguishing them from the apes are normally represented as adaptations making them fitter to survive on the savannah. But most of these adaptations, in the initial stages, must have been positively maladaptive in that environment. A few examples will serve to illustrate the point.

LOCOMOTION

Quadrupedalism characterises the overwhelming majority of ground-dwelling mammalian species. It affords stable equilibrium, is efficient in energy terms, lends itself readily to speed, and is easily learned by the young, often within hours of birth. It allows for emergencies: a quadruped with one injured leg walks on the other three while it heals. The gently arched and cantilevered spinal column has been perfected over millions of years to combine maximum strength with flexibility.

No animal could afford to sacrifice all these assets without an overridingly powerful selective pressure. The cost of habitual plantigrade bipedalism is high. It is the most unstable method of mammalian progress known to zoology. Growing bipeds only perfect the art after years of practice and innumerable tumbles. Even in their prime, damage to one leg can cripple them; once past it, equilibrium again becomes a problem. The bipedal posture, with viscera and male sex organs exposed to attack, is ill designed for confronting an enemy or predator.

In a biped the vertebrae and intervertebral discs are subjected to weights and stresses which the spines of quadrupeds do not have to sustain. The S-shaped curve of the human spine minimises direct downward pressure but creates an area of instability in the lumbar region. The modified angle of the pelvis means that in childbirth the foetus has a more tortuous exit path to negotiate than is the case in quadrupeds. In man, the change from a quadrupedal to a bipedal stance raises the heart roughly twice as high above the ground, and the resultant pooling of the blood in the lower limbs puts additional strain on the vascular system. After millions of years of adaptation to bipedalism we are still plagued by pains and malfunctions such as chronic lower-back pain, inguinal hernia, and varicose veins.

The claim is often made that bipedalism was adaptive because it 'freed the hands'. But an ape's or monkey's hands are perfectly free except when it is moving from one place to another; human beings, likewise, normally engage in skilled manual operations only while sitting or standing, and very rarely while actually walking or running. It could as well be argued that bipedalism reduced our potential for dexterity, since the so-called freeing of the hands was accompanied *pro rata* by the 'enslavement of the feet' (Richards, 1986). This, in the long run, has halved our allowance of serviceable manipulative digits.

It was long argued that the hominid first evolved a big brain and the ability to fashion tools and weapons, and that bipedalism became necessary to enable him to carry a weapon to hurl at his quarry. All theories along these lines had to be abandoned after the discovery of the Afar hominids such as Lucy–small-brained creatures, clearly bipedal, with no evidence of tools or weapons. Three separate lines of argument have emerged in an attempt to replace the weapon-carrying hypothesis.

Carrier (1984) has argued that man's physiology may be evidence of strong selective pressure in favour of endurance running. He has established that, over long distances, bipedal running is an advantage to a human hunter because his four-footed quarry becomes exhausted sooner than he does. This may well have been a fortunate consequence of bipedalism, but it is very unlikely to have been the cause, firstly because the fossil discoveries suggest that bipedal walking was well established before there was any evidence of hunting, and secondly because animals capable of covering short distances bipedally (for example, apes, bears, vervets, beavers) invariably revert to quadrupedalism when speed is required. To justify the contention that game-hunting led to bipedalism, it is not enough to demonstrate that modern *Homo sapiens* runs more effectively on two legs: it is necessary to demonstrate than an unadapted pre-Australopithecine anthropoid could have run more effectively on two legs than on four. Experiments with primates (Taylor and Rowntree, 1973) suggest that bipedalism is slower and consumes more energy.

Lovejoy (1981) envisages a pair-bonded male hominid foraging much farther afield than his mate and walking upright in order to carry food back to her. The concept of a hominid nuclear family is a persistent one, but improbable. Monogamous mammals display minimal sexual dimorphism, whereas *Homo* is unrivalled in the number and variety of epigamic markers. Lovejoy does not specify the type of food being carried. Any ape wishing to transport all or part of a dead animal would carry or drag it with one hand and run on three. Long treks with handfuls of seeds or berries would not repay energy output. The only kind of food conducive to primate bipedalism consists of armfuls of rather bulky items such as large tubers, bananas or coconuts. We need evidence that the savannah yielded such products.

Wheeler (1985) suggests that man descended from a meridional ape, which gained an edge over competitors by reducing the time needed to rest in the shade, and was thus able to devote more time to foraging. For this purpose, it is argued, the ancestral hominid adapted to withstand the sun's noonday heat by minimising the percentage of body surface presented to its perpendicular rays – that is, by standing erect. Some support for this thesis is provided by Newman (1970) and Sakura (1983). The assertion that bipedalism bestowed a competitive edge can only be assessed by considering what other species were competing for the same scant resources. The likeliest candidates would be savannah baboons such as the hamadryads. This successful species shows no signs of being disadvantaged by the habit (common in many primate species) of resting at midday: its siesta is combined with the visit to the water hole, which is obligatory for most savannah species at some time during the day. The marginal putative advantage conferred by day-long non-stop foraging would be unlikely to outweigh the considerable incidental costs of bipedalism and hair loss.

None of these theories offers an entirely satisfactory explanation of habitual bipedalism, a behaviour pattern so specialised that it only emerged in one mammal, and so fraught with drawbacks that it would seem to have been adopted only under some kind of duress.

FUR

Fur is another classic mammalian feature which *Homo* alone is supposed to have found incompatible with life on the plains. It is a prime asset which no land mammal could lightly afford to dispense with: a first line of physical defence against heat and cold and ultraviolet rays. It may also fulfil additional functions such as colour camouflage and threat signalling by pilo-erection.

Primates, particularly, would find it indispensable. Primate mothers are free to swing, leap, clamber, brachiate and run on all fours *only* because the young can hold on to their fur. The hominids were the only primate infants whose hands encountered smooth skin to which they could not cling. No other primate mothers are hampered, except for a brief neonatal period, by having to support their growing offspring in their arms. In the case of the hominid females the hands – even if they had been in any real sense freed by bipedalism – were promptly enslaved again (by the requirement to support offspring because of the loss of body hair) for the greater part of their lifespan.

Theories about hair loss normally refer to the problem of keeping cool during the hot tropical day. (The problem of keeping warm during the cold tropical night has received little attention.) It is not clear why the hominids' need in this respect is thought to have been unique. Reference has been made (Wheeler, 1985) to the lack of a carotid rete, yet the lack of it has not obliged other savannah primate species to shed their fur. The further suggestion that hominids needed new cooling strategies because of their reduced nasal chambers and turbinates is a circular one: if these organs had been important to the animal's well-being, they would not have been reduced.

Experiments with depilation have shown that fur (for example, in the camel) is an efficient barrier *against* heat gain from the environment (Schmidt-Nielsen, Schmidt-Nielsen, Jarnum and Houpt, 1957). The argument therefore hinges on hair loss as an important facilitator of sweat-cooling. But sheep, camels and the desert-dwelling wild ass effectively utilise sweat-cooling without having naked skin. At least one primate (the patas monkey) has, without denuding itself, evolved a highly efficient system of sweat-cooling, adequate to its needs even though it is reputedly the fastest running of all primates and is active all day long in its hot and often arid savannah habitat (Mahoney, 1980). The hominid could presumably have done the same. Newman (1970), exploring the relationship between bipedalism, nakedness and sweat, concluded that nakedness was unlikely to have evolved in order to facilitate sweat-cooling in the heat of the savannah. He believed that nakedness predated sweat-cooling and that 'loss of hair must have stemmed from other causes, or predated the occupation of the habitat in question'.

On the question of hair tracts on the human body, it is doubtful whether their arrangement affords reliable evidence of evolutionary origin. There are some unique features, which Hardy (1960) cited because in his youth it was a subject much researched and debated. Two points should be noted in connection with the new 'aerodynamic' model offered by Wheeler (this volume, chapter 13) to explain the anomalies. Firstly, air currents produced by natural convection would only rise straight up around the body as long as the hominid was not only perpendicular but also stationary, and this would seldom be the case while he was foraging for scattered food sources. Secondly, the convection model does not purport to explain the anomalies in hair tracts on the upper part of the body, yet that is where some of the more striking examples are found (Kidd, 1903).

SWEAT

Sweat-cooling is achieved by the evaporation of a film of liquid from the surface of the skin. In most land mammals which resort to sweat-cooling – other than man – the liquid is a suitable dilute secretion of the apocrine glands, which are found all over the body in association with hair follicles. In humans these apocrine glands are present prenatally but vanish before birth, except for specialised groups in axillary and pubic areas. They are replaced by millions of eccrine glands such as those commonly found in other species on palms, soles, paws and the underside of prehensile tails (volar eccrines). Some higher primates have non-volar eccrines over the body surface, but they are much fewer in number than in man, and in terms of thermoregulation they appear to be non-functional (Montagna, 1972).

A study of thermogenic sweating in three baboons (Hiley, 1976) established that sweating in the area of the chest was the product of epitrichial (that is, apocrine) glands. Another study (Elizondo, 1988) describes thermogenic sweat from the lateral calf of a patas monkey as eccrine; but the methodology fails to establish whether the sweat was exuded by the eccrine glands or by the apocrine glands with which they are interspersed.

In humans the rate of sweat secretion is higher than that of any other known mammal. However, in sweat-cooling, profusion as such is not necessarily an advantage. Sweat exuded more rapidly than it can evaporate is wasted: the excess liquid does nothing to reduce body temperature. That is why in humid conditions sweating affords little or no relief.

Eccrine sweating has two disadvantages. Its onset is delayed (Newman, 1970); it is in the interval between a sudden temperature rise and the beginning of the sweat flow – which can be anything between five and thirty minutes – that human beings may succumb to heat stroke. The second disadvantage is that eccrine sweating continues to flow profusely even when dehydration and/or salt depletion are reaching dangerous levels. Water and salt are both scarce on the savannah, and increased water dependence would limit the range available for foraging. Such an environment would be unlikely to foster the emergence in the hominids of a cooling system so profligate of both these vital resources (Denton, 1982).

THE LARYNX

In all land mammals, with the exception of man, the trachea extends from the lungs via the larynx into the back of the nasal passages; they are known as obligatory nose breathers. The obligation is not absolute: the epiglottis in many animals can, at need, be detached from the palate to afford temporary mouth breathing for purposes of vocalisation or thermoregulatory panting. But as soon as these efforts are relaxed, nose breathing resumes.

This near-universal system is highly efficient. It facilitates olfaction; it ensures that all air reaching the lungs has been filtered, warmed or cooled to near body temperature, and moistened by passing over the mildly bactericidal mucous linings of the nasal passages. It enables an animal to drink and breathe at the same time. It entirely rules out any possibility of an animal being inconvenienced by food and drink entering the airways.

In an adult human being these advantages and safeguards have been lost. The larynx has lost contact with the palate and descended to a point well below the back of the tongue, adjacent to the opening of the gullet. It is a development which mystified Darwin and Negus, among others. No one has been able to suggest any advantage which this change would bestow on a terrestrial mammal. The effects seem uniformly deleterious. The lungs are rendered more vulnerable. During sleep in a supine position the tongue may relapse into the back of the throat, blocking the airway entirely for a short period, and during deeper unconsciousness – for example, from concussion or anaesthetics – the blockage can be fatal. The respiratory tract of young babies initially resembles that of the rest of the animal kingdom. The gradual descent of the larynx at about four to six months coincides with the peak incidence of 'sudden infant death syndrome' and it has been argued that there may well be a causal connection (Crelin, 1978). For example, if a throat infection caused a partial obstruction of the airway, the infant's earliest reflexes would prompt a raising of the larynx to within the nasal passages; but if the larynx had partially descended, this could no longer be achieved and the attempt might cause the airway to be blocked by the uvula.

Current thinking about laryngeal descent envisages it as a fortuitous effect of the change in the angle of the human skull which followed adoption of the erect posture (Laitman, 1983; Lieberman, 1983). But this argument is weakened by the fact that in other animals where the larynx has descended (sea-lion, dugong) the basicranial angle has not changed.

FAT

Man is unique among primates and among most land mammals in his propensity to accumulate comparatively large amounts of adipose tissue, especially in subcutaneous sites. This would seem an unlikely adaptation to a savannah environment, whether the hominids are envisaged as hunters or only as potential prey, since the extra weight would slow them down. The land mammals which regularly accumulate considerable fat stores are the hibernators and estivators, but in them the fat is seasonal, and in man it is not. In a comparison of 23 mammal species ranging from bats to whales, it was found that humans have at least ten times as many adipocytes as would be expected in proportion to their body weight (Pond, 1987; chapter 12).

It used to be argued that loss of body hair to keep cool was followed or accompanied by the acquisition of a fat layer in order to keep warm. But it has been demonstrated (Scholander, Walters, Hook and Irving, 1950) that in the air medium a layer of subcutaneous fat is an inefficient insulator, while in water – for example, in the seal – the fatty layer provides a better insulator against cold than the air layer in its fur.

Fossil evidence cannot establish whether the Australopithecines had already acquired a greatly increased supply of adipocytes, or whether this feature should be attributed to a later date, with the advent of agriculture and a more settled existence. Two considerations militate against the second possibility. One is the human baby. Maternal investment in the fatness of babies is considerable, both before and after birth. In a human neonate, fat constitutes 16 per cent of body weight as compared with 3 per cent in the baboon. For this feature to have become so firmly established in human ontogeny needs a much longer evolutionary history than the period since agriculture. The second consideration is that there are extant human populations practising a non-agricultural economy, but their babies have plump cheeks and their young women have rounded breasts and buttocks. It is reasonable to suppose that this development had its beginning early in hominid history.

THE 'BABOON MARKER'

Even at the level of his DNA, *Homo* emerges as a bafflingly anomalous member of the community of African primates. In the 1970s a team of American cytologists revealed the presence in baboons of a non-defective endogenous type C retrovirus, harmless to the baboons but capable of being released and causing reactions in other primate species (Benveniste and Todaro, 1976). All surviving African primate species contain viral gene sequences closely related to the RNA genomes of the baboon virus and providing protection against it, suggesting that at one time the virus (although subsequently losing its virulence) was both pervasive and life-threatening.

The presence of the 'baboon marker' is thus indicative of ancestral contact with the baboon virus, just as sickle cells in the blood indicate ancestral contact with malaria. Forty different primate species were examined by the American team. Of these it was found that all the 23 African species, including the gorilla and the chimpanzee, carry the marker. None of the 17 Asian species carries it. The surprise discovery was that in *Homo sapiens – of whatever race* – there was no sign of the 'baboon marker'. This strongly suggests that at some time during the onset of their evolutionary separation from the apes, man's ancestors must have been isolated from the baboons and from the other African primates by some geographical barrier which entirely precluded contact. A stretch of ocean would be a classic example of such a barrier.

During this period of separation, the baboon retrovirus raged over continental Africa. Its advent could have been as sudden and threatening as that of the AIDS retrovirus. But it must have differed from AIDS in one respect. Since it affected all non-human primates of African origin, including the small nocturnal prosimians in the forest canopy, the virus was probably airborne. No mainland African primate species failing to develop the protective 'baboon marker' gene sequence has survived. To explain why humans are the only primates native to Africa not bearing the 'baboon marker', Todaro and Benveniste suggested that they descended from a *Homo erectus* strain which first emerged in Asia, and later migrated to Africa at a time when the baboon virus was no longer life-threatening.

The AAT offers an alternative and more parsimonious way of interpreting the facts. One scenario which appears totally untenable is that man's evolution continued unbroken on the baboon-haunted African savannah.

AN ALTERNATIVE HYPOTHESIS

The preceding selection of unsolved questions about human evolution is far from exhaustive, but it supports the contention that the standard scenario of human evolution on the savannah is inadequate. It leaves too many human features unaccounted for.

The Aquatic Ape Theory postulates that hominid speciation was initiated, and its nature determined, by a period of semi-aquatic or aquatic lifestyle. The sea-flooding of north-east Africa (LaLumiere, 1981) could have placed a hominid ape population under duress by marooning it on island habitats, necessitating the exploitation of rich marine food sources as sea levels continued to rise. The bipedal Afar hominids could have descended from survivors of that episode who found themselves once more on mainland Africa as the sea-flooded area first became land-locked and the water finally evaporated.

The split between apes and man is characterised by a genetic divergence of only 1 per cent, but this is accompanied by wide phenotypic and behavioural differences. This combination strongly suggests not only allopatric speciation but also adaptation to widely differing habitats. Coexistence with early ancestors of chimpanzees in forest-edge or savannah habitats would have led to chance encounters and interbreeding, which would have retarded the emergence of strongly divergent phenotypes.

An island would have provided both geographic isolation and a different ecological environment. On the basis of the AAT, many human features which are unique among primates can be explained in terms of convergent evolution, since parallels can be found in semi-aquatic and aquatic animals. Relatively large deposits of subcutaneous fat are found in the majority of aquatic species: it provides buoyancy, streamlining and insulation – and in water the added weight is no disadvantage. Hairlessness is common among aquatic mammals. It is true that small aquatic mammals (such as water-rats) are not hairless, but the hairless species include some, like the river-dolphin and the babirusa, which are as small as, or smaller than, *Australopithecus*. One reason for the descended larynx may have been the need, before a dive, to inhale large quantities of air more quickly than could be achieved through the narrower nasal passages. Wind (1976) reasons that laryngeal descent is unlikely to have been the definitive factor in the emergence of speech. He points to cerebral reorganisation as the decisive element facilitating vocal communication.

There is, however, one other vital prerequisite. When the reorganised brain forms the intention to initiate vocal communication, the message must first be sent not to the vocal tract but to the lungs. Conscious and finely tuned control of respiration (most highly developed in diving animals and man) is indispensable for the emergence of speech. The descended larynx (found nowhere except in some diving animals and man), while perhaps not indispensable, facilitates and enhances the flexibility of the vocal repertoire.

When a species departs from its previous behaviour pattern, firstly the change is normally gradual, and secondly some immediate advantage must accrue from the outset to reinforce the behaviour. In the case of bipedalism these conditions were not fulfilled. Step-by-step change from horizontal to vertical would not be viable; there is no practical halfway house between walking on four legs and walking on two. The disadvantages (instability, prolonged infant dependence, skeletal and vascular malfunctions) would be incurred immediately, would weigh most heavily at the outset, and only gradually decrease through evolutionary modification. Most of the disadvantages relate to the destabilising effect of gravitational forces on the newly orientated bones, blood and other organs. For example, the weight of our own viscera is sustained by a dish-shaped pelvis; the intestines of a savannah ape could not have rested comfortably on the vertical blades of its pongid ilia, as a bipedal gait would have required.

By contrast, the hypothetical advantages accruing to pre-*afarensis* bipedalism on the savannah would be minimal at the outset and only slowly increase. It has been suggested that the descendants of the foraging male might ultimately get into their stride and be able to carry back enough food to cement the pair bond; or that the descendants of the noonday apes might ultimately achieve coolness as their vertical stance was perfected and their body hair diminished. But no immediate benefits would have rewarded the initial clumsy steps in either scenario.

It is tempting to imagine that a time would have come when the graph of decreasing disadvantage intersected with the graph of increasing advantage, but that is a teleological concept. Bipedalism on land would never have begun to become more efficient unless it was already being regularly practised while it was inefficient – a fact which goes far to explain why no other animal ever resorted to it.

If we assume that the initial stage did not take place on land, none of these problems arises. For a wading ape the incentive to bipedalism and the accruing reward would be instantaneous: by standing on two legs it could keep its head above water. The disadvantages would be minimal at the outset because in water gravitational force is counteracted. Equilibrium would be less endangered, the bones would not be compressed, the blood would not pool, the viscera would not sag. Locomotion in water – whether wading or swimming – tends to force the adoption of a 180° angle between spine and hind limbs. Long adaptation to this posture would gradually but inevitably affect skeletal structure – especially in the pelvic region – to a point where the aquatic ape was imperfectly adapted for locomotion on land, whether on four legs or on two. On their return to the mainland, the virtual impossibility, for the female, of carrying a plump, hairless baby while proceeding on all fours would have favoured bipedalism.

Habitual bipedalism is found in no other extant species. However, it may have been characteristic of the fossil 'marsh ape', *Oreopithecus*. Remains of this primate are found in lignite layers, which also contain fossils of crocodiles and turtles, and palaeobotanical remains of reeds, fern spores and swamp algae (Azzaroli, Boccaletti, Delson, Moratti and Torre, 1986). The list of eighteen similarities between *Oreopithecus* and *Homo* drawn up by Hürzeler (1960) has been challenged and whittled down, but the well developed anterior superior and anterior inferior spines of the pelvis, found in *Oreopithecus*, are shared with no other primate but *Homo* (Harrison, 1986). Since the theory that *Oreopithecus* was ancestral to man has been abandoned, convergent evolution is the likeliest explanation of the resemblances.

The hotter and more dangerous environment on the open plains made some form of sweat-cooling desirable. But this does not explain why the hominid once again departed from the mammalian norm by resorting to eccrine glands for thermoregulation. Physiologists have speculated that these glands initially evolved for some other purpose. Montagna (1982) observed: 'The several million glands on the human body act principally as heat regulators, but this function is perhaps too recent to be totally effective'. The previous function may have been excretory. Eccrine glands (as the name implies) do not appear to be secreting anything; the sweat is generally described as being merely diffused or eliminated via the gland. And although non-volar sweat is normally hypotonic (less saline than blood), prolonged sweating causes the glands to become fatigued and to lose their power to keep the saline solution hypotonic (Weiner and Hellman, 1959).

It may be helpful to compare this with another anomalous feature involving a saline solution, namely weeping, or more specifically what Darwin described as 'psychic' as opposed to 'reflex' tears. Psychic weeping is activated by motor pathways in the nervous system different from those which control reflex lacrimation (Ashley Montagu, 1960). Similarly, our non-volar eccrines react to different stimuli from those activating volar eccrines (Weiner and Hellman, 1959). Both eccrine sweat-cooling and human weeping emerged after the ape/hominid split; neither represents the simple quantitative expansion of an existing system. In some pathological conditions such as cystic fibrosis both sweat and tears become very salty.

These facts are consistent with the supposition that human sweat and tears may at an earlier evolutionary stage have been hypertonic, and may have evolved simultaneously and for the same purpose – to perform a function complementary with that of the kidneys in controlling salt equilibrium. Some such auxiliary mechanism has evolved in many marine species to facilitate the excretion of salt from ingested sea water

(Schmidt-Nielsen and Yangè, 1958). In the case of tears, the excretion may have been originally accompanied by an involuntary contraction of the gullet to prevent any more sea water being swallowed; no other explanation has ever been advanced for the cricopharyngeal spasm in the oesophagus ('lump in the throat') which often precedes or accompanies weeping.

Later, in an arid territorial environment, the hominid's now active and abundant eccrine glands would have been pressed into service as thermoregulatory sweat glands, because over most of the human body the apocrine glands are non-existent. An aquatic phase might account for their disappearance. A reduction in apocrine glands and a proliferation of sebaceous glands – also typical of *Homo* – is not uncommon among aquatic mammals (Ling, 1965).

For the period between the initial ape/man split and the appearance of *A. afarensis* no fossil evidence is available. The question confronting evolutionists is where and how the hominids lived during the fossil gap. One way of seeking an answer is to consider what kind of habitat is most likely to have been conducive to the development of the anomalous features in human physiology. Table 2.1 lists some of these features and the environment in which they are found in non-human species. (The 'Yes' in column 2 represents the pachyderms which are found on the savannah, but may have acquired their hairlessness in a different environment.)

Table 2.1 Human features shared with (a) savannah (b) aquatic mammals

Features	1 *In man*	2 *In savannah mammals*	3 *In aquatic mammals*
Loss of body hair	Yes	Yes	Yes
Habitual bipedalism	Yes	No	No
Descended larynx	Yes	No	Yes
Volitional breath control	Yes	No	Yes
180° spine/hind limbs angle	Yes	No	Yes
Increased non-seasonal fat deposits	Yes	No	Yes
Ventro-ventral copulation	Yes	No	Yes
Dorsal hair sparser than ventral	Yes	No	Yes
Proliferation of sebaceous glands	Yes	No	Yes

CONCLUSION

Palaeontology offers no direct evidence about the conditions which triggered the change to bipedalism, because it occurred during the gap in the hominid fossil record. The Savannah Theory, as an explanation of the emergence of man, is therefore based on no hard evidence. It is widely accepted only because it is regarded as the simplest scenario. But man is not a simple animal, and the circumstances combining to produce such a remarkable species are unlikely to have been so commonplace. Many primate species have moved from the trees to the grasslands, but evidence of parallel or convergent evolution between any of these and *Homo* is virtually nil.

As a source of evidence about origins, comparative anatomy is at least as important and reliable as palaeontology. Its findings are often overlooked, or relegated to separate specialist pigeon-holes and forgotten, but once assembled they constitute a catalogue of physical anomalies impossible to reconcile with the orthodox scenario. The AAT claims to represent the 'best-fit' hypothesis of human emergence because it accommodates more of the anatomical data than does any other, and is not ruled out by any of the fossil discoveries to date.

REFERENCES

Ashley Montagu, A., 1960, Natural selection and the origin and evaluation of weeping in man. *Journal of the American Medical Association*, **174** (4), 392–7.

Azzaroli, A., Boccaletti, M., Delson, M., Moratti, G. and Torre, D., 1986, Chronological and paleographical background to the study of *Oreopithecus bamboli*. *Journal of Human Evolution*, **15**, 533–40.

Benveniste, R. E. and Todaro, G. J., 1976, Evolution of type C viral genes: evidence for an Asian origin of man? *Nature*, **261**, 101–8.

Carrier, D. R., 1984, The energetic paradox of human running and hominid evolution. *Current Anthropology*, **25**, 483–9.

Crelin, E., 1978, Can the cause of SIDS be this simple? *Patient Care*, **12**, 5.

Denton, D., 1982, *The Hunger for Salt* (Berlin: Springer-Verlag).

Elizondo, R. S., 1988, Primate models to study eccrine sweating. *American Journal of Human Primatology*, **14**, 265–76.

Hardy, A., 1960, Was man more aquatic in the past? *New Scientist*, **7**, 642–5.

Harrison, T., 1986, The phylogenic relationship of *Oreopithecus*. *Journal of Human Evolution*, **15**, 541–83.

Hiley, P. G., 1976, The thermoregulatory responses of the galago (*Galago crassicaudatus*), and the baboon (*Papio cynocephalus*), and the chimpanzee (*Pan satyrus*) to heat stress. *Journal of Physiology*, **254**, 657–71.

Hürzeler, J., 1960, The significance of *Oreopithecus* in the genealogy of man. *Triangle*, **4**, 164–74.

Kidd, W., 1903, *The Direction of Hair in Animals and Man* (London: A. & C. Black), 89–92.

Laitman, J. T., 1983, The evolution of the hominid upper respiratory system and implications for the origins of speech. In *Glossogenetics*, ed. E. de Grolier, (Amsterdam: Harwood Academic Publishers), 63–90.

LaLumiere, L. P., 1981, The evolution of human bipedalism. *Philosophical Transactions of the Royal Society, London*, **B292**, 103–7.

Lieberman, P., 1983, On the nature and evolution of the biological bases of language. In *Glossogenetics*, ed. E. de Grolier, (Amsterdam: Harwood Academic Publishers), 91–114.

Ling, J. K., 1965, Functional significance of sweat glands and sebaceous glands in seals.

Nature, **208**, 560–2.

Lovejoy, C. O., 1981, The origin of man. *Science*, **211**, 341–50.

Mahoney, S. A., 1980, Cost of locomotion and heat balance during rest and running from 0°C to 55°C in a patas monkey. *Journal of Applied Physiology*, **49**, 789–99.

Montagna, W., 1972, Skin of non-human primates. *American Zoologist*, **12**, 109–24.

Montagna, W., 1982, The evolution of human skin. In *Advanced Views on Primate Biology* (Berlin: Springer-Verlag), 35–41.

Negus, V. E., 1949, *The Comparative Anatomy and Physiology of the Larynx* (London: William Heinemann).

Newman, R. W., 1970, Why man is such a sweaty and thirsty naked animal. *Human Biology*, **42**, 12–27.

Pond, C. M., 1987, Fat and figures. *New Scientist*, **114**, 62–8.

Pond, C. M., 1991, Adipose tissue in human evolution. (This volume, chapter 12.)

Richards, G., 1986, Freed hands or enslaved feet? *Journal of Human Evolution*, **15**, 143.

Sakura, H., 1983, Characteristics of man. In *Evolution*, ed. S. Kondo (Tokyo: Yuzankaku), 211–66.

Schmidt-Nielsen, K., Schmidt–Nielsen, B., Jarnum, S. A. and Houpt, T. R., 1957, Body temperature of the camel and its relation to water economy. *American Journal of Physiology*, **188–9**, 103–12.

Schmidt-Nielsen, K. and Yangè, R., 1958, Salt glands in marine reptiles. *Nature*, **182**, 783.

Scholander, P. F., Walters, V., Hock R. and Irving, L. 1950, *Biological Bulletin*, **99**, no. 2.

Taylor, C. R. and Rowntree, V. J., 1973, Running on two or four legs: which consumes more energy? *Science*, **179**, 186–7.

Weiner, J. S. and Hellman, K., 1959, The sweat glands. *Biological Review*, **35**, 141–86.

Wheeler, P. E., 1985, The loss of functional body hair in man: the influence of thermal environment, body form and bipedality. *Journal of Human Evolution*, **42**, 12–27.

Wheeler, P. E., 1991, Body hair reduction and tract orientation in man: hydrodynamics or thermoregulatory aerodynamics? (This volume, chapter 13.)

Wind, J., 1976, Phylogeny of the human vocal tract, *Annals of the New York Academy of Sciences*, **280**, 612–30.

3 The Evolution of Genus *Homo*: Where It Happened

Leon P. LaLumiere

SUMMARY
This chapter seeks to establish a possible location for an aquatic phase in hominid evolution. It lists the necessary conditions which such a location would have to fulfil and establishes that the highland area known as the Danakil Alps conforms to all of these. Geological evidence for the former isolation of the site by sea-flooding, combined with data from the fossil record, points to a possible scenario for the early stages of hominoid speciation and a suggested locality for further exploration.*

A major obstacle to acceptance of the hypothesis of an aquatic phase in human evolution is the difficulty of envisaging precisely where and when this episode may have occurred, in what type of habitat, what first motivated the change to an aquatic way of life, and what brought it to an end. This chapter discusses some possible answers.

THE NECESSARY CONDITIONS

Reflection upon the Hardy (1960) hypothesis leads to the following conclusions concerning a possible location:

(1) It must have been a forested area inhabited by apes.
(2) It must have been isolated from the rest of Africa during the period in which the evolution of ape-like to man-like creatures occurred. This suggests an island.
(3) The region must have later become reconnected to Africa, enabling the hominids to migrate to other parts of the continent. In combination, (2) and (3) suggest an area of continuing tectonic disturbance.

The first condition – a forested area inhabited by apes – does very little to narrow the field. The Hominoidea originated in Africa, and prior to about 16 million years before present flourished exclusively on that continent (Campbell and Bernor, 1976). But following the establishment of the Africa–Asia–Europe land bridge, they began to expand throughout the Old World evergreen woodland biome, which at its climax, between 12 and 8 million years ago, extended from the Atlantic to the Pacific and southward into subequatorial Africa on the eastern side (Bernor, 1983).

* Some of this material has previously been published in *Philosophical Transactions of the Royal Society of London*, **B292** (1981), and as 'Danakil Island, the evolution of human bipedalism', in Elaine Morgan's *The Aquatic Ape* (1982).

Ramapithecus, formerly proposed as a possible ancestor of the genus *Homo* (Howells, 1967; Leakey, 1976; Leakey and Lewin, 1977, 1978; Mackinnon, 1978), ranged widely over this area. Fossils of this ape from Fort Ternan, Kenya, have been dated at 12.5–14 million years before present, and from the Siwalik Hills in India at 9–12 (Leakey, 1976).

Within this biome, the location most subject in the past to recurrent geological changes such as those envisaged in (2) and (3) is the area of north-east Africa at the junction of the African and Arabian tectonic plates.

EVIDENCE FOR THE HYPOTHETICAL LOCATION

The paradigm of continental drift and sea-floor spreading described by Wegener (1966), Wilson (1963), Bullard (1972), and Dietz and Holden (1972), along with others, provides insight and understanding of the geophysical evolution of the Afar triangle. Near the end of the Oligocene or the beginning of the Miocene, the African plate, of which the Arabian plate was then a part, apparently collided with the Eurasian plate. This collision caused three tectonic events that are germane to this chapter, namely:
According to Hsu, Cita and Ryan (1973), starting at the beginning of the

(1) Doming uplifted the region perpendicular to the axis of the present-day Red Sea, causing cracks in the Afro-Asian plate, and was followed by downfaulting and the formation of the proto-Red Sea, which was connected with the proto-Mediterranean Sea (Hutchinson and Engels, 1970, 1972; Coleman, 1974; Pilger and Rosler, 1976).
(2) Rifting began in the Gulf of Aden (Hutchinson and Engels, 1970, 1972; Coleman, 1974; Pilger and Rosler, 1976).
(3) At the junction of these two regions, tectonic activity produced crustal blocks of assorted sizes (Tazieff, 1970; Tazieff *et al.*, 1972).

Messinian (latest Miocene stage) the Mediterranean Sea was repeatedly isolated and then rejoined to the Atlantic Ocean, causing the sea to dry and then refill. They suggest this cycle of drying and refilling was repeated at least seven times, and perhaps as many as fourteen. During the desiccation of the sea, massive layers of salt were deposited on the bottom of the deeper parts.

After combining the results of biostratigraphic, chronostratigraphic and palaeomagnetic investigations, Cita and Ryan (1973) devised an absolute time scale which they believe is reliable and useful. They suggest that the Miocene–Pliocene boundary should be set at about 5.4 million years ago. They also suggest that the Messinian began shortly after 7.5 million years ago. According to Coleman (1974), the Red Sea was a gulf connected to the Mediterranean Sea during the late Miocene. Stoffers and Ross (1974) suggest that when the Mediterranean was subjected to the cycle of drying and refilling, so also was the Red Sea. During this period, massive layers of salt were deposited on the bottom of the deeper parts of the sea.

Figure 3.1 (p. 31) displays the configuration of the African continent and Arabian plate as it may have been during the late Miocene. It should be noted that the proto-Red Sea and the proto-Gulf of Aden were separated by an isthmus. This land bridge, here called the Afar Isthmus, apparently existed throughout the late Miocene and was an important link in animal migrations between the continents of Africa and Eurasia (Kurtén, 1972; Beyth, 1978; Mackinnon, 1978).

THE ISLAND

Many local populations of terrestrial fauna would undoubtedly have been wiped out as a result of tectonic activity in an area as geologically unstable as the Afar region. But there is evidence to suggest that one particular region may have remained habitable. Tazieff (1970), Tazieff *et al.* (1972) and Barberi *et al.* (1972) have suggested that the northern and central Afar triangle in the past was covered by sea water, with only the Danakil Alps and high volcanoes standing above water as islands. They state that the Danakil Alps are part of a horst, that is, an uplifted crustal block that was broken off and separated from the Nubian plate to the west and the Arabian plate to the east through the action of plate tectonics and sea-floor spreading.

The Afar Isthmus was composed of several such crustal blocks. The Danakil horst, which apparently acted as a 'microplate' (Le Pichon and Francheteau, 1978), is now a mountainous range about 540 km long and up to 75 km wide (Tazieff *et al.*; *Geological Map of Ethiopia*, 1973). In Figure 3.1 the northern end of the horst marks the southern limit of the proto-Red Sea (Frazier, 1970; Barberi *et al.*, 1972).

In the early Miocene the Danakil horst was separated from the Ethiopian escarpment to form a depression extending southward from the north end of the horst about one third to one half its length (Hutchinson and Engels, 1972; Barberi *et al.*, 1972). Within this Danakil Depression, from its inception to the present time, volcanism and sedimentation of marine, lacustrine, evaporitic and continental facies have occurred contemporaneously. The depression apparently was a lake or embayment that formed the locale for the deposition of a detrital formation known as the Red Series. These deposits – with an age range of 5–24 million years before present (Barberi *et al.*, 1972) – currently exist as narrow bands on each side of the Danakil Depression (*Geological Map of Ethiopia*, 1973). Much of the Red Series is overlain by

Quaternary deposits of lava flow. According to Barberi *et al.* (1972), the age of the upper part of the Red Series is 5.4 million years before present. Starting in the early Miocene, volcanoes in the middle of the horst erupted intermittently, producing extensive lava flows that still cover the entire southern portion. Lava also covers the far northern end. In between lies a region about 150 km long and 75 km wide in which the exposed formations are Mesozoic rocks, mainly Jurassic, covered by a discontinuous veneer of Tertiary and Quaternary deposits (Hutchinson and Engels, 1972).

After a long period of relative quiescence, starting about 9–11 million years ago, volcanism increased in the Red Sea, in the Afar triangle, and in the African Rift Valley, indicating renewed tectonic activity (Pilger and Rosler, 1976). About 6.7 million years ago the Danakil Depression was invaded by marine waters (Barberi *et al.*, 1972). Hutchinson and Engels (1972) state that the deeper part of the depression is covered by thick salt deposits. They infer that the deposition of the lower layers may be correlative with the upper Miocene salt deposits of the Red Sea. The cycle of drying and refilling that apparently occurred in the Mediterranean and in the Red Sea probably also occurred in the Danakil Depression.

About the time of the Miocene–Pliocene boundary the African plate began to move away from the Arabian plate, and the Danakil microplate began to rotate anti-clockwise (Tazieff *et al.*, 1972; Le Pichon and Francheteau, 1978). At the same time it began to tilt so that its Mesozoic sedimentary rock formations slope downwards, generally from north-east to south-west (Hutchinson and Engels, 1970; Beyth, 1978). Excluding volcanic peaks, the Danakil Alps today rise to a maximum of 1,335 m. Finally, the microplate was detached from both African and Arabian plates, allowing waters from the Red Sea and the Gulf of Aden to flow into the Afar triangle. Figure 3.2 (p. 31) displays the configuration of the region as it may have been in the early Pliocene. Note that the Red Sea was no longer connected to the Mediterranean Sea (Coleman, 1974) as in Figure 3.1, but was linked to the Gulf of Aden and the Indian Ocean through two straits, one to the east of the Danakil horst (Strait of Bab al Mandab) and the other to the west that will be called the Danakil Strait. Thus, between 6.7 and 5.4 million years ago in the latest Miocene (Messinian), a group of apes along with other animals could have been trapped on Danakil Island.

According to Barberi *et al.* (1972) and Mohr (1978), the central and southern Afar regions have been repeatedly covered by massive flood basalts during the Pleistocene–Holocene, so that the Miocene–Pliocene history of these regions is uncertain. The several volcanoes in the middle of the Danakil horst have been intermittently active from the late Miocene–early Pliocene to the present. About the Miocene–Pliocene boundary the Danakil horst apparently was surrounded by water to the east, the north and the west, while the southern end was covered by extensive flood basalts. The Danakil horst may not have been a geographical island, but for many land animals, under the conditions described above, it would have been a biological island. Examination of the data cited above suggests that the Danakil horst may have become a geographic island sometime before the Pliocene–Pleistocene boundary, and that apes could have existed on it throughout the period of sea-flooding. The southern end of the horst still supports rain-forests, according to Uwe George in an article about the African Rift Valley that appeared in the German edition of *GEO* several years ago.

A SCENARIO FOR THE EVOLUTION OF GENUS *HOMO*

The following is a tentative hypothesis describing what may have happened. Although speculative, it is as well to show that some such course of events may be envisaged.

The Pliocene was a time of increasing desiccation. If the hypothesis of Hsu, Cita and Ryan (1973) is correct, desiccation probably started during the Messinian. Forests probably covered most of Danakil Island at the beginning of the Pliocene, but these must have died in a relatively short period of time. Those near sea level and the coast would be the first to disappear, while those at higher, cooler elevations in the mountains remained longer. The dwindling forest would produce exactly the environmental conditions required by the Hardy hypothesis; those apes near the coast, losing their forest, gradually would be forced into water to find both food and protection from predators. (Their cousins along the Ethiopian escarpments, and elsewhere, undoubtedly retreated with the dwindling forests.)

Witnessing frequent volcanic eruptions and lava flows at both north and south ends of the island, the apes may have made two important discoveries: pebble tools and fire. Hot lavas passing over pebbles scattered along the beaches could have shattered them, to produce keen-edged shards; on meeting water, lavas would be cooled and sundered into sharpened, ready-made tools. Lavas may have cooked plants and animals and so have led the apes to consume and appreciate cooked food. This knowledge would become invaluable to their descendants in the African Rift Valley.

Sporadic and episodic volcanism within the Afar triangle has been a feature since the early Miocene (Barberi *et al.*, 1972; Gass, 1974). Intermittently, the Danakil Strait has been closed and bridged by lava flows as it is today (Frazier, 1970; Hutchinson and Engels, 1972; Lowell and Genik, 1972). Eustatic sea-level fluctuations combined with erosion probably reopened the strait within a short time. However, during the short time the island was connected to the mainland, migration of animals must have occurred, with the Australopithecines among them. The probability is that the aquatically evolving apes were isolated on Danakil Island for at least one and a half million years, and perhaps as long as three million years, before returning to the mainstream of African life.

These hominids had evolved in and near the water, and as they wandered over the lava bridge to the Ethiopian escarpment and then elsewhere, they stayed near water. They did so for two reasons. First, water was their protection against predators. Next, water provided them with food and drink. In their meandering search for food, the hominids drifted southward along the western shores of the Afar Gulf. Whenever possible, they explored the rivers and streams that emptied into the embayment. About three million years ago, some of the hominids settled in a place now called Hadar, near the Awash River (Johanson and White, 1979).

The African Rift Valley is a consequence of the collision and subsequent separation of the African and Eurasian plates. Figure 3.3 (p. 32) displays its location. Since its inception, lakes and rivers have been created. Many have been filled, and this has served to cover and preserve fossils. In particular, the Awash River emptied into the Afar Gulf. The river course follows the Rift Valley in a generally south-western direction from the Afar. The hominids followed the river upstream, eventually arriving at the Omo valley, and then proceeded southward, leaving their remains along the way at such present-day sites as the Omo River, Koobi Fora, Lake Turkana, Olduvai Gorge, Laetoli, Makapansgat, Sterkfontein and Taung (Leakey and Lewin, 1978). These sites are located in Figure 3.3. The oldest known hominid fossil from this region is about 3.5 million years old, with those found at Hadar being more primitive than those found farther south.

THE FOSSIL EVIDENCE

Three facts about the fossil evidence are noteworthy:

(1) No fossils of proto-hominids have yet been found for the two million years before the *afarensis* skeletons at Hadar, the 'fossil gap' during which the split between apes and man took place.
(2) The fossils found at Hadar are more primitive than those found farther south, and possibly are older.
(3) A very high percentage of hominid fossil remains have been found in sites which were close to lakes and rivers. This is usually attributed to the fact that the bones are more likely to have been

preserved in such sites. But it is equally possible that they were in fact the sites where the hominids habitually lived.

Features of Lucy and the other Afar fossils have raised many questions about the kind of life they led. Bipedalism was a surprising feature. Others included the relatively long arms and relatively short legs; the long toes; the stride, relatively as well as absolutely shorter than ours; and the hand grip, better adapted for a precision grip than a power grip (Johanson and Edey, 1981; Charteris, Wall and Nottrodt, 1981; Jungers, 1982). The question arising from these discoveries is how these creatures satisfied the three basic requirements for their survival: namely, (1) fresh water, (2) food, and (3) shelter from predators. Little attention has been paid to the possibility that Lucy may have been a marsh-dweller. This is surprising in view of the fact that the place where the fossils were discovered was, in Lucy's day, the site of a large lake fringed with marshes.

In the film *Lucy in Disguise** Raymonde Bonnefille, the French palynologist, discusses her analysis of pollen obtained at the site where the First Family fossils were recovered. The pollen is mainly from bulrushes, and bulrushes invariably inhabit marshes. Bruce Latimer, after examining the bones of Lucy's foot, concluded that *A. afarensis* was an unusually strong walker and that its long toes would have been invaluable in moving over rough stony ground or in mud, where some slight gripping ability would have been advantageous.

Riverine deltaic marshes are created where a slow-moving river enters a lake or sea. Silts carried by the river water are deposited, forming islets that cause the river to split into several small streams. Thus, marshes often consist of islets interlaced with small streams of depth ranging from a few inches to several feet. In such a habitat the hominid's basic needs would have been met. Such marshes are among the most productive lands in the world. Even the best irrigated agricultural lands yield no more than seven tons of biomass per acre per year; a freshwater marsh may yield up to fifteen tons (Niering, 1985; Teal and Teal, 1969). And much of this – both animal and vegetable – would have been readily available to *A. afarensis*.

Euell Gibbons (1971) describes a variety of marsh-dwelling plants that are, to some extent, edible. For example, the prolific common cat's-tail of the worldwide-distributed family Typhaceae is largely edible, with the exception of the coarse leaves and spike. Moreover, the cat's-tail is easily uprooted from the mud of the shallow waters in which it grows, often in dense stands. The cat's-tail family, along with other marsh plant life, would constitute a dependable year-round source of vegetable food for

* Smeltzer Films, Athens, Ohio, 1981. Produced at Ohio University in co-operation with the Cleveland Museum of Natural History.

the marsh-dwelling apes. In time, either by accident or design and through trial and error, the apes could have learned to catch and consume the various animals that abound in marshes: insects, crustaceans, molluscs, fish, small mammals and birds. Chance discovery of birds' eggs, turtle eggs and crocodile eggs would also have provided a source of food. And the islets would have provided both refuge and places to sleep.

Such an environment would have precipitated and accelerated the adaptation to bipedalism. It offers a possible explanation of Lucy's unusual gait. Any person who has waded barefoot in waist-deep water is acutely aware of the effort required to do so (see Ghesquiere and Bunkens, this volume, chapter 16). He will dig into mud with his toes to acquire a strong forward thrust to move his body through the water, and will take short steps during the process. His wading gait will resemble the 'strolling gait' attributed to the hominids who left their footprints at Laetoli. Many animals which live in, and have become adapted to, an aquatic environment have evolved relatively short powerful legs. (The hippopotamus is an outstanding example.) Both the long arms and the evolution of a precision grip between finger and thumb would have been advantageous in exploring the muddy bottom for edible matter. Even in modern times there are groups of people like those in southern Iraq (see Maxwell, 1957; Schagatay, this volume, chapter 15), who live in marshes and have developed cultures and economies based on them.

Klein (1977) says, 'With respect to site locations, southern African Acheuleans seem to have been quite eclectic. They camped on stream banks or on channel bars, on lake margins, near springs, and in caves . . . The only conclusion that emerges from an analysis of site locations is the trivial one that Acheulean peoples probably never camped far from water'. But the description of this conclusion as 'trivial' is too dismissive. Camping near water was not a behaviour pattern introduced by the Acheuleans. As far back as we can trace our ancestry, the palaeontologic evidence suggests that closeness to water was more essential to hominids than to most animals in the African continent. The physiological reasons which render it essential provide strong evidence that at an earlier stage in our evolution it must have played a crucial part in the emergence of man.

If this analysis is correct, then Danakil Island was the site of the first population bottleneck in the evolutionary line leading to man. It was the crucial one, since it represented the speciating event which originally divided us from the apes and led directly to the bipedalism of *A. afarensis*. A second bottleneck has been identified as taking place probably less than 200,000 years ago in Africa (Cann, Stoneking and Wilson, 1987). The relation between these two great landmarks can be simply stated. Two hundred thousand years ago 'Mitochondrial Eve' marked the beginning of *Homo sapiens*, but she was herself a descendant of the apes marooned on Danakil Island that marked the beginning of *Homo*.

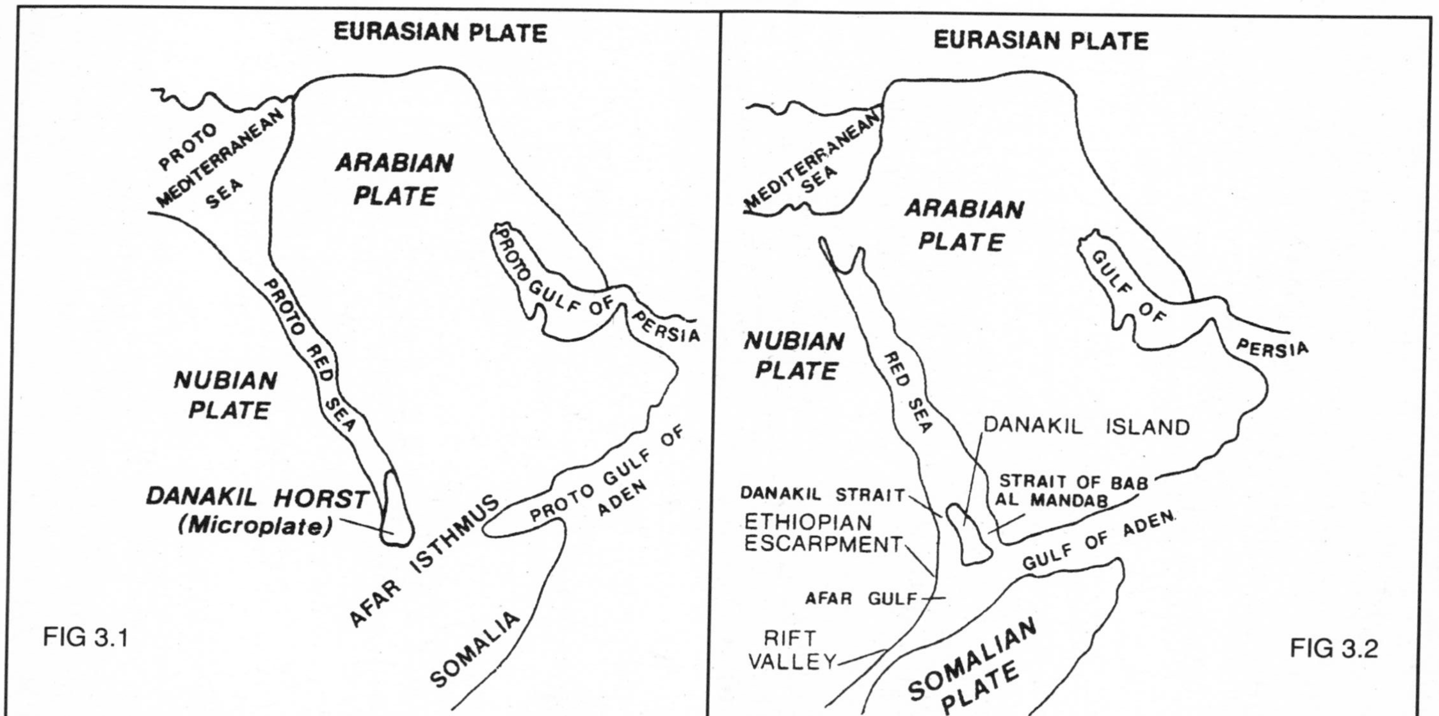

Figure 3.1 The generally supposed relationship of the Nubian plate of the African continent to the Arabian plate during the late Miocene. Figure 3.2 The configureation of the same region as displayed in Figure 3.1, but as it may have been at the beginning of the Pliocene.

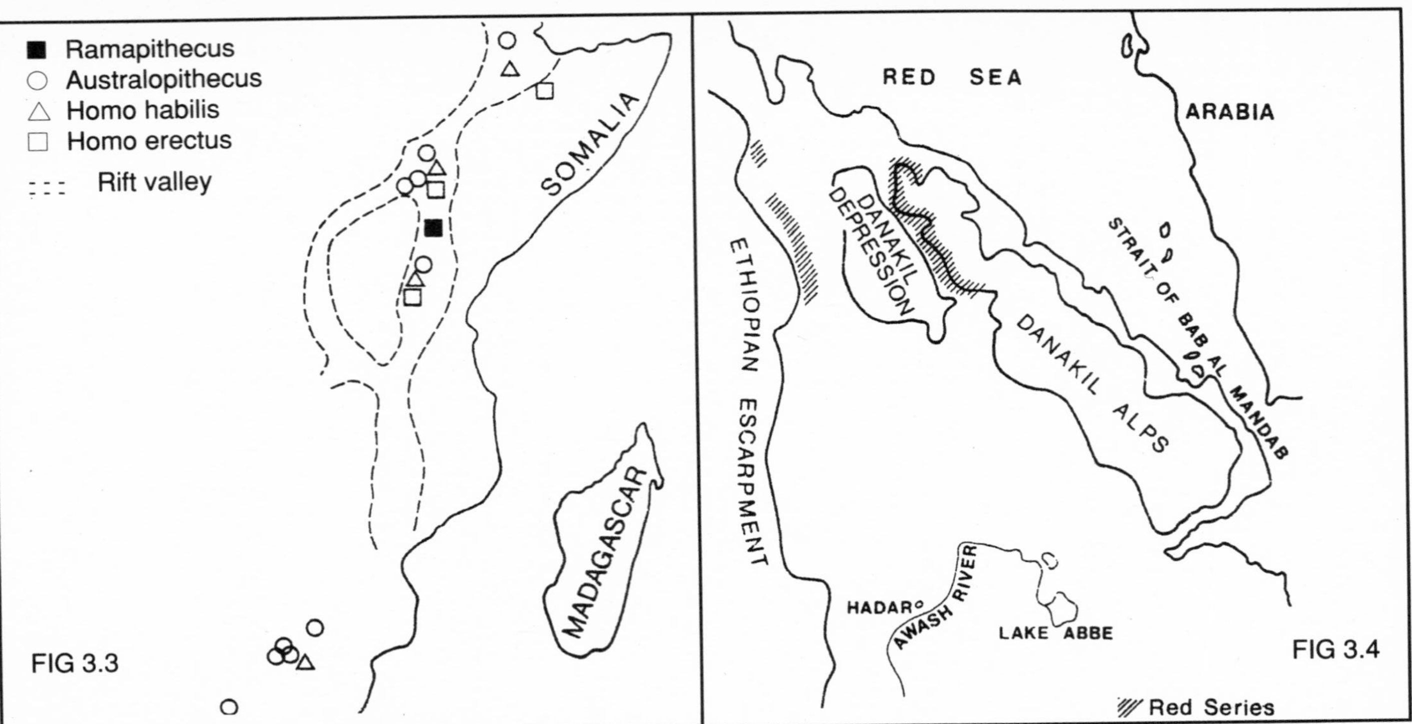

Figure 3.3 The African Valley showing the principal sites where hominid fossils have been discovered.
Figure 3.4 The location of the Tertiary deposits called the Red Series that may yield hominoid fossils if this hypothesis is correct.

SUGGESTED LOCALITY FOR EXPLORATION

Tectonic activity is extremely high within the Afar triangle (Tazieff, 1970). Much of the region is covered by flood or plateau basalts (*Geological Map of Ethiopia*, 1973), and exposed continental basement is limited. Quaternary and recent deposits are more extensive and cover both basement and basalts, especially along the Ethiopian and Somalian escarpments and the coast between the Danakil Alps and the Red Sea. The Red Series are Tertiary deposits that contain Miocene fossils (Frazier, 1970; Beyth, 1978). The radiometric age of the series ranges from 5.4 to 24.0 million years before present (Barberi *et al.*, 1972). Deposits occur along the foothills of the western side of the northern section of the Danakil Alps and east of the Danakil Depression. They also occur along the foothills of the Ethiopian escarpment west of the depression. The location of the Red Series is indicated in Figure 3.4. If this hypothesis is correct, fossils of our ape-like ancestors should be found in them, and fossils of our human-like ancestors should be found in nearby Pliocene and Quaternary formations.

ACKNOWLEDGEMENTS

Elaine Morgan kindly offered to combine my two papers presented at the Valkenburg symposium into one. She has summarised and combined them to create a paper that is manageable in size while retaining the important ideas. I thank her for her time and effort performing the difficult task.

REFERENCES

Barberi, F., Borsi, S., Ferrera, G., Marinelli, G., Santacroce, R., Tazieff, H. and Varet, J., 1972, Evolution of Danakil depression (Afar, Ethiopia) in the light of radiometric age determinations. *Journal of Geology*, **80**, 720–9.

Benveniste, R.E. and Todaro, G.J., 1976, Evolution of type C viral genes: evidence for an Asian origin of man? *Nature*, **261**, 101–8.

Bernor, R.L., 1983, Geochronology and zoogeographic relationships of Miocene Hominoidea. In *New Interpretations of Ape and Human Ancestry*, ed. R.L. Ciochon and R.S. Corruccini (New York and London: Plenum Press).

Beyth, M., 1978, Comparative study of sedimentary fills of Danakil depression (Ethiopia) and Dead Sea rift (Israel). *Tectonophysics*, **46**, 357–67.

Bonatti, E., Emiliani, C., Ostlund, G. and Rydell, H., 1971, Final desiccation of the Afar rift, Ethiopia. *Science*, **172**, 468–9.

Bullard, E., 1972, The origin of oceans. In *Continents Adrift* (San Francisco: W.H. Freeman), 88–97.

Campbell, B.G. and Bernor, R.L., 1976, The origin of Hominidae: Africa or Asia? *Journal of Human Evolution*, **5**, 441–54.

Cann, R.L., Stoneking, M. and Wilson, A.C., 1987, Mitochondrial–DNA and human evolution. *Nature*, **325**, 31–6

Charteris, J., Wall, J.C. and Nottrodt, 1981, Functional reconstruction of gait from the Pliocene hominid footprints at Laetoli, northern Tanzania. *Nature*, **290**, 496–8.

Cita, M.B. and Ryan, W.B.F., 1973, Time scale and general synthesis. In *Initial Reports of the Deep Sea Drilling Project*, ed. W.F.B. Ryan and K.J. Hsu, *et al.* (Washington: US

Government Printing Office), **XIII**, Part 2, 1405–15.

Coleman, R.C., 1974, Geological background of the Red Sea. In *The Geology of Continental Margins*, ed. C.A. Burk and C.L. Drake (New York: Springer-Verlag), 743–51.

Dietz, R.S. and Holden, J.C., 1972, The breakup of Pangaea. In *Continents Adrift* (San Francisco: W.H. Freeman), 102–13.

Frazier, S.B., 1970, Adjacent structure of Ethiopia: that portion of the Red Sea coast including Dahlak Kebir Island and the Gulf of Sula. *Philosophical Transactions of the Royal Society of London*, **A267**, 131–41.

Gass, I., 1974, Complexities of the Afar triple junction. *Nature*, **249**, 309–10.

Geological Map of Ethiopia, 1973. 1/2000000 geological survey of Ethiopia.

Ghesquiere, J. and Bunkens, H., 1991, The burden of locomotion in water: could the aquatic ape have overcome it? (This volume, chapter 16.)

Gibbons, Euell, 1971, *Stalking the Good Life* (New York: David McKay).

Hardy, A. C., 1960, Was man more aquatic in the past? *New Scientist*, **7**, 642–5.

Howells, W.W., 1967, *Mankind in the Making* (Garden City, New York: Doubleday).

Hsu, K.J., Cita, M.B. and Ryan, W.B.F., 1973, The origins of the Mediterranean evaporites. In *Initial Reports of the Deep Sea Drilling Project*, ed. W.B.V. Ryan, K.J. Hsu, *et al.* (Washington: US Government Printing Office), **XIII**, Part 2, 1203–31.

Hutchinson, R.W. and Engels, G.G., 1970, Tectonic significance of regional geology and evaporite lithofacies in north-eastern Ethiopia. *Philosophical Transactions of the Royal Society of London*, **A267**, 313–29.

Hutchinson, R.W. and Engels, G.G., 1972, Tectonic evolution in the southern Red Sea and its possible significance to older continental margins. *Geological Society of America Bulletin*, **83**, 2989–3002.

Johanson, D.C. and Edey, R., 1981, *Lucy: the Beginnings of Mankind* (New York: Warner Books).

Johanson, D.C., Masao, F.T., Eck, G.G., White, T.D., Walter, R.C., Kimbel, W.H., Asfaw, B., Manega, P., Ndessokia, P. and Suwa, G., 1987, New partial skeleton of *Homo habilis* from Olduvai Gorge, Tanzania. *Nature*, **327**, 205–9.

Johanson, D.C. and White, T.D., 1979, A systematic assessment of early African hominids. *Science*, **203**, 321–30.

Jones, J.S. and Rouhani, S., 1986, How small was the bottleneck? *Nature*, **319**, 449–50.

Jungers, W.L., 1982, Lucy's limbs; skeletal allometry and locomotion in *Australopithecus afarensis*. *Nature*, **297**, 676–8.

Klein, R.G., 1977, The ecology of early man in South Africa. *Science*, **197**, 115–26.

Kurtén, B., 1972, *The Age of Mammals* (New York: Columbia University Press).

Leakey, R.E.F., 1976, Hominids in Africa. *American Scientist*, **64**, 174–8.

Leakey, R.E.F. and Lewin, R., 1977, *Origins* (New York: E.P. Dutton).

Leakey, R.E.F. and Lewin, R., 1978, *The People of the Lake* (Garden City, New York: Anchor Press, Doubleday).

Le Pichon, X. and Francheteau, J., 1978, A plate tectonic analysis of the Red Sea–Gulf of Aden area. *Tectonophysics*, **46**, 369–400.

Lewin, R., 1987, Four legs bad, two legs good. *Science*, **235**, 969–71.

Lowell, J.D. and Genik, G.J., 1972, Sea-floor spreading and structural evolution of southern Red Sea. *The American Association of Petroleum Geologists' Bulletin*, **56**, 247–59.

Lucy in Disguise, 1981, Smeltzer Films, Athens, Ohio, USA.

Mackinnon, J., 1978, *The Ape Within Us* (New York: Holt, Rinehart & Winston).

Maxwell, G., 1957, *People of the Reeds* (New York: Harper & Row).

Mohr, P.A., 1978, Afar. *Annual Review of Earth Planetary Science*, **6**, 145–72.

Morgan, E., 1972, *The Descent of Woman* (London: Souvenir Press).

Morgan, E., 1982, *The Aquatic Ape* (London: Souvenir Press).

Morris, D., 1967, *The Naked Ape* (New York: McGraw-Hill).

Morris, D., 1977, *Manwatching* (New York: Abrams).
Niering, W.A. 1966, *The Life of the Marsh* (New York: McGraw-Hill).
Niering, W.A., 1985, *Wetlands* (New York: McGraw-Hill).
Pilger, A. and Rosler, A., 1976, The contemporaneous tectonic events of the Indian Ocean. *Abhandlungen der Braunschweigischen Wissenschaftlichen Gesellschaft*, **26**, 67–90.
Sarish, V.M. and Wilson, A.C., 1967, Immunological time scale for hominid evolution. *Science*, **158**, 1200–3.
Schagatay, E., 1991, The significance of the human diving reflex. (This volume, chapter 15.)
Stoffers, P. and Ross, D.A., 1974, Sedimentary history of the Red Sea. In *Initial Reports of the Deep Sea Drilling Project*. R.B. Whitmarsh, O.E. Weser, D.A. Rose *et al*. (Washington: US Government Printing Office).
Tazieff, H., 1970, The Afar triangle. In *Continents Adrift* (San Francisco: W.H. Freeman), 133–41.
Tazieff, H., Varet, J., Barberi, F. and Giglia, F., 1972, Tectonic significance of the Afar (or Danakil) Depression. *Nature*, **235**, 144–7.
Teal, J. and Teal, M., 1969, *Life and Death of the Salt Marsh* (Boston: Little, Brown).
Wainscott, J.S., Hill, A.V.S., Boyce, A.L., Flint, J., Hernandez, M., Thein, S.L., Old, J.M., Lynch, J.R., Falusi, A.C., Weatherall, D.J. and Clegg, J.B., 1986, Evolutionary relationships of human populations from an analysis of nuclear DNA polymorphisms. *Nature*, **319**, 491–3.
Wainscott, J., 1987, Out of the Garden of Eden. *Nature*, **325**, 13.
Wegener, A., 1966, *The Origins of Continents and Oceans*, trans. John Biram from 4th rev. German ed. (New York: Dover Publications).
Wilson, J.T., 1963, Hypothesis of earth's behaviour. *Nature*, **198**, 925–9.

4 Is an Aquatic Ape Viable in Terms of Marine Ecology and Primate Behaviour?

Derek Ellis

SUMMARY

Tropical marine wetlands, often several types near each other, occur as mangrove salt-marshes, lagoons, and reef back-channels with islands. They are highly productive ecosystems with a diverse fauna and flora available as food for a dextrous, simple-tool-using, learning, wading ape, especially one capable of shallow dives. Three species of extant primates are known to use such habitats, and at least 15 primate species are able to swim and to perform some diving. In marine wetlands, a critical habitat requirement for safe nocturnal roosts is provided by cliffs and trees while, during daylight, home ranging is an expected primate behaviour.

The African Rift Valley, including the Red Sea, must have provided a suitable combination of sea level and habitat changes, about 5 million years ago, for an ape to become geographically isolated in marine wetlands, where aquatic selective pressures could have operated. Many modern humans' characters appear, in fact, to be adaptive to living in wetlands, and, once evolved, could have been functional in allowing the hominid stock to compete with baboons on inland riverine savannah. An aquatic ape is a likely ancestor of humans in terms of primate behaviour, marine ecosystems and geophysical timing.

INTRODUCTION

This chapter brings together information about marine ecosystems, African rifting, the behaviour of primates, and some concepts of evolutionary theory, as a biologist's contribution to discussion of the Aquatic Ape Theory of human evolution. Marine ecosystems have not previously been considered in any great detail in this context, even when the theory was being expressed by marine biologist Hardy (1960). There is now an enormous literature on relevant habitats – for example, tropical marine wetlands. Primate behaviour is an overwhelmingly documented subject, too. But certain aspects which are relevant to the Aquatic Ape Theory are not well known, such as swimming and the behaviour of coastal populations. Or their relevance may not be immediately apparent: for instance, home ranging and circadian cycles. My point is that any postulated ancestor was a living, behaving animal with an integrated set of activities allowing it to survive and breed.

The third subject area, eco-ethological and evolutionary theory, is yet another that is enormous in scope, but nevertheless it must be taken into account by anyone hypothesising lines of descent. Several examples – the concept of optimality theory, anagenesis–cladogenesis and allopatry–sympatry (two fundamental and simple pairs of evolutionary concepts), cline formation and subspeciation, punctuation and stasis – illustrate that relevant theory must be considered in developing a scenario for any postulated hominid clade.

My starting-point in getting involved in this topic was a very simple one, and based on several tenets of evolution theory. It was, in particular, the obviously over-simplified summary statement about the conventional (savannah) theory of human evolution: 'Apes came down from the trees out on to the savannah'. Whether or not this arose under the selective pressure of reducing forests from Pliocene desertification does not matter. The 'Direct Habitat Shift' theory presents the difficulties listed in Table 4.1. How did apes survive on the savannah when there were fierce, fast predators there, day and night? How did they outcompete the several species of widely distributed baboons already there? And how were they isolated from the ape clade leading to chimpanzees and gorillas?

Table 4.1 Difficulties with the Savannah Theory of human evolution

1 The variety of predators: e.g., lions, cheetahs, leopards, African hunting dogs
2 Safety at night: e.g., from hyenas. Could it be secured by trees? Cliffs? Thorn barricades? Fire?
3 Competitors: five or six species of baboons, widely distributed
4 How was the prehuman stock isolated from the ape stock leading to chimpanzees and gorillas?

The following information is set in the context of five general conclusions from the relevant literature.

The area of interest

The geographical area of interest is in the eastern half of Africa, particularly the Rift Valley; but, also, it approaches the coastline at the Red Sea (the Danakil Depression) and the Zambezi River (Figure 4.1). That this area is the focus of attention is partly the consequence of the distribution of hominid fossiliferous beds from South Africa to Ethiopia (e.g., Lewin, 1984), and partly because the specific arguments of Kortlandt (e.g., 1972) are based on these fossils. And the area is also partly indicated by the implications of habitat diversity, clinal subspeciation and ecological catastrophe in a long (over 5000 km) rifting valley, continental and oceanic. Richards (1987) provides a comprehensive review of most aspects.

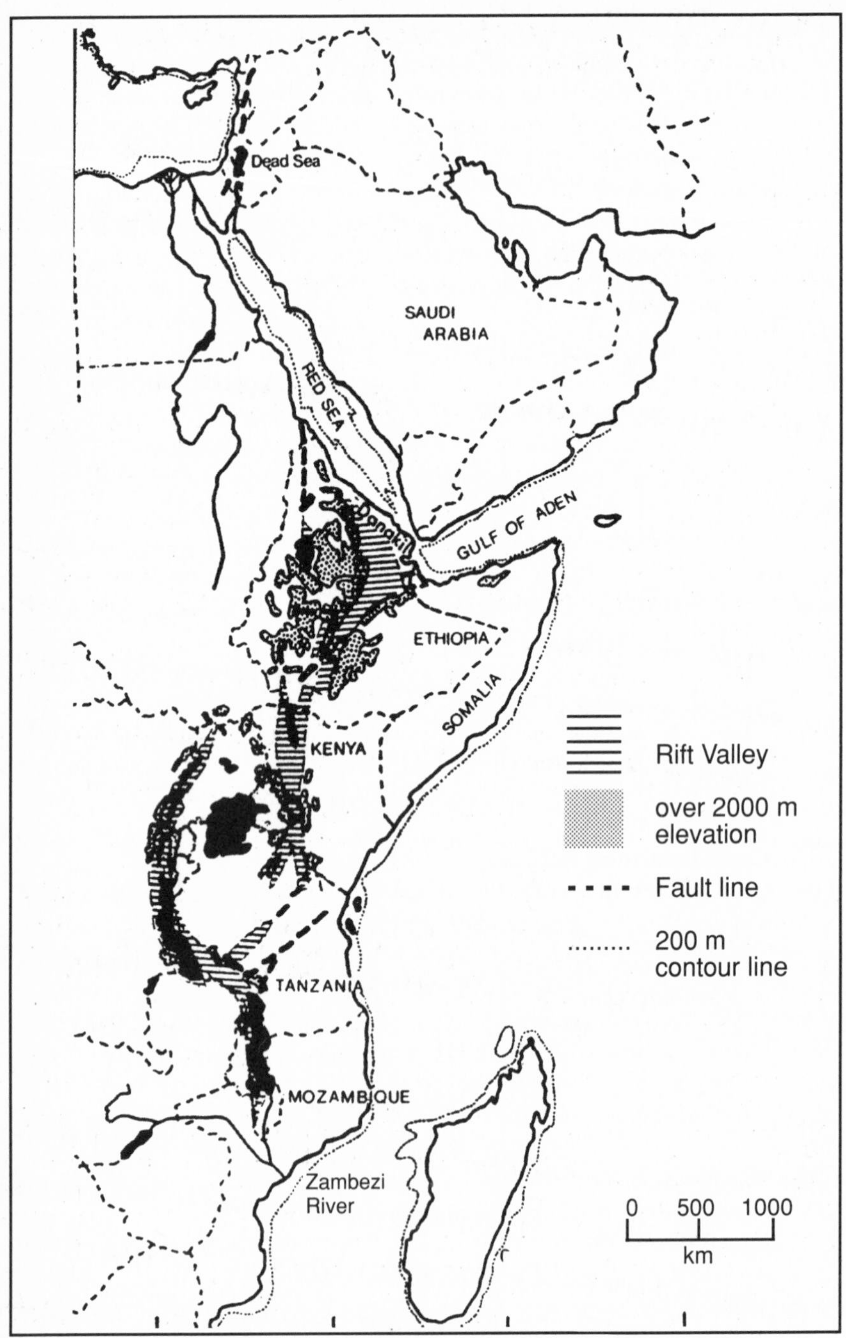

Figure 4.1 The African Rift Valley, including the Red Sea.

African wetlands and Red Sea rifting

An aquatic ape would have been adapted to marine, rather than riverine–lake, wetlands. In principle, tropical marine ecosystems are richer in immobile and slow-moving food, and are less dangerous than freshwater wetlands. That the former offer a greater food supply is conventional wisdom among aquatic biologists, although I know of no one who has actually documented the relative diversity and abundance of edible aquatic plants, crustacea, bivalves, other invertebrates, fish, and so on. The relative danger is also difficult to document and I do not intend to do so, but it seems a reasonable conclusion to someone who has toured rivers infested with crocodiles and hippopotamuses as well as swum and scuba-dived in shark-inhabited lagoons. I do not swim in African rivers; I do swim, with care, in clear seawater there.

However, both arguments are subsidiary to an important African geomorphological event in the Pliocene. This is the oceanic Red Sea rifting, starting approximately 5 million years ago, which widened the previously formed sea-bearing extension of the African rift there (Cochran, 1983; Girdler, 1984; Girdler and Southren, 1987). This oceanic rifting will inevitably have created a geomorphologically active coastline with archipelagos, the result of fluctuating water levels arising partly from the rifting process and partly through climatic and sea-level changes. The Red Sea is a region with a geomorphologically dynamic aquatic (marine) regime appropriate to the Aquatic Ape Theory. Also, the continental Rift Valley will have been volcanically active and subject to catastrophic habitat destructiveness, lava flows and inferno at this time.

Forest and savannah habitat

The forest habitat is a complex of sub-habitats (Richards, 1952), each occupiable by similar species with different adaptations. Thus there can be an upper canopy (with specialised primates such as the indri, howler monkey and gibbon), and several strata below down to the forest floor. These strata vary regionally depending on the amount and seasonality of rainfall, and the local topography creating standing or flowing water, such as swamps, rivers, lakes and estuaries. Thus there are rain-forests, and swamp, riverine and mangrove forests (Figure 4.2), as well as those on drier ground. Extensive stretches of these wet and dry forests in Africa, South-East Asia, Madagascar and South America support diverse species of primates, from upper canopy to ground.

The statement, 'Apes came down from the trees out on to the savannah', is misleading about forest and grassland ecology, as well as about primate biology. The common ancestors of catarrhine monkeys and hominoids, and of pongids and hominids, need not have been and probably were not upper-canopy species with their specialisations, even though both catarrhines and hominoids now have convergent species

Figure 4.2 Proboscis monkey on the ground in a mangrove swamp forest (G. Radcliffe, photo).

occupying that niche. The evolutionary problem is to transfer one or more stocks of apes from their niche as generalised lower-strata forest residents on to woodland savannah (tropical parkland) or riverine treed grassland, not the open savannah (tropical long-grass prairie).

Savannah is occupied by specialist long-ranging and fast cursorial herbivores and carnivores. Food would be hard to get there, hard to keep, and getting it would be dangerous enough for hunting parties, let alone camp-followers comprising elders, pregnant females and infants. In the process of adapting to parkland, not only the adult males, but also females and infants, would have to be viably adapted to the complexities of whatever ecosystem they were inhabiting at any one time (especially to predation) during the long series of anatomical, physiological and behavioural changes on the way to becoming human. And they would have to be able to push their way into the new ecological niche by adaptiveness superior to that of the baboons which had 'come down from the trees' before them.

Timing

The period of interest must encompass not only the (roughly) 5 million-year separation of gorilla–chimpanzee–human stock (Lewin, 1984), but also the scale of Rift Valley formation (Bonatti, 1987) and the cladogenesis of apes from catarrhine monkeys. There are some intriguing anatomical differences between the two clades (Napier and Napier, 1985). For example, the survival value and behavioural implications of loss of the tail in apes needs considering, since apes and monkeys thereby had different anatomical starting-points when they produced their ground-living species. The time frame considered here thus extends back to the beginning of the Miocene epoch, some 25 million years ago. Note also that, if sexual maturity lay within the age range five to ten years, the number of generations for ape stocks would be 200,000–100,000 per million years.

Marine mammal adaptation

The various clades of aquatic and semi-aquatic animals have different sets of adaptations. These match the Maynard-Smith (1975) concept of the equilibrium value of traits, the Evolutionarily Stable Strategies (ESSs). Thus the Cetacea are hairless, fully oceanic, with blubber, stern-oar tail-fluke and sonar. Soricidae and Mustelidae are amphibious with water-resistant hair, and land-usable legs functioning in water as paired side-oars or rear paddles. They are generally freshwater, but the coastal sea-otter *Enhydra lutris*, the rare sea-cat *Lutra felina*, and the Pacific coast so-called river-otter *Lutra canadensis* are notable exceptions. Another aquatic group is the pinnipeds and sirenids, with hair reduction and blubber. They are coastal, and the pinnipeds retain land birthing, and some, at least, much infant hair. These families are all derived from quadripedal forms, present members of which, such as otters, show only occasionally opportunistic bipedal behaviours of grazing and stare-round.

Primates frequently show opportunistic bipedalism, including when in water (see photographs and movies of wading proboscis monkeys with arms up high). They could generate yet another aquatic Evolutionary Stable Strategy, balancing both known and novel aquatic adaptations in an original way. There is no need to require wetlands primates to converge exactly on cetacean, pinniped or even mustelid aquatic ESSs. Starting from primate arboreal body capability, they have new combinations of adaptive opportunities open to them, or forced on them – for instance, by the ape lack of tail – and superior vertical flexibility.

MARINE WETLANDS ECOSYSTEMS

A generalised model of a marine wetlands ecosystem is presented in Figure 4.3. Such systems encompass salt-marsh and mangrove swamp, lagoons, rock shores, surf beaches and sand dunes, in a progression from wettest to driest. They can occur adjacent to each other, separated or intermixed in diverse ways. They are universal, distributed almost from poles to tropics. The general principles of their biology have been documented many times.

Some information is available about tropical and semi-tropical variants (Figures 4.4–4.7), including their forms extant in the Red Sea and East Africa. Bally (1986), for example, lists 1247 references to the biology of African sandy beaches, 49 from Somalia, 31 from the Red Sea, 30 from Mozambique, and lesser numbers from Kenya and Tanzania. As we know the general principles of coastline formation from geomorphology and climate, we can draw some conclusions about their Miocene–Pliocene–Pleistocene forms in the area of interest. Wetlands occur in archipelagos as well as on mainland coasts (Figure 4.6).

Resource content of marine ecosystems

Salt-marshes are the high tide and brackish water component of the marine wetlands ecosystems. They comprise the edges of river channels, and soft ground with streams connecting pools of varying sizes (Ranwell, 1972). They are overgrown by various grasses and salt-tolerant plants. The vegetation is populated by many land animals, worms, birds, small mammals, but especially insects, which in wet or warm seasons may swarm in large numbers. At the seaward side of the marsh, salinity becomes noticeable, and there appear in the fauna and flora various forms of algae and a variety of molluscs and crustacea. Fish of varying size and activity inhabit the pools, streams and rivers, especially at high tide when

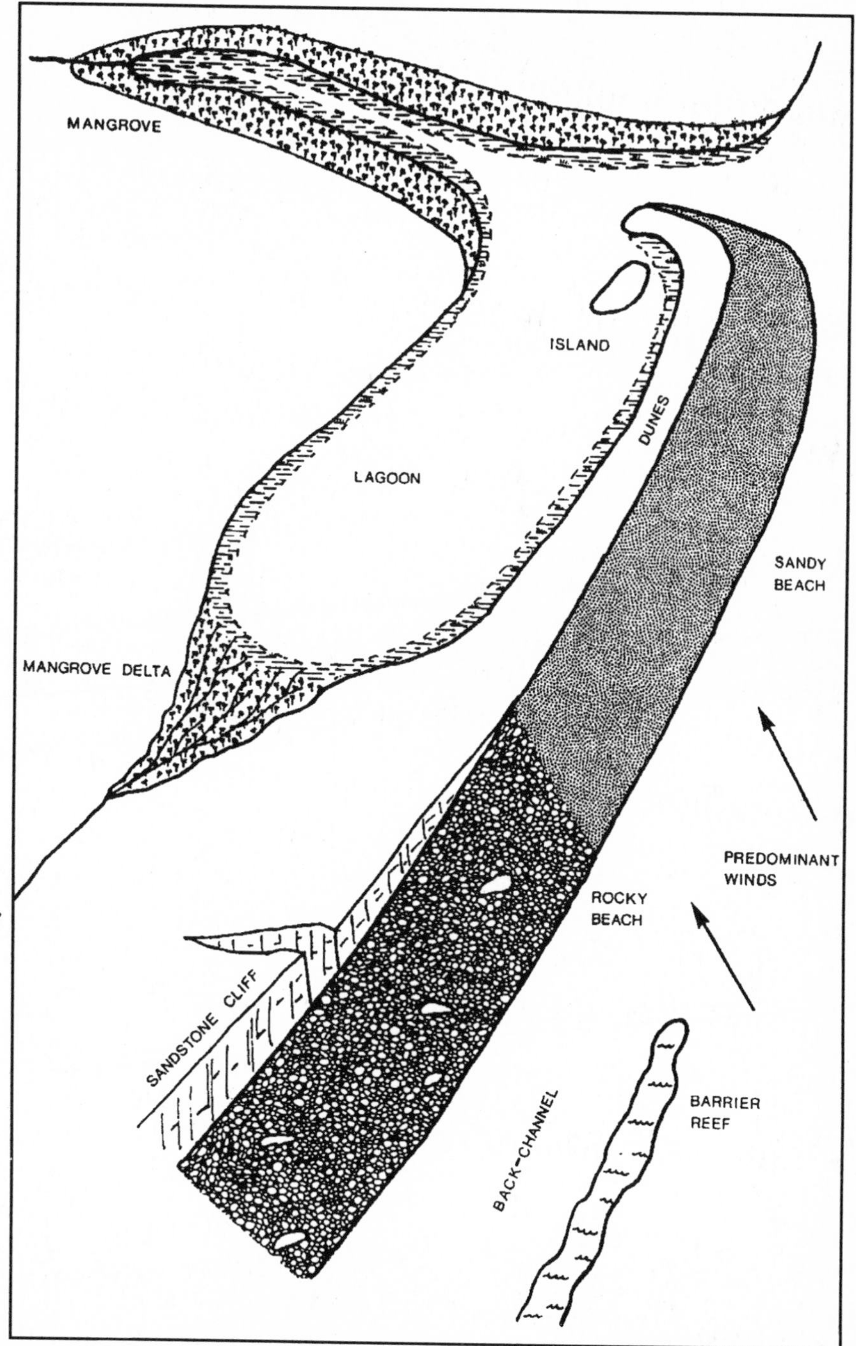

Figure 4.3 Model of marine wetlands ecosystem.

brackish water forms can swarm upstream. In tropical latitudes trees also feature. These are mangroves of several species (Figure 4.2). They greatly diversify the ecosystem and provide more niches than the salt-marshes of temperate regions, with an accompanying diversification of the microflora and especially the sedentary fauna (snails, hermit-crabs) on the trunks of trees (MacNae, 1968).

Lagoons are the lakes of marine wetlands. They occur on the landward side of barrier coral reefs as back-channels (Figure 4.4), and on the landward side of sandy depositional features (Figure 4.5) such as the spits which occur wherever the physical forces of wind, waves and an erosional feeder cliff create a longshore drift, thrusting materials across a shoreline embayment. However, any depression connected to the sea within the range of high tide will fill with brackish, salt- or hypersaline water, depending on river flow, tidal prism and air temperature. Being sheltered from direct wind and wave action, lagoons can be mud-bottomed with growth of salt-tolerant marine grasses and other plants, and a variety of marine but osmotically tolerant invertebrates and fish. Coral reef lagoons (back-channels) and atolls (Figure 4.6) tend to be well flushed and sandier-bottomed. Lagoons attract migratory water birds, often temporarily in enormous numbers, and support such mammalian herbivores as the sirenian dugongs and manatees. Invertebrates may be present in enormous numbers, the result of a few opportunistic species quickly responding to stressful changes of salinity (above 35‰) and temperature (above 25°C) (Moore, 1972). The diversity of species declines as salinities reach about 45‰ and temperatures about 30°C.

On rock shores (Figure 4.7) the stable hard surface is covered by marine algae, generally microphytic at high tide, grading to macrophytic at low tide, and with pools supporting marine grasses as well. At high tide, snail and crustacean grazers use the ephemeral unicellular or filamentous algae, often only during the cool of the night. In the pools there is an enormous diversity of attached, sedentary, and mobile invertebrates and fish herbivores and carnivores. Birds and mammals range on to the system as tides fall. At low tide the rock shore is particularly productive, with diverse algal forests of kelps and understorey red, green and brown algae, and their herbivore–carnivore food chains. In the tropics these are supplanted in many places by even richer coral reefs, the upper parts of which are accessible to swimmers by shallow diving, and occasionally to waders at times of unusually low tides. There is a serious risk on rock shores, though. They can be physically dangerous, particularly during winds with an incoming tide. Wave action, and especially freak surge waves, can break unpredictably higher upshore than usual, and catch unsuspecting foragers.

Figure 4.4 Coral reef back-channel lagoon, with island.

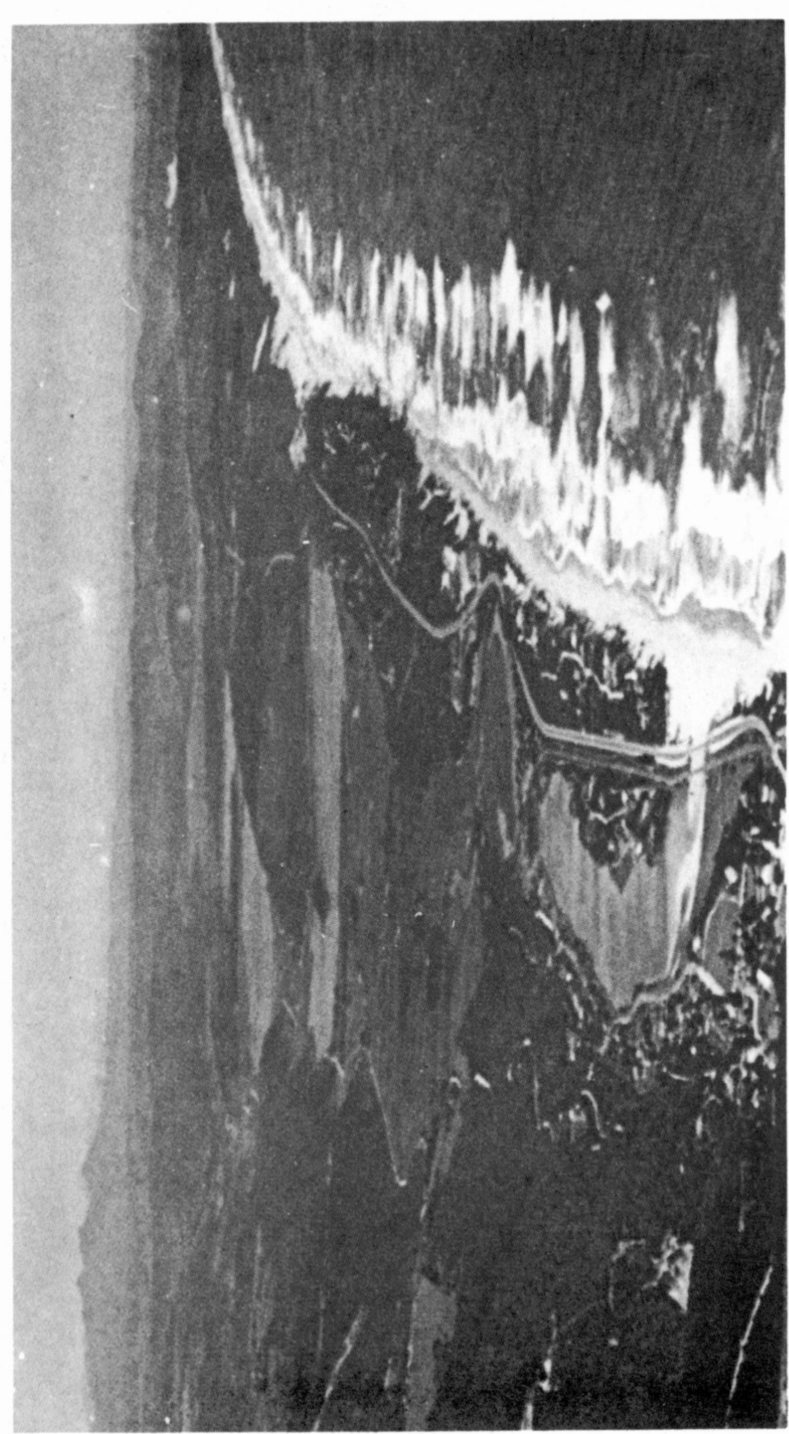

Figure 4.5 Estuarine lagoons.

Figure 4.6 A tropical archipelago.

Figure 4.7 Chacma baboons on a surf shore with sand beach and rock habitats.

Sand beaches (Figure 4.7) are relatively unproductive in the mid-tide zone. In wet areas they support a variety of burrowing worms, molluscs and crustacea, some of which (*Donax*, the sand mussel) are visibly transient up and down the beach with the tide, and in upper levels many ocypodid and other crabs. Beaches are the main point of arrival for edible flotsam such as marine mammal carcasses. They support highly productive high-tide strand lines of algal and other debris, which in turn support enormous numbers of beach fleas and other crustaceans, readily available at night. Their disadvantage is that beaches are also vulnerable to surge waves; and a non-flying opportunist forager has to keep careful watch to start running upshore in good time. Sand dunes must be included in marine wetlands ecosystems, since they occur landward of beaches in many places. They respond vigorously to irregular rainfall by the growth of dormant plants, and can maintain oases and damp soil in the dune-slacks (depressions between the dunes).

The relative environmental risks and stresses, and the resource accessibility and adaptive demands of the various wetlands for a primate, are summarised in Table 4.2.

Finally, it should be noted that tsunamis, the so-called tidal waves, can be catastrophic over extensive areas of low-lying prograding coastline, such as is formed by millennia of longshore drift and estuarine discharge.

Contemporary tropical examples

A few tropical coastlines have been comprehensively investigated, or reviewed. The most relevant to our area of interest are the shores of West Africa (Lawson, 1966), the coast of India (Natarajan, 1975), and the south Somalian coast. The West African review describes shoreline geomorphology as well as biology; the Indian review has more detailed biology of the various wetland types. The south Somalian coast investigations are described in many papers of *Monitore Zoologico Italiano*. In addition, there is a vast literature on tropical forms of most of the noted habitats: for instance, for mangroves (MacNae, 1968), for sandy beaches (McLachlan and Erasmus, 1983) and for coral reefs (Stoddart, 1969). Tropical lagoon biology is not well known. Tropical rock-shore biology closely follows similar shores in temperate zones, but is more productive and diverse (Stephenson and Stephenson, 1972).

Wetlands of the Red Sea can be used as examples in hot, dry climates. Fringing coral reefs are known to be productive, and their shallows are exposed at unusually low tides (Fishelson, 1971, 1980). Old reefs can be found above present high tides. Mangrove swamp forests occur in patches, as do salt-marshes (Kassas, 1957). Occasional seasonal convectional rainstorms flood to the sea; and run-off is absorbed in ground water to reappear at inland and shoreline oases. Even the Dead Sea has such oases. Climatic maps show relatively higher rainfall inland at

Table 4.2 Relative environmental stresses and risks, resource accessibility and adaptive demands in tropical marine wetlands

	Environmental stresses			*Other risks*		*Adaptive demands*			
						Nocturnal activities			
	Salinity	*Insolation temperature*	*Waves*	*Competition severity*	*Predation risk*	*Sleeping*	*Food-gathering*	*Utilisation of complex vocalisation*	*Potential for tool-using*
Mangrove coastal forests	Least	Least	Least	Highest	Moderate	In trees	Unlikely	Moderate	Low
Lagoons –embayed	High(est)	High(est)	Low	Low	Moderate	Dangerous	Possible	High	Highest
–reef back-channels	High	High	Moderate	Low	Moderate	Dangerous	Possible	Moderate	High
Near-shore islands	High	Moderate	Low	Low	Lowest	Safest	Possible	Moderate	Moderate
Rocky shore and tide-pools	High	High	Highest	Low	Moderate	On cliffs (if present)	Moonlight, low tides	Low (noisy)	High (shellfish)
Surf beaches	High	High	Highest	Low	High	Dangerous	Moonlight, low tides	Low (noisy)	Low
Sand dunes, including dune-slacks	Low	High(est)	Low	Low	High	Dangerous	Unlikely	Moderate	Low

the south-east and south-west of the Red Sea (up to 150 cm per year). Monsoonal rains are features of other tropical areas, including the south Somalian coast (Vannini *et al.*, 1977).

The physical and chemical oceanography and fisheries resources of the Red Sea and off the east coast of Africa have been investigated by a variety of expeditions and coastal marine stations (Venema, 1984). Essentially, surface waters can be productive in terms of fish and shellfish. Hartnoll (1975) reports collecting over one and a half years forty-three species of ocypodid and grapsid intertidal crabs on the Tanzania coast, distributed over rocky and sandy shore and mangrove forests, and extending into fresh water.

Miocene–Pliocene–Pleistocene considerations

The African Rift Valley (Figure 4.1) has been forming, possibly in one or two episodes of continental splitting (40 and 25 million years ago), since late Cretaceous–early Miocene times; then about 5 million years ago oceanic splitting of the Red Sea area started (Cochran, 1983; Girdler, 1984; Girdler and Southren, 1987). When a sea has been contained within the rift it has often approximated the present Red Sea, but has on occasions intruded inland beyond the present coastline – for example, the Afar triangle (Tazieff, 1970), containing the Danakil Depression. Island distribution would have been quite different from now. This inland sea, and the African coastline in general, has been complicated in terms of water levels (hence current flows, tides, and so on) by the sea varying ± 100–200 m from present levels (Figures 4.1 and 4.8), arising from global climate changes and glacial isostasy (Stanley, 1984). At a 200-m lower water level the Red Sea would be an inland sea subject to evaporation, supersalination and later inundation as water level rose. The Zambesi end of the rift would not have the same geomorphological and habitat diversity facilitating evolutionary isolation.

Thus, allowing for species changes through our period of interest, marine wetlands ecosystems will have occurred in the Red Sea as they do today; they would have been dynamic biological systems, with fluctuations over time scales of one day to the next, over seasons (annual wet–dry) over hundreds of years as the result of local geomorphological forces, over glacial periods, and over geological time. At any one time, biologically productive wetlands ecosystems, modified by regional climate, can be expected on appropriate coastal habitats in the Red Sea and the Danakil Depression. Under hot dry conditions, temperature and salinity stresses would constrain upper tidal wetlands to relict oases at unusually favourable sites, as occur today in Melita Bay and the Dahlak Islands of the southern Red Sea (Lewinsohn and Fishelson, 1967). When climates were cooler and wetter than today, marine wetlands would have been expected, and mangroves would have been the coastal represen-

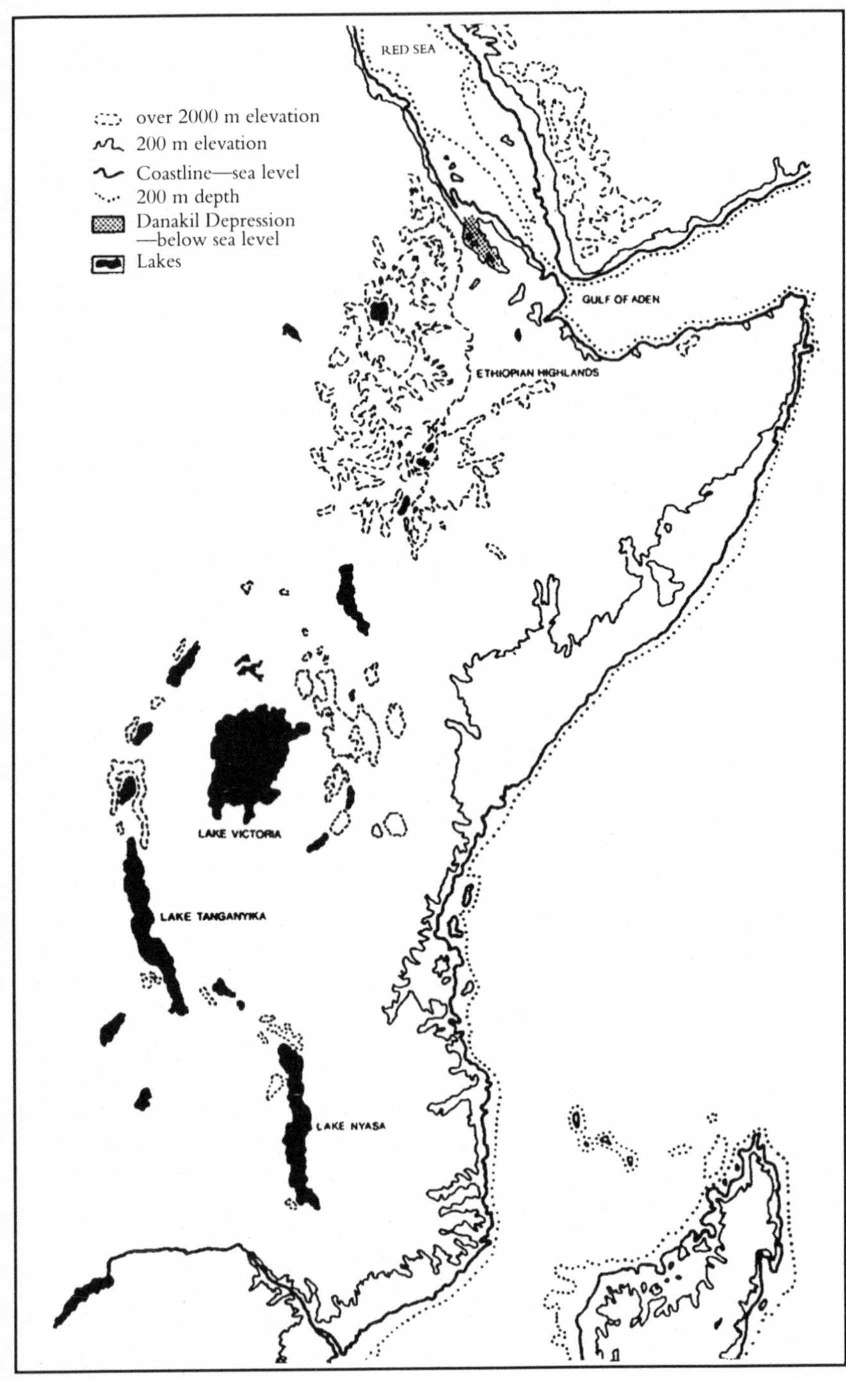

Figure 4.8 Topography of the African Rift Valley.

tative of extensive forest stretching either continuously inland or up river valleys, including the great rift, sometimes contiguous with tropical rain-forests and cooler montane forest.

Under warmer and drier climates than today, drying-out, with parkland or savannah formation and possibly regional desertification, would have constrained and isolated the remaining montane and rain-forests from the Rift Valley and the coast. A primate fauna is to be expected throughout these forests, whether extensive and contiguous or constrained and isolated. This would include the coastal forests, as, for example, in Borneo today, where proboscis monkey *Nasalis larvatus*, crab-eating macaque *Macaca fascicularis* and silvered leaf monkey *Presbytis cristata* coexist (Ellis, 1986). It is hard to imagine what would have prevented lower-canopy or ground apes (Dryopithecines?) being present in forests along the African rift, as the Red Sea first became a marine embayment (25 million years ago?) and then started the oceanic rifting of 5 million years ago.

PRIMATE BEHAVIOUR

An ethogram (an inventory of the behaviour of a species (Tinbergen, 1969)) for a primate would be a long list, with many categories and lengthy descriptions of variable behaviours. Nevertheless, we should attempt to compile an ethogram when hypothesising ancestral species. It is a salutory experience, forcing one to consider the whole animal as an integrated behavioural–anatomical–physiological system in a realistic habitat. This section presents comments on a few primate behaviours which appear relevant to preparing an ethogram for a human ancestor.

Swimming

At least six species of primates have been recorded as swimming when free-ranging (Table 4.3). A further twelve have been recorded swimming or wading in zoos. All four primate major taxa are represented: prosimians, platyrrhine and catarrhine monkeys and apes. Three of the four ape species groups have been recorded as swimming or wading in zoos (Figure 4.9), and the pygmy chimpanzee *Pan troglodytes pygmaeus* in the wild also (Nishida, 1980; Uhara, 1976). From information obtained from primate keepers, it appears that many, if not most, primates can learn to swim during infancy. In the wild they would learn to do so from peers and seniors, with the first of the stock doing so fortuitously, surviving, benefiting either by food, escape or comfort (cooling), and responding similarly again when the situation was repeated. Once established as part of the culture of an ape or monkey stock, swimming would be perpetuated down the generations, as with the Koshima stock of Japanese macaques *Macaca fuscata* (Napier and Napier, 1985).

Table 4.3 Swimming and other water activities of primates (extended from Ellis, 1987)

Species	*Species that swim in*		*Species that wade/play in zoos or wild*	*Other littoral wetlands species*	*Comments and references*
	wild	*zoos*			
Prosimians					
Gentle grey lemur (*Hapalemur griseus*)	X				Lake Alaotra troop swim (Kavanagh, 1983)
New World monkeys					
Spider-monkey (*Ateles geafroyi*)		X			(Chaffee)
Dusky titi (*Callicebus moloch*)				X	Swamp and riverine forest (Kavanagh, 1983)
White-faced capuchin (*Cebus capucinus*)				X	Shoreline occupants harvest oysters (Kavanagh, 1983)
Old World monkeys					
Cercopithecinae					
Allen's swamp monkey (*Allenopithecus nigroviridis*)	X	X			Has foot-webbing (Gilbow, 1985; Forney, 1985; Wolfheim, 1983)
White-collared mangabey (*Cercocebus torquatus*)				X	Can occur in swamps (Grizimeck, 1972). The most ground-dwelling of several rain-forest mangabey species (Napier and Napier, 1985)
Mandrill (*Mandrillus sphinx*)		X			(Bourne)
Mona monkey (*Cercopithecus mona*)		X			(Kagan)
DeBrazza's monkey (*Cercopithecus neglectus*)		X			(Bourne)
Japanese macaque (*Macaca fuscata*)	X	X			(Kagan, Bourne; Kavanagh, 1983)
Crab-eating/long-tailed macaque (*Macaca fascicularis*)		X			(Shumaker, Ruhe)

Species	*Species that swim in*		*Species that wade/play in zoos or wild*	*Other littoral wetlands species*	*Comments and references*
	wild	*zoos*			
Rhesus monkey (*Macaca mulatta*)	X	X			(Lindberg, 1971; O'Neill)
Celebes-crested macaque (*Macaca nigra*)		X			(Shumaker, Kagan, Ruhe)
Barbary macaque (*Macaca sylvanus*)		X			(Shumaker)
Talapoin (*Miopithecus talapoin*)	X				(Kavanagh, 1983)
Yellow baboon (*Papio cynocephalus*)				X	(Messeri, 1978)
Chacma baboon (*Papio ursinus*)				X	Cape stock beach-dwelling (Ellis, 1985; Davidge, 1976)
Baboon (unidentified)		X			(Ruhe)
Colobinae					
Proboscis monkey (*Nasalis larvatus*)	X	X			(Ellis, 1987; Hutchins)
Dusky leaf monkey (*Presbytis obscurus*)			X (rarely)		(Kagan)
Silvered leaf monkey (*Presbytis cristata*)				X	Inhabit coastal forests (Kavanagh, 1983)
Olive Colobus (*Procolobus verus*)				X	Low-stratum riverine forests (Napier and Napier, 1985)
Apes					
Gorilla (*Gorilla gorilla*)		X			(Brown *et al.*, 1982; Golding, 1972)
Chimpanzee (*Pan troglodytes*)			X		(Uhara, 1976; Nishida, 1980)
Orang-utan (*Pongo pygmaeus*)			X		(Ellis, 1987)

Respondents providing information referenced above:

Bourne, D., Toronto Zoo; Chaffee, P., Fresno Zoo; Dotts, C., San Diego Zoo; Hutchins, M., Bronx Zoo; Kagan, R., Dallas Zoo; Lindberg, D.G., San Diego Zoo; Marsh, L., University of California, Davis; O'Neill, P., National Institute of Health, Dickerson, MD; Ruhe, L., Baby Zoo, San Jose; Shumaker, R.W., National Zoological Park, Washington, DC; Tong, M., Houston Zoo.

Figure 4.9 Orang-utan wading in the moat at the Singapore Zoo (reprinted from Ellis, 1987).

The comment is often made that apes and monkeys cannot swim and are afraid of the water, and 'that is why zoos have moats around monkey compounds'. However, zoos that use moats have to check carefully that their expensive apparently non-swimming apes and monkeys really cannot or will not swim. Young apes and monkeys are like young children. Given the right instruction or peer models, they will quickly learn, particularly from a socialising attendant who likes to swim with them (Ellis, 1987; see also Wind, chapter 17, this volume). Indeed, zoos with moats had better not teach their curious, attention-seeking young monkeys and apes how to swim. Or their moats will no longer work, as was found with two gorillas at the University of Ibadan Zoo (Golding, 1972): 'Both animals soon learned to run across the compound and either leap diagonally into the water in a tremendous belly-flop or twist about at the last minute and plunge in backwards . . . the male was able to launch himself with a kick from the mud bottom, travelling several feet in a horizontal "breast stroke" position.'

Coastal monkeys and home ranging

Three species of catarrhines have coastal stocks. They all show pronounced home-ranging behaviour: that is, they routinely patrol daily a limited range of their shoreline habitat. The species are the proboscis monkey *Nasalis larvatus* (Ellis, 1986; and Figure 4.2), the chacma baboon *Papio ursinus* (Davidge, 1976; and Figure 4.7) and the yellow baboon *Papio cynocephalus* (Messeri, 1978).

The limit to shoreline stock vagility appears to be set by a critical path of safe roosting places. Proboscis monkeys select high riverine trees, from which they can escape (their main predator is the clouded leopard) by dropping into the water below. The two coastal baboon stocks sleep on predator-inhibiting cliffs. The daily patrols, although circumscribed by the roughly twelve-hour light–dark cycle, vary from day to day opportunistically according to food availability, need to drink (for the baboons) and proximity of the nearest roosting place.

Social (kin) grouping

Table 4.4 summarises levels of social organisation in terms of numbers of individuals commonly grouping together and kin relationships within the groups. The term 'solitaries' may be misleading. It can mean a scale of individual territoriality beyond easy recognition by an observer, with the animals (such as orang-utans) knowing who their neighbours are, and with males maintaining a larger territory than females, and encompassing theirs.

An important pattern in the tabulated information is that the different types of social grouping occur in the four major primate taxa. In other words, type of social group is a flexible behavioural property which can change easily over evolutionary distance (as well as historically in human society). An ancestor to chimpanzee, gorilla and human need not have had a social organisation similar to any one of the three extant species. Martin and May (1981), using arguments based on ape and human genitals, suggest that an early ancestor had single male breeding groups. Nevertheless, social group flexibility in primates is so great that other ancestral stages could have had substantially different forms of social grouping.

Table 4.4 Group organisation of primates (modified from Chalmers, 1979, and Ellis, 1985)

Group type	*Group size*	*Home-range size (hectares)*
Solitaries	1	c.1 or less
Several lemurs and lorises		
Orang-utan		
Male especially		
Female with young to 4–5 years		
Juveniles may group		
Monogamous family groups – Breeding male, female and young	2+	4–50
Indri, some monkeys		
Gibbon, siamang		
One-male, several-female groups	10–20	10–5000
Many monkeys		
Gorilla (may tolerate some mature males)		
Hamadryas and gelada baboons (groups may aggregate)		
Multi-male, multi-female groups	10–100	1–2500
Some lemurs		
Many monkeys, including macaques and baboons		
Chimpanzee – frequent subgrouping, between kin and 'friends'		

Dispersal phases – young adults?

Goodall (1986) has shown that female chimpanzees tend to wander as they mature sexually, and subsequently settle in one troop or another. Strum (1975) and Ransom (1981) have shown that male baboons can bully, bluff or wheedle their way into a new troop. The consequence of these dispersals is to reduce the risk of inbreeding. It is to be noticed that although the dispersing sex differs between the two species, the common pattern is that dispersal is by young adults. An implication of this pattern is that species vagility (hence gene spread) is quite limited compared to potential gene spread by, for example, a wandering sexually active male consorting with stranger females over many years and long distances.

Day–night cycles

The majority of primates have a wake–sleep cycle closely related to the day–night light–dark cycle. They roost at dusk and rise at dawn. Table 4.5 presents some data that I recently obtained at a twenty-seven-cage arena in the San Diego Zoo. The various species settled down for the night by preliminary quiet sitting, then progressed to sleeping over about two hours before and after dusk. They started to rise about an hour before dawn. The times seem to be similar in the wild. A few species, while still tied to the day–night cycle, reverse it (the lorises and the Douroucouli, *Aotus trivirgatus*) (Kavanagh, 1983), waking at dusk, being nocturnally active and roosting at dawn. At least one diurnal lemur is an exception – for example, *L. fulvus* (Harrington, 1975) – and can be active at night (Schilling, 1979) as well as during the day.

The issue is significant, since the twenty-four-hour activity pattern of one primate species, ourselves, can break the usual environmental constraints. We can stay awake after dusk for culturally determined activities, and rouse ourselves for prolonged activities at night: for instance, the graveyard shift in a factory, and the first mate's midnight–4 a.m. watch at sea. This potential (for opportunist nocturnal foraging) would not have been unimportant to an omnivorous human ancestor: for example, during seasons of nocturnally swarming insects, at times of full moon illumination, and at the coast during night-time low spring tides.

Communication

Primates communicate by a mixture of scents, badges and displays, and by calls including extended songs in canopy species (indri, howler monkeys and siamangs). Scents, particularly, are a feature of ground-dwelling forms. Complex sound communication is a feature of oceanic and aerial mammals. Both Cetacea and Chiroptera use high-frequency direction-finding sonar in their open habitats, unencumbered by

Table 4.5 Observations on primate roosting and waking in a 27–cage arena at the San Diego Zoo, 8–9 April 1987

	Cage	14:00 hrs		NO	18:00hrs					19:00 hrs						20:00 hrs	NO	05:00 hrs						06:00 hrs			
	no.	10	40	DATA	13	20	30	40	50	00	10	20	30	40	50	00	DATA	01	10	20	30	40	50	00	10	20	30
												↑ Sunset														↑ Sunrise	
Allenopithecus	1											S	S	R	—	—		—	—	—	—	—	—	—	—	—	
nigroviridis	2															R		—	—	—	—	—	—	—	—		
Presbytis	1											R		R	—	—		—	—	—	—	—	—	- -	- -	- -	- -
francoisi	2					S	- -	- -	- -	- -	- -	- -	- -	- -	- -	R		—	—	—	—	—	—	- -	- -	- -	- -
Presbytis entellus														R	—	—		—	—	—	—	—	—	—	—	—	—
Alouatta pigra					S	- -	- -	- -	- -	R	—	—	—	—	—	—		—	—	—	—	—	—	- -	- -	- -	
Alouatta	1	S	- -		- -	- -	R	—	—	—	—	—	—	—	—	—		—	—			—	—	—	—	—	—
seniculus sara	2		S		- -	R	—	—	—	—	—	—	—	—	—	—		—	—		S	—	—	—	—		
Macaca niger											S	- -	- -	R	—	—		—	—			—	—	—	—	—	—
Mandrillus	1										R	—	—	—	—	—		—	—	- -	- -	- -	- -	- -	- -	- -	- -
leucophaeus	2										R	—	—	—	—	—		—	—	- -	- -	- -	- -	- -	- -	- -	- -
	3				S	- -	- -	- -	R	—	—	—	—	—	—	—		—	—	—	—	—	—	—	—	—	
	4	Out of sight all periods																									
Pithecia pithecia		Out of sight most periods																								Active	
Callicebus moloch					R	—	—	—	—	—	—	—	—	—	—	—		—	—	—	—	—	—	—	—	—	—
clonacophilus																											
Cercocebus	1										S	R	—	—	—	—		—	—	—	—	—	—	—	—	—	
torquatus	2								R	—	—	—	—	—	—	—		—	—	—	—	—	—	—	—		
torquatus	3		S		R	—	—	—	—	—	—	—	—	—	—	—		—	—	—	—	—	—	—	—		
Cercopithecus cephus												S	- -	- -	- -	- -		—	—	—	—	—					
Lemur catta												?	?	?	R	?		?	?	?	?						
Varcia variegata												?	?	?	R	?		?	?	?	?						
Cercopithecus												S	- -	- -	R	—		—	—	—	—	—	—	—	—		
talapoin																											
Macaca silenus											R	—	—	—	—	—		—	—	—	—	—	—	—	—		
Cercopithecus					S						R	—	—	—	—	—		—	—	—	—	—	—	—			
hamlyni																											
Cercopithecus												?	?	?	?	?		?	?	?	?	—	—	—			
diana roloway																											

Key R = all roosting; S = some roosting; Blanks = cage occupants active; ? = uncertain; ——— all roosting; - - - - some roosting complex three-dimensional fine-habitat structures, such as tree and algal forests. The sonar of the Cetacea also produces complex vocalisations, apparently meaningful between individuals.

There is another potential use of sound by aquatic species, employed by the young of the sea-otter. This is the property of distant transmission through reflectivity of the water surface. The infant sea-otter will utter a piercing scream after being left by its parent for more than a few minutes of a feeding dive, and the call travels very effectively, particularly when the surface is calm. On a calm day in coastal waters the conversation of boaters can be clearly understood kilometres distant. Lagoon living, particularly, would provide both selective pressure and calm-water habitat for evolving complex vocalisations effective over long distances. The new complexity would add to demands on the brain.

Feeding and omnivorousness

Apes and monkeys are dextrous enough to use fine probes for termiting (Goodall, 1986), and to wash food in water (Napier and Napier, 1985). Many are insectivorous and nut-cracking. Some chimpanzees catch and eat living small mammals. At least some of these behaviours may be learned. A coastal ape would have no difficulty in using such learned abilities to catch and break into the sedentary and sessile animals that are there on shore, in pools, lagoons and wetlands in enormous numbers, especially at low tide. In learning to adapt the abilities to new foods in a wet habitat, new and complex selective pressures would be put on the brain.

SOME RELEVANT ECO-ETHOLOGICAL AND EVOLUTIONARY CONCEPTS

Behavioural integration and optimalisation

An animal's behaviour and anatomy is a system: an ethosystem. The system is integrated so that the animal survives and breeds, even though it may perform some actions that seem risky, and lack some structures that seem useful. Krebs and Davies (1981) have called this 'optimality'; 'trade-offs between costs and benefits will give the maximum net benefit to the individual'.

An example relevant to hominid evolution comes from the loss of the tail by the ape stock. The best-known benefit to primates of being tailed arises from the prehensile form: that is, where the tail is a grasping device supplementing the four limbs for moving through the forest canopy. Gibbons and orangs have to do without a tail, and have adapted to canopy living by brachiation (gibbons) and slow movement (orangs). Catarrhine monkeys and prosimians derive other benefits from the tail, even though it is not prehensile. It can be a touch sensor, which can be used in the trees and on the ground, providing information from behind and to the side. In addition, it is often used in social displays, as a contact device when sleeping and resting, and in balancing.

Apes have lost the tail, along with its considerable survival advantages. Presumably, at some stage in the catarrhine–hominoid split, apes were in an adaptive situation where the benefits of a tail became too costly for survival. A selective explanation is needed, since the tailless ape on the ground was eventually able to compete with the tailed baboons already there, and establish itself in spite of the baboons very successfully occupying the parkland niche. Lack of a tail, plus other ape characters, could well be important to the human stock in coexisting with baboons.

The tail might have been lost in the following way. An isolated ancestral monkey stock came to spend increasingly more time on the ground than in the lower canopy, such that the tail was less needed as a touch sensor. The animals were exposed continuously to a range of daytime visually-hunting ground predators that could detect them by their movements, including tail waving. The optimum balance had changed, and long-tailed specimens were at a disadvantage. Such a scenario for one character is too simple, and needs expanding, so that all the anatomical–behavioural–physiological differences between apes and catarrhine monkeys (Andrews, 1981, 1985) are explained in terms of benefits and costs. Also, the various characters must have a net benefit during all life stages, for infants and juveniles, and for females as well as mature males.

Evolutionary theory

Primates, like any other clade, evolve either by straight-line evolution (anagenesis) or by line-splitting (cladogenesis). If anagenesis occurred, an ape could have evolved to human by adapting to a reducing forest drying out to parkland and savannah. There are problems with this, in that gene flow would continue over a wide area between the grassland and remaining forest stocks (sympatry). The alternative of cladogenesis means that ape stocks evolving to chimpanzees, gorillas and humans were isolated one from another. Appropriate forest clusters would have occurred during a Pliocene drying: for example, as mountain-mist forests, river-valley and coastal forests. Elevations over 2000 m in Africa are shown in Figures 4.1 and 4.8. Mountains group in patches over several hundred kilometres in East Africa, and the southern patches are several hundred kilometres from the coast.

Any scenario for human evolution must pinpoint the area and explain human descent in terms of biologically and geographically appropriate anagenesis/cladogenesis and sympatry/allopatry.

There is a great range of theoretical biological concepts which must be considered in developing theories of human evolution and lines of descent. The concepts of Hennigian cladistics (e.g., Wiley, 1981; Ciochon, 1982), molecular biology (e.g., Sarich, 1971), punctuation and stasis (e.g., Eldredge and Gould, 1972) and molecular drive (e.g., Dover, 1986) are all highly relevant, and should be brought together into human evolutionary theory.

AN ALTERNATIVE TO THE SAVANNAH THEORY

Table 4.1 lists some difficulties in evolving humans on the savannah. These difficulties can be avoided if the clade spent an evolutionarily significant period of time in a habitat where characters changed in such a way that on later entry to riverine savannah the ape–human stock had a set of characters allowing it to feed omnivorously, to survive predators there day and night, and to do so more efficiently than the baboons already present. The situation is summarised in Figure 4.10 and Table 4.6. We need a habitat other than a forest–savannah boundary ecotone for the separation of ape and human stocks.

Table 4.7 shows that many human characters can be arranged in sets ordered by different levels of functioning in an aquatic habitat.

To explore an aquatic descent scenario in some detail, we must use the concept of the ethogram, hierarchically arranged (Ellis, 1985). The upper-level categories used here are: habitat and its use, food-gathering, avoidance of and escape from predators, sleeping, social grouping and organisation, comfort behaviours and juvenile behaviours.

The scenario starts with a generalised ape convergent with coastal monkeys now extant. It is hard to see what could have stopped lower-canopy and ground apes from inhabiting the African Rift Valley, and the forested coasts of East Africa and the Red Sea by 5 million years ago, after separation of catarrhines and hominoids 20 million years before. The second stage of the scenario explores how an aquatic ape could have been viable as a localised rapidly evolving form. This would be sometime during the oceanic rifting, sea-level changes, archipelago appearance and drowning, supersalination and inundations, starting about 5 million years ago. It would represent the extreme aquatic stage and form of a clinally varying Rift Valley ape. It would be localised at the geomorphologically dynamic Red Sea end of the rift, not the Zambezi end. The third stage explores whether transition to *Australopithecus* or *Homo* or both, inland, is a viable process. This last stage must be developed, as the Aquatic Ape Theory can only be convincing if it can bring back inland up the Rift Valley (at least once) the hominid stock in a way strictly conforming to biological–evolutionary forces. In so doing, the aquatic ape ancestral species must become extinct.

Table 4.6 An alternative theory for human evolution

1	An ape stock was isolated in a habitat unusual for a primate
2	The stock, by adapting to that habitat, evolved characters which were functional there
3	Loss of the habitat or population pressure due to successful adaptation forced the stock towards riverine savannah
4	The stock survived in riverine savannah, since a subset of the new unusual primate characters allowed them to out-compete the baboons already there and to avoid predators

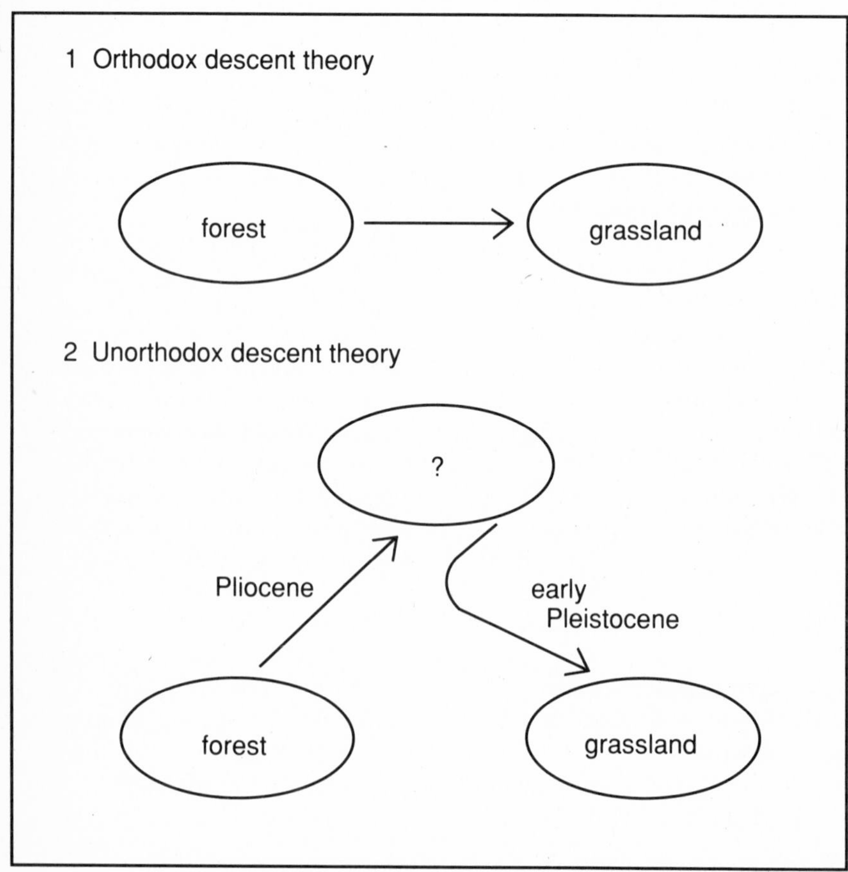

Figure 4.10 Models of direct and indirect habitat-shift descent theories for humans.

Table 4.7 Some human characters, arranged in four sets with comments on aquatic adaptiveness

Characters	Comments
Set 1	
Hairlessness, or almost Subcutaneous fat, or blubber Dilute urine Salty tears The diving reflex Ventro-ventral mating Floating infants, able to breathe	These characters are commonly found in various combinations in aquatic mammals of different evolutionary origins, but rarely in terrestrial, and particularly not dry savannah, mammals
Set 2	
Sheltered nostrils Head hair, with rest of body almost hairless (see Set 4)	These characters would be adaptive in an aquatic ecosystem
Set 3	
Upright stance Fine hand-grasping ability Communication by diverse calls, not by badge-displays and pheromones Enlarged and complex brain	These characters would be adaptive in an aquatic ecosystem, and would also be preadaptive to riverine savannah, thus allowing humans to enter the ecosystem, out-compete baboons and minimise predation
Set 4	
Feet not grasping Black skin, with pubic and underarm hair Capable of nocturnal as well as daylight activity	These characters are unique for a primate, and require adaptive explanations. They could be adaptive to an aquatic habitat

Coastal and riverine forest ape stock: Stage 1

Effective present-day utilisation of habitat by coastal and riverine-parkland monkeys derives from home-range opportunism, with troops returning daily from roosting sites to remembered feeding grounds, exploring as they go. Baboons penetrate far on to low ground-cover habitat (including maritime dunes) and even shoreline. An omnivorous coastal primate – that is, a baboon-sized, nut- and beetle-cracking insectivore–frugivore (Kay, 1984) – would find no shortage of foods on shore, in marshes and in tide-pools, on dunes (nesting birds) and beaches (breeding turtles) and in eruptions of foliage, fruits, insects, and so on at various times (Davidge, 1976). Even folivorous primates, such as the proboscis monkey, are well provided for. Tool use for termiting, clam-breaking and so on would be possible. Occasional small flotsam would be eaten, or larger fresh corpses torn apart.

The apes, however, would need to be fairly large, especially the males, and socially organised and aggressive for group defence against predators. Sleeping quarters would be either (remembered) suitable stands of trees high over water, or cliffs, or both. Only a few such sleeping quarters would be needed within the home range of a particular troop, but they would need to be spaced conveniently, and this factor would be the critical path limiting range size and resources availability. The social organisation would be based on large-troop self-defence, so would probably be a multi-male harem, resembling one or other of the two extant baboon strategies, with expendable young males functioning as sentinels. Young male dispersal would reduce inbreeding of such a kin group. Grooming would be an important social bonding device, and the productive ecosystem would allow plenty of time for it. Juveniles would have familiarised themselves with wading and swimming. Water entry for travel and feeding would follow, even by heavy adults, and especially in emergencies.

At this stage, the ape stock would be limited to the Rift Valley and coastal wetlands forests and open spaces by the postulated African Pliocene desertification. Thus stocks would be scattered over some 5000 km or more along the rift and the coasts of the Red Sea, if not more widely along the coasts of East Africa. Low-vagility-induced social grouping and limited juvenile wandering would generate clinal differences, possibly extensive enough to qualify as subspeciation, with those stocks most dependent on aquatic food and safety starting the appropriate anatomical and cultural changes, leading the clade to a uniquely primate set of aquatic adaptations – Stage 2.

An aquatic ape: Stage 2

The extreme aquatic habitat is now island and coastal open ground of marsh, lagoons, reef back-channels, beaches, rocky shores and dunes and restricted forest around the Red Sea, as water levels, temperatures and salinities fluctuate relative to the continuous or disjunct Gulf of Aden and Mediterranean Sea. Home ranging, including on to land, would continue. Night feeding opportunities would be taken at full moon and low spring tides. Stone-pounding to crack oysters, mussels, crabs and so on would occur (Figure 4.11). Sharp stones would be used to cut into freshly beached corpses. Much time would be spent exploiting lagoon and reef back-channel ecosystems with their marine grasses, invertebrate and fish faunas. Individuals would reach under water and make shallow dives for food. They would range these sheltered sea-water highways by wading and swimming. Ranging might be restricted to certain times of day and be undertaken cautiously, especially in turbid water, because of predation at certain sites by sharks and crocodiles (Figure 4.12). Escape from land-based predators, when the apes were on shore, would be by running back to water and swimming away.

Sleeping would be on islets (a significantly new resource, for nocturnal safety) or cliffs, or (less frequently) up trees, with safe locations remembered by troop elders. Social groups would be smaller and less rank-structured than in the earlier coastal apes, as a result of greater availability of safe habitat (lagoons and islets). Open-ground social defence by large and powerful individuals would be less necessary. Many social activities, including grooming, resting and playing, and ventro-ventral mating, çould occur in the water. Calls would travel long distances over calm water without distortion, and with reduced visual and chemical signalling, calls would become more complicated and meaningful.

Infants would float instinctively, the right way up, and adults would also float, especially in hypersaline sea water. The nose would have developed, and so would other anatomical and physiological adaptations to prolonged aquatic wading and swimming – for instance, bipedalism, an appropriate diving reflex, hair loss and subcutaneous fat (Morgan, 1972, 1982, this volume, chapter 2; Verhaegen, 1985, this volume, chapter 5), in part by neotenic mechanisms.

Some troops would be more land-based than others, reflecting learned differences in resource exploitation. (The aquatic ape was really a wading ape.) The changing archipelagos of the rifting Red Sea, however, would keep gene pools mixing between island and mainland, in spite of a low vagility between separated, largely swimming, troops. At this stage in the actively rifting African valley, the continentally moving section was subject to catastrophic habitat destruction by volcanoes, lava and fire. The oceanic rift of the Red Sea and Danakil Depression would be safer. At some stage the clade was reduced to one or more highly aquatic stocks in which novel adaptive features appeared, making up a unique primate aquatic ESS.

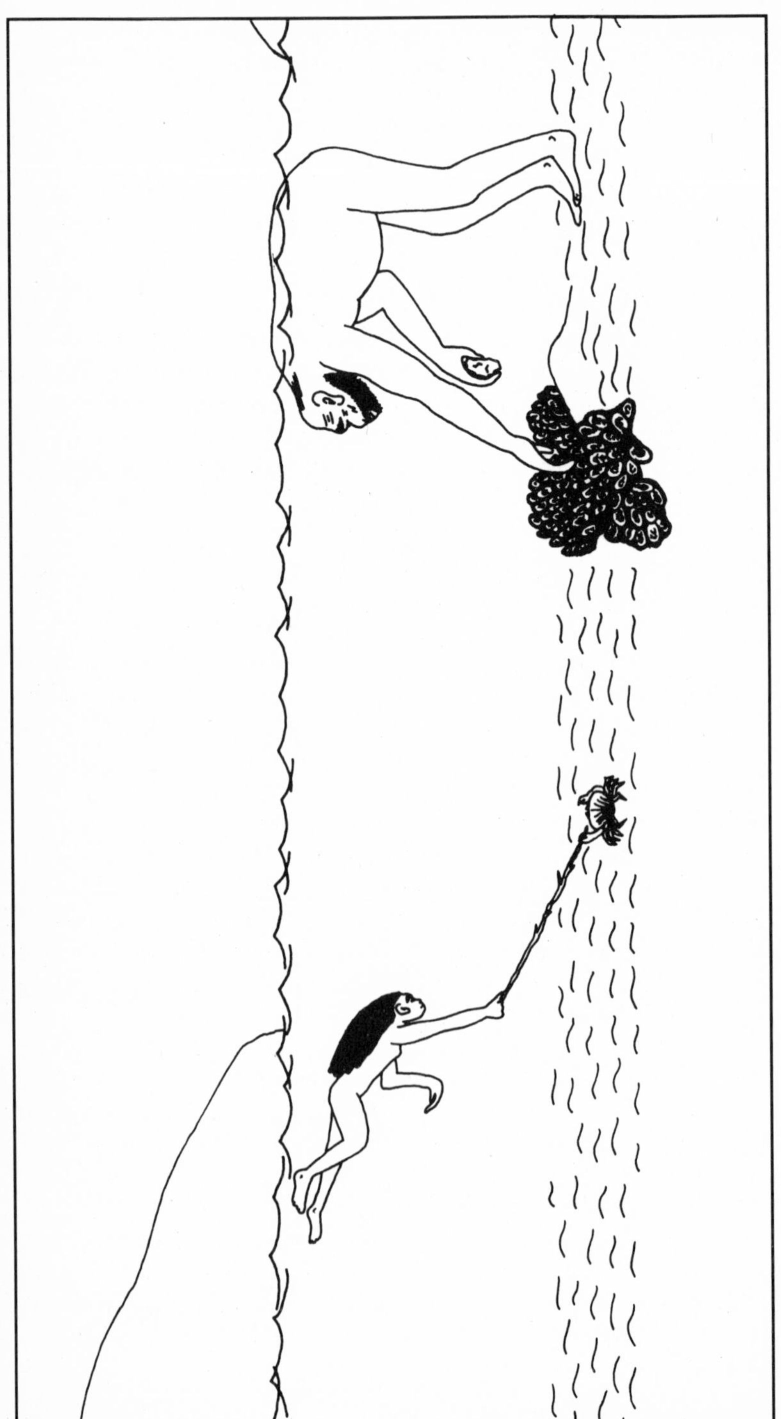

Figure 4.11 Active aquatic apes in a shallow lagoon.

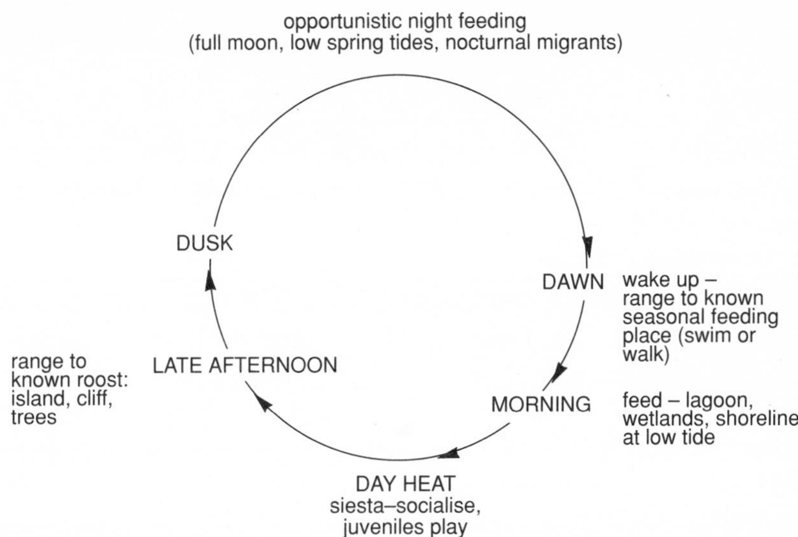

Figure 4.12 The daily cycle of an aquatic ape.

The return inland: Stage 3

The more land-based troops, now bipedal, gradually spread along Rift Valley riverine parkland during one or more cooler, less catastrophic, periods. This spread is the product of troop-splitting and the wandering of young adults, penetrating into a habitat now empty of competing ancestors. Baboons would be present, but can be out-competed. The spread inland is driven by population pressure. This arises from great success in exploiting the limited but productive wetlands habitat of the rift, and a climate providing riverine parkland for range expansion. Possibly it arises also from constraints to the aquatic ape heartland habitat by climatic or water-level changes, or both – for instance, a drying-out Danakil Depression. These hominids are either still largely herbivorous or omnivorous, depending on what stage in the aquatic ape clade the range expansion occurred, and whether it occurred more than once.

The Behrenmeyer sketch in Lewin (1984) shows some of the important habitat features. However, lake and river foraging is limited, due to underwater predators and large, intolerant species such as hippopotamuses. Aquatic foraging is limited to safe pools and shallow wading–gathering places. Anti-predator social defence on land is supported by rock-throwing, shouting, and waving and hammering branches. Sleeping spots are safe islets, narrow river spits, ox-bows, and so on. Trees can still be used. Perhaps thorn-barricading has already been learned. Social grouping is less intense now, with some separation into transient subgroups.

If omnivorous, males – largely young adults but led by a troop-dominant or high-ranking subordinate – periodically range grassland (but not penetrating far into the relatively dry and dangerous savannah) as hunting and scavenging parties. The troop, led by the most assertive and intelligent males or females, supported by the benevolent dominant, mostly range near the home base, gathering small foods and scouting for new sources, especially during new growth seasons. Both hunting and gathering groups carry food and materials back to the home base. Inactives (elders, infants, injured) may remain in the home safe spot during the daily ranging.

Monogamy occurs, not necessarily exclusively, as a consequence of a particularly complicated optimality balance between greater intelligence and the amount to learn (especially in developing language), some Darwinian selection by females for the mix of hominid qualities, and simple environmental management through tools and weapons, rendering the world a less dangerous place and thus allowing smaller groups. Meanwhile, juveniles are the academics and inventors of the troops, exploring and inventing from the examples of elders, so that new routes and practices work their way into the troops' repertoires of behaviours.

The aquatic ape is now poised as a proto-hominid for radiation into *Australopithecus* and *Homo*, along and near the African Rift Valley.

Extinguishing the aquatic ape is the part of the scenario that offers the most options. Restriction to limited habitat in the Red Sea through climatic change – for example, to the Danakil Depression only – could have been part of the population pressure dispersing fringe populations progressively inland. One or other form of coastal unsuitability could have occurred, such as cooling of sea water, or heating, super-salination and drying-out. If this did indeed happen, the aquatic ape disappeared anagenetically, and we are effectively the aquatic ape ourselves.

A second option is the elimination of the limited-distribution aquatic ape by catastrophic change, such as a tsunami caused by one or other of possibly several inundations of a Red Sea evaporated below the levels of an interglacial Gulf of Aden or the Mediterranean Sea.

A third option is that the aquatic ape was a victim of Pleistocene extinctions (Martin and Wright, 1967), as hominid descendants arrived at the coast and either out-competed or preyed on their ancestor; or that it succumbed to glacially induced climatic changes.

CONCLUSION

Responses to the question that forms the title of this chapter are as follows:

(1) In terms of marine ecology, the tropical coastal environment provides productive ecosystems exploitable by a range of extant monkeys. There is no evident reason to believe that an ape could not converge to successful adaptation there, nor that coastal ecosystems were unsuited for such convergent apes during similar, warmer or cooler, Pliocene and Pleistocene periods. The oceanically rifting Red Sea provides a uniquely suitable timing (starting about 5 million years ago) and location (mainland coast and archipelagos, open embayments and enclosed sea, at various times).

(2) In terms of primate behaviour, a number of species occupy a limited range of coastal ecosystems, with the critical path to the system presented by protective sleeping sites. Extant species resolve the problem by home ranging from a few remembered roosting places to opportunistically available and remembered foraging grounds, supplemented by a variety of predator-escape strategies, such as climbing trees and cliffs, and group defence. The aquatic ape clade could have resolved its predator avoidance and escape problems in similar primate ways, supplemented by water escape, nocturnal roosting on islands, and avoidance of remembered dangerous sites with underwater predators.

(3) An aquatic ape is a viable creature in terms of marine ecology and primate behaviour, and the hypothesis of its existence is testable by appropriate fossil search, as previously suggested by LaLumiere (1981). To a biologist there is no problem in evolving an aquatic ape: the biological problems come in clading it to humans and in later making it extinct.

The characters in Table 4.7 meet the need for a balanced and integrated behavioural set (an ethosystem), producing a viable animal in an aquatic habitat. What is more, it is a set of characters with potential for more efficient utilisation of riverine savannah than by the baboons already there. The combination of dexterity, intelligence and complex vocalisations is the preadaptation. The characters in Table 4.7 show that the primate line of descent, although including characters in the several acknowledged aquatic clades, nevertheless developed its own unique set, functional for an opportunistically upright, tailless, socialising, tropical, insectivorous–herbivorous ape living in and beside shallow water.

Savannah Theory protagonists also should, for comparison, produce a balanced eco-ethological adaptive descent scenario for primate ancestors at the right time (late Miocene and Pliocene) and in the right place. Most authors avoid the critical time punctuated in at 4–5 million years ago, although Kortlandt (1972) showed what was needed almost twenty years ago.

ACKNOWLEDGEMENTS
I am grateful for discussions over the years with Elaine Morgan, and correspondence with Marc Verhaegen. I have appreciated critical questions by my more reactionary students. My thanks go also to support staff: Greg Allen, Monique Van Hoek and Zena Rojak, my draftspersons; typists Kathleen Russell and Eleanore Floyd; and research assistant Tina Frisch.

REFERENCES

Andrews, P., 1985, The origin of the Cercopithecidae. In *Catalogue of the Primates in the British Museum (Natural History)*, ed. P.H. Napier (British Museum (Natural History)), Part III, 2.

Andrews, P., 1981, Species diversity and diet in monkeys and apes during the Miocene. In *Aspects of Human Evolution*, ed. C.B. Stringer (London: Taylor & Francis), 25–61.

Bally, R., 1986, A Bibliography of Sandy Beaches and Sandy Beach Organisms on the African Continent. *South Africa Natural Sciences Progress Report*, 126.

Bonatti, E., 1987, The rifting of continents. *Scientific American*, **256** (3), 97–103.

Chalmers, N., 1979, *Social Behaviour in Primates*, (London: E.J. Arnold).

Ciochon, R.L., 1982, Hominid cladistics and the ancestry of modern apes and humans. In *New Interpretations of Ape and Human Ancestry*, ed. R.L. Ciochon and R.S. Corruccini (New York: Plenum Press), 783–837.

Cochran, J.R., 1983, A model for development of the Red Sea. *Bulletin of the American Association of Petroleum Geologists*, **67** (1), 41–69.

Davidge, C., 1976, Activity patterns of baboons (*Papio ursinus*) at Cape Point. Unpublished MSc thesis, University of Cape Town.

Dover, G.A., 1986, Molecular drive in multi-gene families: how biological novelties arise, spread and are assimilated. *Trends in Genetics*, **2** (6), 159–64.

Eldredge, N. and Gould, S.J., 1972, Punctuated equilibria: an alternative to phyletic gradualism. In *Models in Paleobiology*, ed. T.J. Schopf (San Francisco: Freeman), 82–115.

Ellis, D.V., 1985, *Animal Behavior and its Applications* (Chelsea, USA: Lewis).

Ellis, D.V., 1986, Proboscis monkey and aquatic ape. *Sarawak Museum Journal*, **36** (57), 251–62.

Ellis, D.V., 1987, Swimming monkeys and apes – know their biology. *Proceedings of the 1987 Western Region Conference, American Association of Zoological Parks and Aquaria*, 361–7.

Fishelson, L., 1971, Ecology and distribution of the benthic fauna in the shallow waters of the Red Sea. *Marine Biology*, **10**, 113–33.

Fishelson, L., 1980, Marine reserves along the Sinai Peninsula (Northern Red Sea). *Helgolander Meeresuntersuchungen*, **33**, 624–40.

Girdler, R.W., 1984, The evolution of the Gulf of Aden and Red Sea in space and time. *Deep-Sea Research*, **31** (6-8A), 747–62.

Girdler, R.W. and Southren, T.C., 1987, Structure and evolution of the Northern Red Sea. *Nature*, **330**, 716–21.

Golding, R.R., 1972, A gorilla and chimpanzee exhibit at the University of Ibadan Zoo. *International Zoo Yearbook*, **12**, 71–6.

Goodall, J., 1986, *The Chimpanzees of Gombe* (Harvard: Belknap).

Hardy, A., 1960, Was man more aquatic in the past? *New Scientist*, **7**, 642–5.

Harrington, J.E., 1975, Field observations of social behavior of *Lemur fulvus fulvus* E. Geoffroy 1812. In *Lemur Biology*, ed. I. Tattersall and R.W. Sussman (New York: Plenum Press), 259–79.

Hartnoll, R.G., 1975, The Grapsidae and Ocypodidae (Decapoda: Brachyura) of Tanzania. *Journal of Zoology*, London, **177**, 305–28.

Kassas, M., 1957, On the ecology of the Red Sea coastal land. *Journal of Ecology*, **45**, 187–203.

Kavanagh, M., 1983, *A Complete Guide to Monkeys, Apes and Other Primates* (London: Cape).

Kay, R.F., 1984, On the use of anatomical features to infer foraging behavior in extinct primates. In *Adaptations for Foraging in Non-Human Primates*, ed. P.S. Rodman and J.G.H. Cant (New York: Columbia University Press), 21–52.

Kettlewell, H.B.D., 1959, Darwin's missing evidence. *Scientific American*, **200** (3), 48–53.

Kortlandt, A., 1972, *New Perspectives on Ape and Human Evolution* (Amsterdam: Stichting voor Psychobiologie).

Krebs, J.R. and Davies, N.B., 1981, *An Introduction to Behavioural Ecology* (Sunderland: Sinauer).

LaLumiere, L.P., 1981, Evolution of human bipedalism: a hypothesis about where it happened. *Philosophical Transactions of the Royal Society of London*, **B292**, 103–8.

Lawson, G.W., 1966, The littoral ecology of West Africa. *Oceanography and Marine Biology Annual Review*, **4**, 405–48.

Lewin, R., 1984, *Human Evolution. An Illustrated Introduction* (New York: Freeman).

Lewinsohn, C. and Fishelson, L., 1967, The Second Israel South Red Sea Expedition 1965 (general report). *Israel Journal of Zoology*, **16**, 59–68.

MacNae, W., 1968, A general account of the fauna and flora of mangrove swamps and forests in the Indo-West-Pacific region. *Advances in Marine Biology*, **6**, 73–270.

Martin, P.S. and Wright, H.E. Jr (eds), 1967, *Pleistocene Extinctions* (New Haven, Conn.: Yale University Press).

Martin, R.D. and May, R.M. , 1981, Outward signs of breeding. *Nature*, **293**, 8–9.

Maynard-Smith, J., 1975, *The Theory of Evolution* (London: Penguin Books).

McLachlan, A. and Erasmus, T., (eds), 1983, *Sandy Beaches as Ecosystems* (The Hague: Junk).

Messeri, P., 1978, Some observations on a littoral troop of yellow baboons. *Monitore Zoologico Italiano* (abstract only), **12**(1), 69.

Moore, H. B., 1972, Aspects of stress in the tropical marine environment. *Advances in Marine Biology*, **10**, 217–69.

Morgan, E., 1972, *The Descent of Woman* (London: Souvenir Press).

Morgan, E., 1982, *The Aquatic Ape* (London: Souvenir Press).

Morgan, E., 1991, *Why a new theory is needed.* (This volume, chapter 2.)

Napier, J.R. and Napier, P.H., 1985, *The Natural History of the Primates* (London: British Museum (Natural History)).

Natarajan, R. (ed.), 1975, *Recent Researches in Estuarine Biology* (Delhi: Hindustan Publishing Corporation).

Nishida, T., 1980, Local differences in responses to water among wild chimpanzees. *Folia Primatologica*, **33**, 189–209.

Ransom, T.W., 1981, *Beach Troop of the Gombe* (Bucknell University Press).

Ranwell, D.S., 1972, *Ecology of Salt Marshes and Sand Dunes* (London: Chapman & Hall).

Richards, C., 1987, *Human Evolution. An Introduction for the Behavioural Sciences* (London: Routledge & Kegan Paul).

Richards, P.W., 1952, *The Tropical Rain Forest. An Ecological Study* (Cambridge: Cambridge University Press).

Sarich, V., 1971, A molecular approach to the question of human origins. In *Background for Man: Readings in Physical Anthropology*, ed. V. Sarich and P. Dolhinow (Boston:

Little, Brown) 60–81.

Schilling, A., 1979, Olfactory communication in prosimians. In *The Study of Prosimian Behaviour*, ed. G.A. Doyle and R.D. Martin (New York: Academic Press), 461–542.

Stanley, S.M., 1984, Mass extinctions in the ocean. *Scientific American*, **250** (6), 64–72.

Stephenson, T.A. and Stephenson, A., 1972, *Life Between Tide-Marks on Rocky Shores* (San Francisco: Freeman).

Stoddart, D.R., 1969, Ecology and morphology of recent coral reefs. *Biological Review*, **44**, 433–98.

Strum, C., 1975, Life with the Pumphouse Gang. *National Geographic*, **147** (5), 671–91.

Tazieff, H., 1970, The Afar triangle. *Scientific American*, Dec. 133–41.

Tinbergen, N., 1969, *The Study of Instinct* (Oxford: Oxford University Press).

Uhara, S., 1976, Pygmy chimpanzees in Nkele, Zaire. A photographic introduction to the ecology. *Monkey*, **20**, 6–11.

Vannini, M., Chelazzi, G., Chelazzi, L., Ercolini, A., Ferrera, F., Messana, G., Messeri, P. and Pardi, L., 1977, Researches on the coast of Somalia. The shore and the dune of Sar Uahle. 13: Physical environment: geomorphological notes, climate and tides. *Italian Journal of Zoology* (new series, supplement 11), 249–71.

Venema, S.C., 1984, Fishery resources in the North Arabian Sea and adjacent waters. *Deep-Sea Research*, **31** (6–8A), 1001–18.

Verhaegen, M., 1985, The Aquatic Ape Theory: evidence and a possible scenario. *Medical Hypotheses*, **16**, 17–32.

Verhaegen, M., 1991, Aquatic features in fossil hominids? (This volume, chapter 5.)

Wiley, E.O., 1981, *Phylogenetics* (New York: Wiley-Interscience).

Wind, J., 1991, The non-aquatic ape: the Aquatic Ape Theory and the evolution of human drowning and swimming. (This volume, chapter 17.)

Young, J.Z., 1962, *The Life of Vertebrates* (Oxford: Oxford University Press).

5 Aquatic Features in Fossil Hominids?

Marc Verhaegen

SUMMARY

The hominid fossil record is examined in this chapter in the light of comparative anatomy and molecular biology. Four hypotheses are proposed:

(1) Nothing in the palaeontological data invalidates the idea of semi-aquatic adaptations in hominid evolution from more than 4 million years ago until less than 1 million years ago.
(2) African hominoids – humans, chimpanzees and gorillas – are descended from australopithecine ancestors.
(3) Early australopithecine locomotion resembled that of the modern proboscis monkey, with potential for hanging from branches with the arms, swimming and diving, and wading bipedally.
(4) *Homo erectus* and *H. neanderthalensis* possessed adaptations for littoral diving, and lost the arboreal adaptations of their australopithecine ancestors.

PALAEO–ENVIRONMENTAL EVIDENCE

Hominid fossils have been found in places that either are or were the sites of rivers or lakes. Pre-, gracile and robust Australopithecines, as well as early *Homo* (Tables 5.1, 5.2; Figure 5.1), stem from very wet palaeo-environments with algae, sponges or reeds, and bivalves, swamp-snails, crabs, fish, frogs, aquatic turtles, crocodiles, water-fowl and hippos, often in the shallow water of a lake margin, lagoon or river delta (for example, Pickford, 1975; Ward and Hill, 1987; Martyn and Tobias, 1967; Radosevich and Retallack, 1988; Johanson, Taieb and Coppens, 1982; Bonnefille, 1976; Brain, 1981, p. 189; Carney *et al.*, 1971; Leakey, Clarke and Leakey, 1971; Ninkovich and Burckle, 1978; Potts, 1988). Lucy, the most complete skeleton of an *Australopithecus afarensis*, from Hadar, was discovered amid crocodile and turtle eggs and crab claws in near-shore deposits, and Johanson and Taieb (1976) preclude the possibility that Lucy's remains had been moved over any great distance. Also, the *Homo erectus* boy WT–15000,* an even more complete skeleton, was found amid typical lacrustine forms: 'the only other fauna found so far in the fossiliferous bed are many opercula of the swamp snail *Pila*, a few bones of the catfish *Synodontis* and two fragments of indeterminate large mammal bone' (Brown, *et al.*, 1985). Some fragmentary fossils – often skull bones or mandibles, the skeletal parts that

* See Table 5.2 for abbreviations used to denote East African fossil sites.

Table 5.1 Survey of fossil hominids

Species	
Australopithecus afarensis, c.4–3mya,* E. Africa: e.g., Lucy from Hadar	
A. africanus, c.3–2.5 mya, S. Africa	
A. robustus, c.2–1.5 mya, S. Africa	the robust Australopithecines
A. boisei, c.2.5–1 mya, E. Africa	the robust Australopithecines
Homo (Australopithecus?) habilis, c.2 mya, E. Africa	
H. erectus, less than 2 mya, Africa, Java, China	
H. neanderthalensis or *H. sapiens neanderthalensis*, prior to 35,000 years ago, Europe and Middle East	

Not all species are well defined, nor do all hominid fossil remains fit well into one of these 'species'. E.g., *A. afarensis*, *H. habilis* and *H. erectus* are not very homogeneous (Ferguson, 1987a, 1987b). The large intraspecific variation could be due to being composed of different taxa (*afarensis* or *habilis*), to a wide geographical (*erectus*), or temporal (*boisei* or *erectus*) distribution or to large sexual dimorphism. The Australopithecines prior to 4 mya are often referred to as *A.* cf. *afarensis* or pre-Australopithecines.

Table 5.2 Some East African fossil sites: abbreviations used

Abbr.	Site		
AL	Afar locality, Hadar in Ethiopia		
ER	East Rudolf, e.g., Koobi Fora		KNM = Kenya National Museum
WT	West Turkana or West Lake Rudolf		KNM = Kenya National Museum
CH	Chesowanja (late *A. boisei*)		KNM = Kenya National Museum
KP	Kanapoi	pre-Australopithecines (Figure 5.1 (b))	KNM = Kenya National Museum
TH	Tugen Hills	pre-Australopithecines (Figure 5.1 (b))	KNM = Kenya National Museum
LT	Lothagam	pre-Australopithecines (Figure 5.1 (b))	KNM = Kenya National Museum
OH	Olduvai hominid	Tanzania	
LH	Laetoli hominid	Tanzania	

* Million years ago.

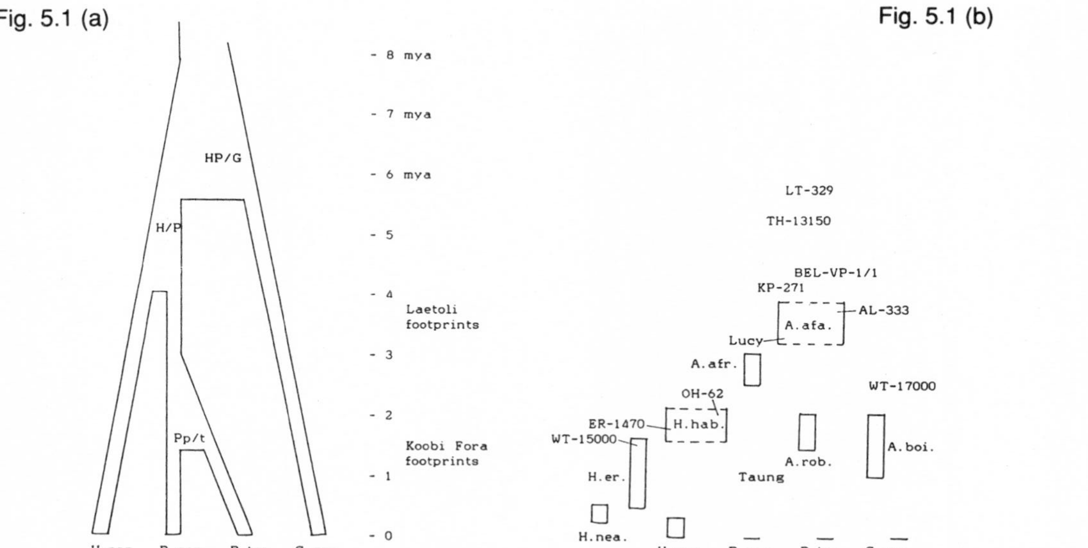

Figure 5.1 Evolutionary tree of African hominids.

(a) *Molecular tree* (after Hasegawa, Kishino and Yano, 1985; 1987)
HP/G = split between *Homo-Pan* and *Gorilla*; H/P = split between *Homo* and *Pan*; Pp/t = split between pygmy chimp (bonobo) and common chimpanzee.

mya = million years ago

(b) *Fossil tree* (after Delson, 1987)
BEL–VP–1/1 = pre-australopithecine frontal bone from Ethiopia (Clarke *et al.*, 1984); LT–329 and TH–13150 = *A.* cf. *afarensis* mandibles (Ward and Hill, 1987); KP–271 = Kanapoi distal humerus.

are left until last in the consumption process of large cats (Morden, 1988) – of *A. afarensis* from Laetoli come from wind-worked tuffs, but even these were found not far from ancient rivers (Leakey *et al.*, 1976). Also, the australopithecine remains found in South African cave deposits were probably the left-overs of sabre-tooths or leopards that were eating their prey in a riverside tree (Brain, 1981).

The findings do not constitute proof that the early hominids lived exclusively in or near the water. Watery sites provide silt in which bones are more likely to be preserved, and in river-valley locations there may be later water erosion to expose the layers which contain the fossils. It is possible to argue that while some of these hominids lived and died by the lake, others may have been living out on the open savannah, and that the prevalence of watery locations is indicative of the preconditions for fossilisation rather than of the hominid's habitat.

One palaeo-anthropological objection advanced against the Aquatic Ape Theory is the negative one that 'long-term adaptation along African coastlines should have left some traces, particularly if early hominids were exploiting shellfish (whose remains preserve remarkably well)' (Jurmain *et al.*, 1981, p. 326; see also Washburn and Moore, 1980, p. 132). But 'aquatic' does not necessarily mean 'marine'. Our ancestors could have been semi-aquatic in tropical lagoons, or in gallery or mangrove forests. They could have eaten vegetables instead of animal food. Besides, primates are not in the habit of collecting food and taking it back to a base. If they ate shellfish they would have originally eaten them only a few at a time *in situ*, as sea-otters do. Dating from at least about 0.3 million years ago, when *Homo* had acquired the practice of communal eating, traces of shellfish exploitation are found, for example, at Terra Amata in southern France.

COMPARATIVE ANATOMY OF FOSSIL HOMINIDS

Body size

Body enlargement, when comparison is made with Old World monkeys, is obvious in fossil and living hominoids (see Tables 5.3, 5.4). A body weight of more than 30 kg is rare in arboreal animals, whereas increased body mass is a striking feature of all aquatic mammals as compared with their closest terrestrial relatives.

However, increased body weight cannot in itself be regarded as evidence of aquatic influence, since it can also be seen – though usually on a less spectacular scale – in other circumstances (Simpson, 1959; Clutton-Brock and Harvey, 1977). For example, animals tend to be larger when they live in colder environments (Bergmann's Rule), when they live in open grasslands as opposed to forests, or in seas as opposed to rivers. A shift from insectivorousness to frugivorousness, or from frugivorousness to folivorousness, could also favour a larger body size. Ground-dwellers tend to be larger than climbers, so that ceasing to be arboreal may in itself have been a major factor leading to increased body size.

Brain volume

The cranial capacity of the Australopithecines ranged from 375 to 525 ml, which is about as large as that of apes (Tobias, 1983; Falk, 1985, 1987). There has been a marked increase since early *Homo* ER–1470, who had a cranial capacity of probably more than 750 ml (Falk, 1980). Neanderthal man had a brain 15 per cent larger than modern man. Various theories have been advanced to account for the brain enlargement in *Homo* (Table 5.5). One is the evolution of speech (Verhaegen, 1988); songbirds also have large relative brain size (as measured by encephalisation quotient) compared with other birds (Wyles, Kunkel and Wilson, 1983). Other suggested explanations are the danger of over-heating the brain (Fialkowski, 1986), the need for throwing accuracy (Calvin, 1983), and the possible intellectual demands imposed by tool use, hunting or warfare (McHenry, 1982).

Most of these explanations are related to behaviour rather than to habitat, but one environment which appears to increase brain size is *water.* Brain enlargement is very common in aquatic mammals, notably pinnipeds (seals, walruses and sea-lions) and toothed whales (sperm and killer whales, dolphins and porpoises). A few years ago it was thought that a higher basal metabolism in marine mammals accounted for this (Armstrong, 1983), but recently more accurate measurements have failed to discern a difference in metabolic rate between terrestrial and aquatic mammals (e.g., Folkow and Blix, 1987). Another suggestion is made by Michael Crawford: since omega–3 fatty acids result from a marine or a mixed land/water diet, the very high content of these marine-based fatty acids in the human nervous system could have permitted – as in dolphins – the evolution of very large brains (S.C. Cunnane, personal communication). On the other hand, brain enlargement may be due to the same reason as body enlargement: the need for miniaturisation of the body and especially of the brain is low in an aquatic milieu, because the surrounding water greatly reduces the energy costs of sustaining the extra weight (Verhaegen, 1988).

Explanations advanced for modern man having a somewhat smaller brain than his ancestors and than Neanderthal man are summarised in Table 5.6.

Brain endocasts

Fossil brain endocasts make it possible to attempt to date the emergence of typically human brain centres. Two of these are closely connected

Table 5.3 Classification of living primates

I Strepsirhini (e.g., lemurs, indris, loris, galagos)
II Tarsiers
III Anthropoids (monkeys, apes and man):

- A Platyrrhini or New World monkeys (e.g., spider-monkeys, marmosets)
- B Catarrhini or Old World monkeys (Africa and Asia)
    - 1 Cercopithecoidea or Old World monkeys:
        - (a) Colobinae (e.g., langurs, proboscis monkey (*Nasalis larvatus*))
        - (b) Cercopithecinae (e.g., macaques, baboons)
    - 2 Hominoidea (apes and man):
        - (a) Hylobatidae or lesser apes (gibbons and siamang, S. E. Asia)
        - (b) Large hominoids (great apes and man):
            - – orang-utan
            - – African hominoids: man, chimp and bonobo, gorilla

Table 5.4 Living hominid and pongid species

Pongo pygmaeus or orang-utan, the great ape from S.E. Asia

Gorilla gorilla	)
	)
Pan troglodytes or common chimpanzee	) the great apes from Africa
	)
Pan paniscus or bonobo or pygmy chimp	)

Homo sapiens sapiens or anatomically modern man

Table 5.5 Brain weights of various mammals, adult and premature, weighing 50–70 kg (Smith, 1984)

Man	c.1300 g
Porpoise	537 g
Great apes	c.400–450 g
Zebra	410 g
Ruminants	140–334 g
Suids	125–178 g
Carnivores	154–175 g

Table 5.6 Explanations for neolithic reduction of cranial capacity in man (partly after Henneberg, 1988)

- auto-domestication (domestic animals have 20–30% less brain tissue than their wild relatives)
- 'stasis' between two punctionalistic leaps
- selection for smaller body size (e.g., after leaving the aquatic habitat, or as a result of population growth and subsequent food shortages)
- relaxation of selection for intelligence, with the development of more complex societies (cf. auto-domestication)
- internal reorganisation of the brain superseding further increases in size (cf. computer miniaturisation)
- decreased protein consumption in the Holocene
- reduced muscle robustness or muscle control
- by-product of generalised structural reduction (gracilisation of the skeleton)
- selection for smaller brain weight (e.g., after leaving the aquatic habitat)

with speech. *Broca's area* in the left frontal lobe coordinates the primary motor cortex that commands the muscles of mouth and larynx, for instance, for speaking. *Wernicke's area* in the left parieto-temporal lobe is used in decoding spoken language.

Tobias (1983) was unable to detect Wernicke's area in fossil endocasts earlier than *H. habilis*, around 2 million years ago. Both Tobias and Falk (1983) believe that the Australopithecines, lacking this structure, could not have been capable of verbal communication. Tobias detected signs of a Broca-like expansion in *A. africanus* fossils of about 2.5 million years ago, but this is questioned by Falk, who believes that only early *Homo* ER–1470 of about 2 million years ago had an obvious Broca's area, and that the Australopithecines still had an ape-like frontal lobe. Morgan and Verhaegen (1986) speculated that the earliest Broca-like structures were an adaptation for improved control of mouth and breathing muscles as required in a diving mammal, an essential precondition for the evolution of speech.

Falk (1986) also studied the cranial venous sinus system in fossil hominid endocasts, and found that the occipital/marginal venous sinus was enlarged in *A. afarensis* and the robust Australopithecines, but seldom in other hominoids (except human foetuses and neonates). She believed that the enlarged occipital/marginal sinus was a haemodynamic adaptation to incipient bipedalism. Extensive, valveless, anastomotic vertebral venous networks are found in man (Falk and Conroy, 1983) and also in a variety of other mammals subjected to frequent and sudden changes in head and trunk position, possibly because they operate in a medium where movement is three-dimensional – that is, water or air. Examples include climbing or flying mammals such as sloths, cats and bats, and especially diving mammals such as seals, sea-cows and whales. Slijper (1979) suggests that aquatic mammals use these venous networks to buffer the sudden pressure changes they encounter when diving.

Still another suggestion is made by Cabanac (1986). He believes that our extensive venous networks at the skull base are part of a cooling system of the brain (see also Wheeler, 1985; but cf. Verhaegen, this volume, chapter 11).

Table 5.7 Explanations for skull vault thickening in fossil *Homo* (partly after Foster, 1987)

- the insertion of very powerful masticatory and/or nuchal muscles on the skull vault
- mechanical protection of the brain
- a negative correlation with brain capacity
- a positive correlation with cranial capacity
  - with certain hunting habits
  - with inter-group aggression
  - with sexual dimorphism

Cranial vault

H. erectus, even more than *H. neanderthalensis*, had very thick cranial vaults, thicker than those of monkeys and apes, or of modern man; and thicker also than those of *H. habilis* and the Australopithecines (Kennedy, 1985). Several explanations have been proposed for this feature (Table 5.7). Most of them are variations on the theme of mechanical protection for the growing brain: they relate this to behavioural factors such as hunting, inter-group aggression and sexual dimorphism.

The heavy cranial vault of *H. erectus* was accompanied by very dense bones in the rest of the skeleton (humerus, ulna, pelvis, femur, tibia). These cannot have been directly related to protection of the brain, and would be less obviously advantageous in a hunting hominid for whom speed was at a premium. Really heavy skeletons are only seen in slow littoral bottom-feeders like sea-cows, probably compensating for their abundant subcutaneous fat (density 0.9) in a milieu with a density of 1.026 instead of the 1.000 of pure water (Hildebrand, 1974, pp. 586–7; Wilson, 1979, pp. 793–4). The fast-swimming seals have thinner skulls than dogs (van Nie, personal communication), but the slow walruses have extremely thick cranial vaults, presumably for keeping the head down easily while seeking shellfish. If *H. erectus* had thick skull bones for the same reason, he too must have sought food at the lake or sea bottom.

We can deduce that at least some of the Neanderthals were habitual divers. Skulls of middle-aged Shanidar I and Chapelle-aux-Saints males had extensive and bilateral ear exostoses, while the *H. erectus* skull–X from Zhoukoudian demonstrated a discrete lesion in one ear (Kennedy, 1986). In modern man, these anomalies are only seen in populations who exploit marine or freshwater resources through diving in water of 18°C or less; they are almost invariably 'associated with a history of cold water exposure over long periods of time'; 'a long and impressive history of aquatic habits, usually beginning before their teenage years, was described by all patients' (quoted in Kennedy). There is no reason to believe that this was different in *H. neanderthalensis*. It strongly suggests that the male Neanderthals – at least in some seasons – dived regularly, probably every day, in the cold rivers along which they lived.

Another feature of the cranial vault in *H. erectus* and *H. neanderthalensis*, especially the males, is the pronounced supra-orbital torus (bony eyebrow ridge), found also in robust Australopithecines, African apes and baboons. It is weakly or variably developed in modern humans, orang-utans, gibbons and some Old World monkeys, and is absent in all smaller primates and most other mammals. Masticatory and eye-protective explanations are usually advanced (Table 5.8).

Table 5.8 Explanations for supra-orbital torus development in *H. erectus* and *H. neanderthalensis* (after Russell and replies, 1985)

- a differential growth process among various regions of the skull due to non-mechanical factors
- an allometric correlation with large body size
- a defence against possible blows, especially in primates with their frontally placed eyes
- an adaptation that resists the stress over the eyes during anterior biting, e.g., before the use of fire (cooking)
- a consequence of powerful masticatory muscle insertions just dorsal to the torus (cf. Table 5.9)

Compatible with these explanations is that the presence of a well-developed torus in fossil man in contrast with modern man is a result of the more dorsally placed brain. In *H. erectus* and *H. neanderthalensis* the brain case is placed behind the face rather than above it, and it is also flattened (platycephalic), with its widest point behind the ears, at the base of the skull and not well up in the vault as in *H. sapiens* (Stringer, 1978). Both the flattening and the dorsal shift of the brain case seem to indicate a streamlining of the skull, such as would be required by the diving lifestyle suggested by other features of fossil man (Figure 5.2 (b)). For other reasons suggested for the long, low skulls of *H. erectus* and *H. neanderthalensis*, see Table 5.9.

Table 5.9 Traditional explanations for platycephaly in *H. erectus* and *H. neanderthalensis*

- a much stronger development of the posterior sensory brain cortex in Neanderthal man than in modern man
- the presence in *H. erectus* and *H. neanderthalensis* of strong masticatory and nuchal muscles that kept the skull vault low
- a correlation with skull vault thickness (see Table 5.7)
- obstetric factors
- a lowering of the superiorly projecting skull as in modern man, according to Allen's Rule that projecting body parts are shortened in colder environments

Skull pneumatisation

All apes and monkeys have maxillary and sphenoidal paranasal air sinuses, but frontal and ethmoidal sinuses are only present in adult African hominoids. They are absent in orangs, gibbons and monkeys (Blaney, 1986). In fossil hominids the volumes of air sinuses in different skull regions are difficult to assess. Nevertheless, a few trends may be discerned (Table 5.10). Most fossil hominids, especially early Australopithecines and early *Homo*, had larger air sinuses than living hominoids. As we approach modern man, pneumatisation became more concentrated in the paranasal region, in particular the frontal region in the Neanderthals. For sinus morphology in other animals, see Table 5.11. Little is known about the role of these structures. Blanton and Biggs (1968), after listing nine possible roles for the air sinuses, found none of them convincing (Table 5.12).

In freshwater animals that usually swim with their heads above the water surface, large air sinuses could be advantageous. Freshwater crocodiles are among the few reptiles with large paranasal sinuses (Romer and Parsons, 1977, p. 457), and A. W. Proetz proposes that in crocodiles the sinuses 'have no other function than to lighten the skull, permitting better floatability of the head and therefore maintaining the nostrils above the surface' (quoted in Blanton and Biggs). It is conceivable that the Neanderthals developed strongly enlarged frontal sinuses for a similar purpose – to keep their noses more easily above the freshwater surface (Figure 5.2 (c)).

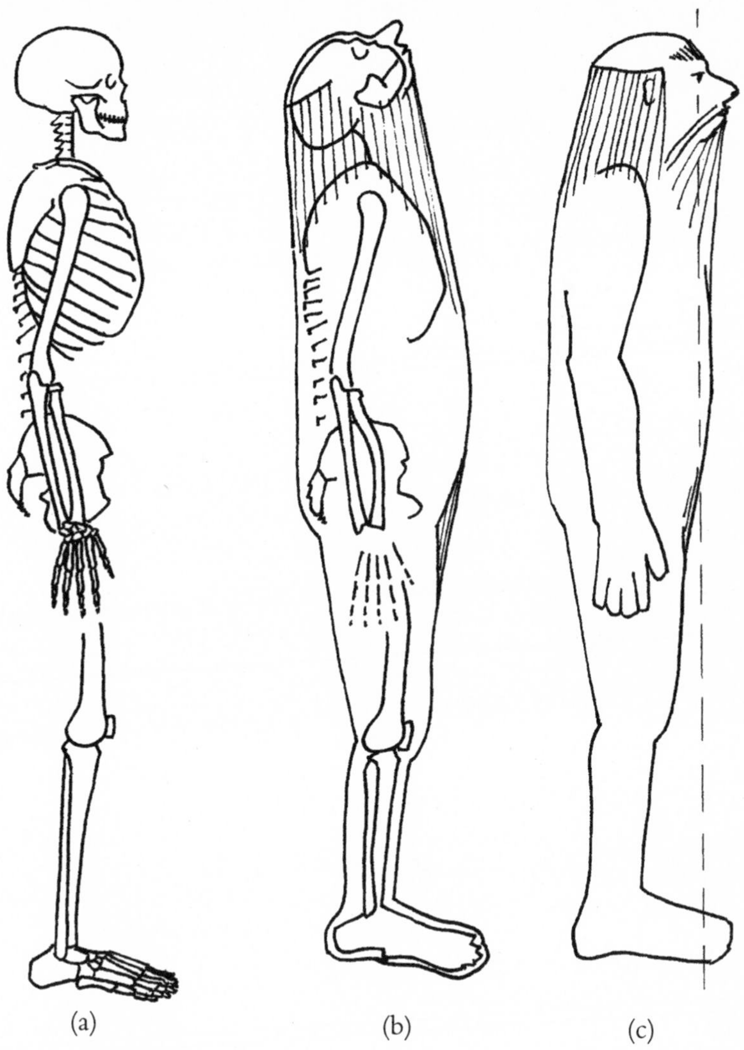

Figure 5.2 Side view of a male Neanderthal compared with modern man.

(a) modern skeleton; (b) diving Neanderthal (note streamlining of head and body); (c) floating Neanderthal (note projection of nose above water surface).

A reconstruction is necessarily speculative in respect of the soft tissues. The assumptions made in (b) and (c) are that the nostrils were anterior, the hair long, the belly thick and the head bald on top (Verhaegen, 1985, 1987a, 1987b). (b) and (c) are based on comparisons of Neanderthal fossils with modern man: skull lower and longer; mid-face projects anteriorly, jaws more robust; spinous processes of vertebrae longer and more horizontal; superior pubic rami reach more anteriorly; hand slightly broader, little finger longer; radius and femur bowed more strongly; patella larger; tibia somewhat shorter.

Table 5.10 Pneumatisation in fossil hominids

- *A. afarensis* AL–199 and AL–200–1 had large maxillary sinuses (Johanson and Taieb, 1976)
- Temporal squama pneumatisation in *A. afarensis* AL–333–45, early *A. boisei* WT–17000, and some gorillas and male chimps, was more pronounced than in later *A. boisei*, S. African Australopithecines and *H. habilis* (Kimbel, White and Johanson, 1984; Johanson, 1985; McHenry, 1986; Walker *et al.*, 1986)
- Robust Australopithecines generally show more extensive paranasal pneumatisation and inflated mastoids, but less inflated temporal squamae (Leakey and Walker, 1988; Wood, 1978; Kimbel, White and Johanson, 1984)
- The S. African Australopithecine from Taung shows a much larger maxillary sinus than comparable chimp or human juveniles; pneumatisation has also extended into the hard palate (as in *A. robustus* and *P. troglodytes*) and zygoma (Conroy and Vannier, 1987)
- Early *Homo* ER–1470 had extensive mastoid, maxillary and especially frontal pneumatisation (Day *et al.*, 1974)
- The mid-Pleistocene *H. erectus* from Bodo had extensive maxillary sinuses (Conroy *et al.*, 1978)
- The frontal sinuses in modern man (in blacks more than in Eskimos and Australian aborigines), and certainly in Neanderthal man, are much larger than in apes (Blaney, 1986)

External nose

The human projecting external nose became apparent in *H. erectus*, most markedly in the superior nasal region (Franciscus and Trinkaus, 1988b). In Neanderthals the whole mid-face region was very protruding, with the large, broad, highly placed nasal aperture projecting anteriorly (Figure 5.2 (c)). The Monte Circeo skull from the Tyrrhenian coast, which had the lowest skull vault of all Neanderthals, also had the most highly placed nasal aperture (Moerman, 1977, pp. 265, 144). When Otto Hauser discovered the Moustier Neanderthal in 1908, the external nose was still recognisable, and the nostrils were directed more anteriorly instead of inferiorly as in modern man (Moerman, p. 80).

Special adaptation of the nasal aperture is a feature of all aquatic mammals, and of mammals with an external nose: the proboscis monkey and some closely related colobine monkeys, saiga, elephant seal and bladder-nose seal, elephants, tapirs, swine and peccaries, coati and some other carnivores, and diverse sniffing insectivores. In *Homo*, the external nose has been viewed as a compensation for the reduction of the anterior dentition, or as an adaptation for moisture conservation in arid environments (Table 5.13). The Neanderthal protruding mid-face has been explained as a masticatory adaptation for better opposing rotational forces on the anterior teeth (Rak, 1986), or as an adaptation to extreme cold (Coon, 1962; but see Rak). An aquatic explanation is the lengthening of the airways for better closure, the streamlining of the head when diving (Figure 5.2 (b)), and the projection of the nose above the water surface when swimming on the back (Figure 5.2 (c)), as sea-otters do when opening shellfish, or proboscis monkey babies clinging to their swimming mothers (Ellis, 1986).

In contrast with *Homo*, the Australopithecines still had the flat, non-protruding nose of their primate ancestors. Nevertheless, a few peculiarities may be noticed. As in all hominoid taxa, the nasal region is highly variable (Eckhardt, 1987, 1988). Guttered margins of the nasal aperture are especially prominent in robust Australopithecines (Walker *et al.*, 1986). Robust Australopithecines also display a unique inferior tapering of the nasal bones. The only living primate in which a similar condition exists is the snub-nosed langur, a close relative of the proboscis monkey (Corruccini and Ciochon, 1979). The function of these adaptations is not clear, but might be connected with incipient aquaticness.

Table 5.11 Pneumatisation in other animals

Extensive pneumatisation	*Small paranasal sinus*
Crocodiles (freshwater)	Most reptiles
Most fossil hominids	Monkeys, carnivores
Swine	Hippopotamuses
Elephants	Marine mammals

- Most mammals (e.g., monkeys, lions and cats) have small sinuses with broad ostia, unlike man (Blanton and Biggs, 1968; Harrison, 1958)
- Dogs have larger frontal sinuses, which are almost completely filled with ethmo-turbinates used in olfaction (V. E. Negus, in Blanton and Biggs, 1968)
- Most herbivores (e.g., koalas, horses, ruminants and especially swine) have well developed sinuses (Loeffler, 1981, pp. 111–31; Kratzing, 1984)
- Elephants have very large sinuses, hippos (which usually stand and walk on the river bottom) very small ones
- Marine mammals have reduced or absent sinuses other than those associated with the middle ear (Hempleman and Lockwood, 1978, p. 27)

Table 5.12 Possible explanations for skull pneumatisation

1 *As surveyed by Blanton and Biggs (1968):*
- to impart resonance to the voice
- to humidify and warm the inspired air
- to increase the area of the olfactory membrane (dog frontal sinus, see Table 5.11)
- to absorb shock applied to the head
- to secrete mucus for keeping the nasal chambers moist
- to thermally insulate the nervous centres
- to aid facial growth and architecture
- to exist as evolutionary remains and/or unwanted space
- to lighten the bones of the skull for maintenance of proper balance of the head

2 *Other or more detailed possibilities:*
- to set wider apart eyes or ears (stereo), horns or antlers (herbivores), teeth or tusks (elephants); or to permit the insertion of masticatory (herbivores) or other cranial muscles
- to make the head look bigger for intra- or inter-specific intimidation
- to narrow the nasal passages, e.g., for better closure during diving
- to keep more air – and oxygen – in the body during diving
- to lower the specific gravity of (parts of) the head for floatability and/or for stabilising the position of the head in or outside the water

Table 5.13 Possible functions of an external nose

- preparation of inspired air: e.g., dust-filtering, wet cleaning, purification, humidification and temperature modification (Franciscus and Trinkaus, 1988b)
- water and/or heat retention from expired air: e.g., moisture retention in dry climates in *H. erectus* and *H. neanderthalensis* (Franciscus and Trinkaus, 1988a,b)
- water and/or heat dissipation: e.g., heat dissipation through broad nares of a possibly hyperactive Neanderthal man (Franciscus and Trinkaus, 1988a)
- secondary response to the primary reduction of facial and dental dimensions
- visual intra-specific intimidation (as in the bladder-nose seal, and possibly the proboscis monkey)
- sound resonance (see also Ellis, 1986)
- odour detection: e.g., when sniffing in wet ground (swine, coati, etc.)
- manipulation of objects (elephant), or rooting in wet ground
- snorkel or nose-closing device in the water, by lengthening and/or narrowing the airways (Morgan, 1982, pp. 80–2)

Spine

The Australopithecines had the foramen magnum located relatively farther back on the skull base than modern man, but less so than the gorilla or common chimp. Some of the males, especially, had a large and steeply rising nuchal plane, almost similar to that in apes (Kimbel, White and Johanson, 1984; Johanson, 1985). *H. erectus* also had a much larger nuchal plane than *H. sapiens*. These features could have been correlated with an often more dorsiflexed head, and perhaps with the smaller brain case.

A. afarensis, like *Homo*, exhibits a univertebral pattern for the first rib: the head of this rib articulates only with the body of the first thoracic vertebra, and there is no articular facet for the first rib on the seventh (the most inferior) cervical vertebra as in other mammals (Ohman, 1986). The only exceptions are some kangaroos which have a different sort of univertebral first-rib articulation, and some chimpanzees, which are intermediary in showing quasi-facets on the seventh vertebra. Ohman postulates four hypotheses: the univertebral pattern 'increases the volume of the neck, which would compensate for the loss of the laryngeal airsac system in hominid vocalisation; it is a consequence of the barrel-shaped thorax in hominids; of functional modifications in the hominid shoulder girdle; and/or modifications in the hominid first rib while breathing in an upright stance'.

A more barrel-shaped thorax (as in aquatic mammals), certain shoulder girdle modifications (for example, for swimming with arms above the head, or for streamlining), and a greater capacity for a deep intake of breath would also be needed in an aquatic milieu. The univertebral pattern may also have allowed a greater cervico-thoracic dorsiflexion of the head (Figure 5.2 (b)), and probably a greater flexibility of the first rib. More flexible ribs are a feature of aquatic mammals (Hildebrand, 1974, p. 591; Hempleman and Lockwood, 1978, p. 27).

The spinous processes of the vertebrae are longer and less inclined in *A. afarensis*, *H. erectus* and *H. neanderthalensis* than in modern humans (Johanson and White, 1979; Brown *et al.*, 1985; Trinkaus, 1987). Probably this was related to a thicker muscle layer, and perhaps a thicker fat layer, than in modern man, so that the dorsal mid-line reached farther backwards, which made the trunk rounder, less dorsoventrally flattened than in *H. sapiens*. In aquatic mammals a round trunk helps to withstand the water pressure on the lungs, especially in the deep-diving species (C.J. van Nie, personal communication).

Thorax

Quadrupedal terrestrial mammals have latero-laterally flattened thoraxes (Figure 5.3 (a). So do most monkeys (Figure 5.3 (b)). The human thorax, however, is rather broad, and it is flattened in the opposite plain, dorsoventrally. It is difficult to reconstruct the precise shape of the thorax in the different fossil hominids. P. Schmid believes that Lucy had an ape-like thorax (inverted funnel-shaped), while C.O. Lovejoy considers that it more nearly resembled our own barrel-shaped thorax (Ohman, 1986). The Neanderthals must have had a very wide thorax (Moerman, 1977, pp. 133, 235).

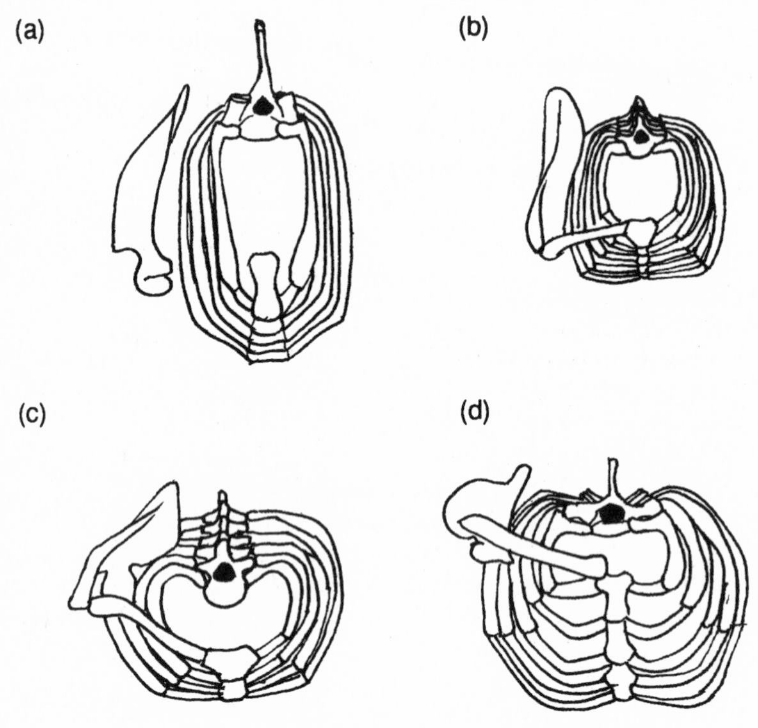

Figure 5.3 Comparison of thorax form, after Campbell (1974, figure 4.10) and Hildebrand (1974, figure 20.6).

Cranial view of thorax and shoulder girdle (scapula and clavicle, right half) of (a) a quadrupedal terrestrial mammal: deer (*Odocoileus*); (b) a quadrupedal arboreal mammal: monkey (*Macaca*); (c) a bipedal mammal: man (*Homo*); (d) a semi-aquatic mammal: beaver (*Castor*).

Bipedality or normally upright position is the classic explanation for having a round thorax. A barrel-shaped thorax was noted by E.J. Slijper in a goat born without forelimbs, which jumped forward on its hind limbs in a semi-upright position (Ohman). The narrow chest of quadrupeds can best be explained as an adaptation for reducing the distance between the points of support of the forelimbs, and for allowing the scapula to rotate in the same plane in which the leg swings (see Figure 5.3 (a); and Hildebrand, 1974, p. 494). A broad thorax is seen in arm-hangers like the great apes (inverted funnel), gibbons (barrel-shaped) and spider-monkeys (Hildebrand, figure 22.9). Perhaps these brachiators do not need a latero-laterally flattened chest because they hang with their arms rather than lean upon them. Or the broad thorax could be an adaptation for maintaining an erect posture (as in Slijper's goat), or for being able to reach farther laterally with the arms with more dorsal scapulae (Figure 5.3 (c)).

Most marine mammals have round, barrel-shaped thoraxes (Slijper, 1979). Human foetuses, too, have round thoraxes, but adults have broader thoraxes, as do the common seals (van Nie, 1983) and freshwater mammals like the duck-billed platypus, hippopotamus and beaver (Figure 5.3 (d)).

Arms

The shoulder blades of the gracile Australopithecines resembled those of apes. Lucy had a smaller antero-posterior diameter of the humeral head (as in the wholly arboreal orang-utan), while *A. africanus* was more chimp-like in the larger height of the glenoid fossa (the humeral articulation surface of the scapula) (McHenry, 1986). In both fossils, the glenoid fossa was orientated 15° more upward than in man. The usual explanation for this ape-like orientation is that they were partly arboreal (brachiating), but Morgan (1984) remarked that swimmers and divers also spend part of the time with their arms extended above their heads. Very long arms are especially typical of tree-hangers such as sloths, spider-monkeys and apes, but could also have evolved for other purposes, such as knuckle-walking, collecting (whether fruits or, for example, mussels), swimming, or throwing.

Lucy had a relatively short humerus (Jungers, 1982), and a rather ape-like humerus and ulna (Stern and Susman, 1983). The Kanapoi distal humerus, of 4 million years ago, resembled that of man more closely than did some much later specimens of *A. boisei* (Oxnard, 1975, pp. 96, 121; Feldesman, 1982). The ulna of *boisei* was about 30 per cent longer than that of *H. sapiens*, and morphologically intermediate between man and apes (Feldesman). Also, OH–62, possibly a *H. habilis*, had relatively longer arms than modern man (Johanson *et al.*, 1987). While the Neanderthal humerus was no longer than ours, the forearm of the Kiik Koba child was about 10 per cent longer than in a comparable human baby (Moerman, 1977, p. 130). (This contradicts the hypothesis, quoted earlier, that the Neanderthals' extremities were reduced as an adaptation to withstand cold, according to Allen's rule.)

Several features of the Neanderthal skeleton suggest a hypertrophic upper limb, especially for ab- and adduction and for exo- and endo-rotation (Trinkaus, 1976; Trinkaus and Churchill, 1988; Churchill and Trinkaus, 1988; Ben-Itzhak and Smith, 1988). Swimming certainly is one of the activities in which strong arm muscles would be needed. One remarkable finding is that the right humerus in male Neanderthals was much broader and heavier than the left (Moerman, 1977, pp. 253–7; Ben-Itzhak and Smith; Ben-Itzhak, Smith and Bloom, 1988). This could be explained by arm specialisation in collecting (fruits, mussels), or in making or manipulating tools (pebbles, harpoons, spears), and by vascular anomalies such as patent ductus arteriosus with right-to-left shunt, or preductal coarctatio aortae (see also van Nie and Roede, this volume, p.292).

In OH-62, which is said to belong to *H. habilis*, the shaft of the radius exhibits mediolateral bowing (Johanson *et al.*, 1987). This is also seen in Neanderthal man. It has the effect of broadening the forearm, which may be a paddle-like adaptation, but is usually considered a result of stronger muscularity.

Hands

There is no evidence that any of the fossil hominids ever used their front limbs for walking on their knuckles, as the African apes do. In *A. afarensis* from AL–333, the wrist and hand were strikingly chimp-like, with strongly curved phalanges as in the pygmy chimp, which suggests climbing or arm-hanging, but it lacked the very short thumb and the knuckle-walking features of the African apes (Stern and Susman, 1983; Bush, 1980). The hands of *A. robustus* from Swartkrans showed features of both chimpanzees and humans; like *afarensis*, they lacked the knuckle-walking adaptations and probably also the diminished importance of the thumb, but the phalanges, as in man, were less curved than in apes or *afarensis* (Lewis, 1977; Susman, 1987). *H. habilis* OH–7 did show strongly curved phalanges, very broad at mid-shaft, suggesting powerful grasping potential like the chimpanzee (Napier, 1962; Susman and Stern, 1982). Most fossil hominids had phalanges with even broader shafts than man. Humans have relatively broader hands than other primates, but the Neanderthals had even broader hands with relatively longer little fingers and – in contrast with their long limb bones – even less curved hand bones than humans (Moerman, 1977, pp. 52, 256, 129).

The curved phalanges with broad mid-shafts of *A. afarensis* and *H. habilis* are usually seen as a hanging or climbing adaptation, and certainly this palmar concavity is different from the ulnar deviation of the phalanges seen in sea-turtles, penguins, sea-lions, or dolphins (Hildebrand, 1974, figure 23–14). The broad Neanderthal hands could be explained by strong muscularity (grip); their cup form, for drinking or digging up tubers (van Nie, personal communication); or flipper-like adaptations: broad hands with broad phalanges are seen in all aquatic mammals.

Pelvic girdle

Abitbol (1987) found that the lumbo-sacral angle in Lucy (about 30°) was greater than in dogs (9°) and human new-born babies (20°), only slightly greater than in macaques and spider-monkeys (27°), but less than in chimps (44°), gibbons (60°) and man (77°). A wide lumbo-sacral angle was thought to have evolved to accommodate the large foetal head at the time of delivery, but it is more likely to correlate with habitually extended thighs (Abitbol, 1987), which are found in striding mammals (humans, and gibbons walking on branches), and in all swimming mammals. Morgan (1982, pp. 58–61) regarded aquaticness as a preadaptation for erect stance and locomotion.

The pelves of Lucy and *A. africanus* were very similar, and different from both apes and man (Stern and Susman, 1983). The bi-acetabular diameter was relatively much broader than in man and apes (Berge and Kazmierczak, 1986). The auricular articulation (with the sacrum) and the acetabular (with the femoral head), as in apes, were relatively much smaller than in humans (Oxnard, 1975). The lateral enlargement of the iliac blades was more ape-like, but the ilia, as in man, were much lower than in apes and monkeys. Both apes and monkeys have longer iliac blades than *Australopithecus* and *Homo*, but otherwise the apes' pelves are distinct from the monkeys' (Steudel, 1978).

Suggested explanations for these features of gracile Australopithecines' pelves have included: a bipedal gait different from and less efficient than our own, but with a better abductor mechanism for the thigh; semi-arboreality; obstetric factors; and the requirements of visceral accommodation and support during erect locomotion (Berge and Kazmierczak, 1986; Tague and Lovejoy, 1986). Some of the factors suggesting that bipedality was not well developed in the early Australopithecines are perhaps the small articulation surfaces and long and more horizontal femoral necks, which would make for less efficient weight-bearing, and the larger bi-acetabular diameter which would have made it more difficult to retain balance (Figure 5.4). In a semi-aquatic context, the broad pelvis could be compared with the broad trunk of aquatic mammals, especially freshwater species, and the small iliac height is comparable with the pelvic reduction characteristic of all aquatic mammals.

The pelvis of the adolescent *H. erectus* WT–15000, as well as his proximal femur, retained some Australopithecine-like aspects, but the bi-acetabular diameter was much narrower (Johanson *et al.*, 1987; Brown *et al.*, 1985). The femoral neck was orientated much more horizontally (with a neck-shaft angle of only 110°) than in robust Australopithecines (115–120°), Lucy (123°) or man (121–133°), and was much longer – in accordance with the strong iliac flare and small bi-acetabular diameter – than in man and certainly apes, and relatively as long as in robust Australopithecines; the femoral head was as large as in man, and much larger than in Australopithecines and apes (Brown *et al.*; Stern and Susman, 1983).

The meaning of the long and horizontal femoral neck in fossil hominids is not clear (Tompkins, Heller and Franciscus, 1988), but it is difficult to explain in an arboreal or bipedal context, although the narrower bi-acetabular diameter and larger femoral head of *H. erectus* could suggest a more frequent bipedality than in gracile Australopithecines (see Figures 5.4 (a) and 5.4 (b)). More horizontal femoral necks and flared ilia are also seen in the Neanderthals. Their pelves had slender, elongated, and very ventrally reaching superior pubic rami, clearly different from modern man (Rak and Arensburg, 1987). The broad sacrum (Ivanhoe, 1985), iliac flaring and long and ventrally reaching superior pubic rami are evidence of a larger trunk diameter than in man. Obstetric adaptations to the larger head of the Neanderthal foetus are unlikely to have been the cause (Rak and Arensburg).

Legs

The early hominids up to and including OH–62 had much shorter legs than later *Homo* (Figure 5.4). The relative length of the australopithecine leg resembled that of the orang-utan, the most arboreal of the great apes. But, as opposed to the orang, their legs are more reduced at the knees and still more at the ankles, rather than at the hip end (Oxnard, 1975). This distal leg reduction could be compared with that of aquatic mammals. WT–15000, the sub-adult *H. erectus*, had a long femur, slightly longer than in a present-day twelve-year-old boy, but a relatively shorter tibia (Brown *et al.*, 1985). Neanderthals also had somewhat shorter tibiae (Moerman, 1977, pp, 53, 253). The shortening is sometimes said to be an adaptation to cold, but this does not fit with considerations of time and space (Rak, 1986).

In *H. erectus* and *H. neanderthalensis* not only was the femur long, but also its shaft showed an anterior convexity, and in *erectus* it was compressed dorso-ventrally as compared with these features in modern man (Geissmann, 1986; Moerman, pp. 34, 61). All this could be correlated, for example, with different muscular arrangements in the thighs, with a different pattern of weight transmission in the legs (Kennedy, 1985), or with the broader pelves. It would also be consonant with paddle-like adaptations, since femoral broadening would improve the propulsive force of thigh-stretching in swimming. Dorso-ventrally flattened femora are characteristic of pinnipeds (Wyss, 1988).

The cortex of femora and tibiae of *neanderthalensis*, and certainly of *erectus*, is much thicker than in man, Australopithecines and apes. As Kennedy commented:

> the presence of such thickened bone is extraordinary; very few animals show similar generalised thickened bone. Manatees and dugongs show not merely thickened bone and medullary stenosis, but complete loss of a medullary canal . . . The adaptive advantage of such heavy, dense bone to the sirenians is apparently to counterbalance the buoyancy of their large lung volume while submerged. Amedullary bones, presumably reflecting a similar selective pressure, are also found in certain Mesozoic marine reptiles and in living humpback whales.

Sea-cows 'graze' lying or 'walking' with the front limbs on the sea bottom. Tertiary freshwater sirenians had much less massive bones than marine ones (Sickenberg, 1934, pp. 173–4). Surface-feeding ducks have a density of only 0.6; most fish are about as dense as the water that surrounds them; but bottom-dwellers are much denser (Hildebrand, 1974, pp. 584–9; Wilson, 1979, pp. 793–5; McFarland *et al.*, 1979, pp. 167–8, 212–16, 613–17).

It is, of course, impossible to know the body density of the fossil hominids. Man has a density of 1.02–1.09, partly depending on whether the lungs are inflated (Patrick, and Ghesquiere and Bunkens, this volume, chapters 14 and 16, respectively). This is slightly lower than the 1.07 of sheep, dogs and cats (Wind, 1976). Aquatic mammals have very thick subcutaneous fat layers – up to half of the body weight in slow-diving species – and smaller lung volumes, especially in deep-diving species. Humans standing in water of 25°C have their lungs compressed by almost half a litre (Choukroun, Kays and Varène, 1989), and long-distance swimmers have much more subcutaneous fat than normal (Pugh and Edholm, 1955). So we may assume that our semi-aquatic ancestors – with much more fat than us, and somewhat smaller lungs – would have had less density than modern man, other things being equal. This would make diving more difficult.

Perhaps in *H. erectus* and *H. neanderthalensis* the dense bones were adaptations to the density of (salt) water to compensate for the thick fat layers. The high density could anchor the body against water currents; in diving mammals that do not go very deep, the time below is longer than that between successive dives. The heavy bones would also enhance the descent rate; human divers frequently use counterweights during descent,

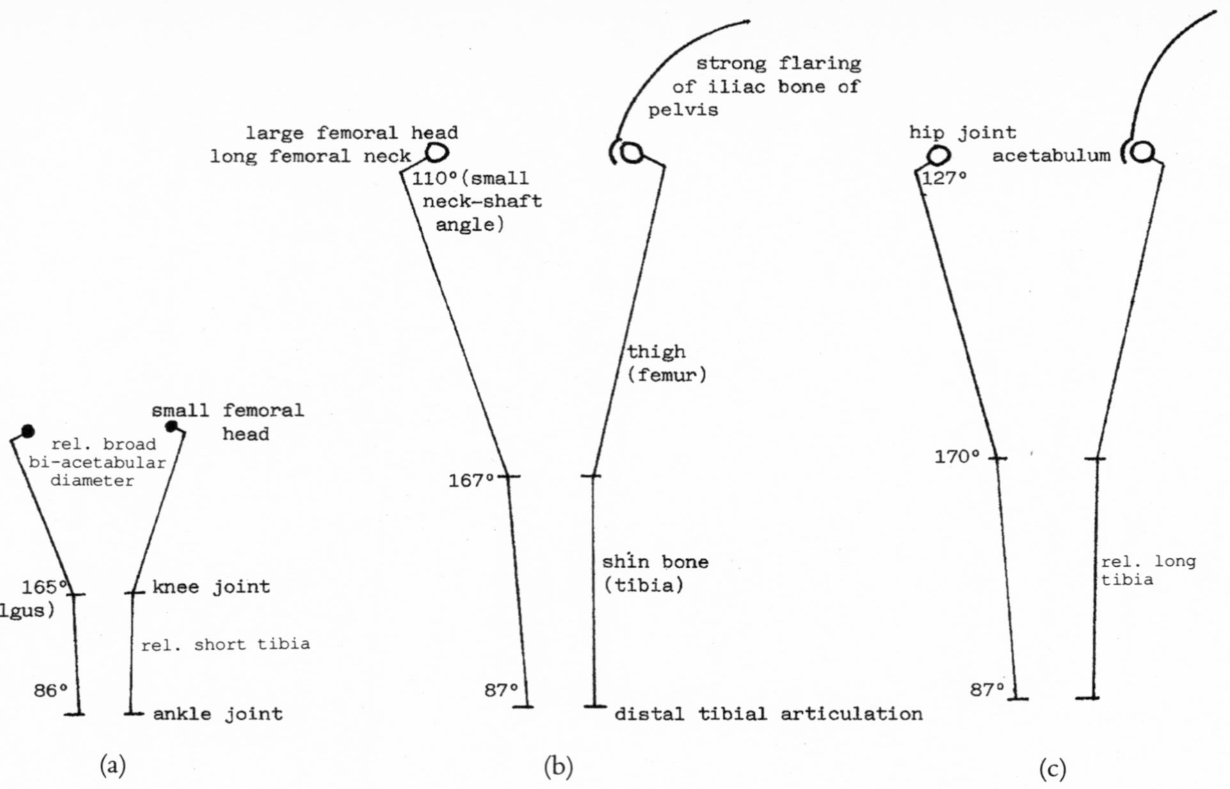

Figure 5.4 Schematic anterior view of hominid lower limbs (broadly to scale).
(a) 'Lucy', AL–288–1, a small *A. afarensis* c.3 mya; (b) WT–15000, a sub-adult *H. erectus*, c.1.6 mya; (c) modern *H. s. sapiens*.

whereas, during ascent, too rapid decompression can cause accidents (Hong, 1988). The massive skull, and more specifically the thick occipital part of it, could have stabilised the head while floating on the back (Figure 5.2 (c)). The heavy leg bones, and in particular the dense distal femora as in *H. erectus* from Trinil, suggest kneeling on the bottom while collecting food. The heavier right humerus of male Neanderthals could suggest collecting with the right arm.

Homo erectus fossils from inland sites (Zhoukoudian, located near a big river and possibly a lake) have denser femora than island specimens from Trinil. This could perhaps be explained by thicker fat layers (more weight on land and less density in water) in colder climates, by sexual dimorphism (Trinil–I was probably a woman), and by the immediately preceding evolution of these groups (phylogenetic inertia). For other – not necessarily conflicting – speculations for medullary stenosis, see Table 5.14.

Table 5.14 Possible explanations for medullary stenosis of femur and tibia in *Homo erectus* (after Kennedy, 1985, and references therein)

- a greater need for resisting torsional or bending stresses
- fatigue stress
- more weight, e.g., a broader trunk or more muscle or fat
- certain growth disturbances
- hypothyroidism (with lower basal metabolism and body temperature, which would allow longer dives)
- vitamin A, vitamin D, parahormone and calcium anomalies, e.g., by cyclic consumption of fruits instead of meat
- a reservoir for calcium, phosphorus or other minerals

The Neanderthals displayed very large patellae. This is in accordance with the robustness and the large epiphyses of most of their long bones (Moerman, 1977, pp. 52, 253). The human knee is unique among living primates in that only *H. sapiens* has a posterior insertion for the lateral meniscus on the tibial plateau. *A. afarensis* had no posterior insertion, but early *Homo* ER–1481 had two insertions like us (Tardieu, 1986). This means that the knee of *A. afarensis* was less stable than that of *Homo*.

Femur and tibia form an angle of about 165° in gracile Australopithecines and 3–4-year-old human children (valgus knee); 170° in the large Hadar specimens (AL–333) and in adult humans; 175° in orang-utans and spider-monkeys; and 180° in other apes and monkeys (Stern and Susman, 1983; McHenry, 1986). J. Prost (in Stern and Susman) suggested that the hominid valgus knee could have evolved to meet the demands of climbing, since among non-human primates the greatest degree of valgus is found in orangs and spider-monkeys. But more often it is believed to be a sign of bipedality, because it places the foot more directly under the centre of gravity of the body during the phase of single-limb support in walking (Stern and Susman, 1983). Yet a valgus knee is likely to be less stable than a straight one. In an aquatic milieu, centrally placed distal legs (Figure 5.4) would be even more indispensable, as we can see in the streamlined hind limbs of marine mammals.

The distal tibial articulation faces infero-laterally in apes, and makes an angle of about 75° with the tibial shaft in chimps. It faces more inferiorly in man and fossil hominids for which information is available (85–90°). This suggests that *A. afarensis* had a more perpendicular tibia than apes, and it is thought to be an adaptation for bipedality (Latimer, Ohman and Lovejoy, 1987). Equally likely, it is simply correlated with the valgus knee (Figure 5.4).

Among living primates only man had a highly positive (that is, external) tibial torsion (toeing-off), but Lucy, like many human children still, had a pronounced negative tibial torsion (Sarmiento, 1987). Toeing-in could be an advantage for better grasping trees or branches. Toeing-out, in contrast, is typical of sea-lions (Morgan, 1982, figure 9). If the central position of the hominid shin bones was an adaptation for bipedality, it may be asked why we developed toeing-out instead of either toeing-in (which was probably the ancestral condition) or, alternatively, the absence of torsion (which would have been more effective for terrestrial locomotion).

Feet

The bipedal footprints discovered at two Laetoli sites, of about 3.5 million years ago, provide one landmark for dating the evolution of bipedalism. Of the two sets of prints, those at site A prove controversial. White and Suwa (1987) called them 'enigmatic', and Tuttle (1985) believed they could have been made by a bear. It is more probable, however, as affirmed by Leakey and Hay (1979), that they must be attributed to a hominid. The prints are relatively very broad and the stride is very short, suggesting that the gait could perhaps best be compared with that of a penguin on land (Morgan, 1982, p. 61). The footprints at site G bear a much clearer resemblance to human footprints: they are relatively broader than those of modern man, and the stride is shorter. These features, together with the long and adducted first metatarsals (mid-foot bones) but 'oblique alignment of the ray I phalangeal impressions' and 'anterior encroachment of the lateral toes' (White and Suwa) would be compatible with the hypothesis of flipper-like adaptations.

Fossilised foot bones of *A. afarensis* from the same period yielded other details about the anatomy. An examination of three heel bones from AL–333 established that they were nearer to apes in size and perhaps morphology (Stern and Susman, 1983; Deloison, 1985; but see Latimer and Lovejoy, 1989). The virtual absence of the human lateral process (which enlarges and stabilises the supporting surface of the heel) led Deloison to conclude that '*A. afarensis* could not rest its foot on the ground and walk as modern man does'. Aspects of heel and mid-foot are suggestive of a plantigrade foot with strong plantar ligaments (Stern and Susman); the phalanges were 'strikingly ape-like', slender but with mid-phalangeal thickening, highly curved and much longer than in man (Stern and Susman). As in the case of the curved hand bones, this is usually regarded as a climbing adaptation. Another view is that the curved toes served partly to keep a foothold on rough, stony or muddy ground (Latimer *et al.*, 1982). The foot of *afarensis*, plantigrade and with somewhat less developed heel and longer forefoot than in modern man, also bears remarkable resemblances to that of the sea-lion (Figure 5.5).

More recently, the OH–8 talus, possibly from a *H. habilis*, was much less human-like than that of *H. erectus* ER–813 of a similar period (Wood, 1974). The OH–8 foot bears several close resemblances to the chimpanzee, but with human-like exceptions such as a limited rotation of the calcaneo-cuboid joint, a less divergent first metatarsal, and a fifth metatarsal which was even more robust than in modern man (Lewis, 1980; Day and Napier, 1964, figure 2). The impression of a flat foot is reinforced by the OH–10 terminal first toe phalanx of about the same time, which was relatively much broader than that of man, and certainly than that of a chimpanzee (Oxnard, 1975, figure 62). Also, the Neanderthals had broader feet than most people have today (Moerman, 1977, pp. 257, 129, 64).

Long, flat, broad feet with robust first and last digital rays are typical of wading, swimming and diving birds and mammals (Figure 5.5), but terrestrial and arboreal animals have narrower feet with the central digits being those most emphasised (Wyss, 1988). Indeed, the rather human-like (though still shorter-strided) Koobi Fora footprints, possibly from a *H. erectus* of about 1.6 million years ago, appear to have been made in water less than ten centimetres deep (Behrensmeyer and Laporte, 1981). They confirm that, as in modern man, the common integumentary covering of the foot encloses a much higher percentage of the toe bones than in any extant primate. It extends in humans to approximately the mid-point of the basal phalanx, and F. Wood Jones once referred to it (albeit in quotation marks) as 'webbing' (Morgan, personal communication).

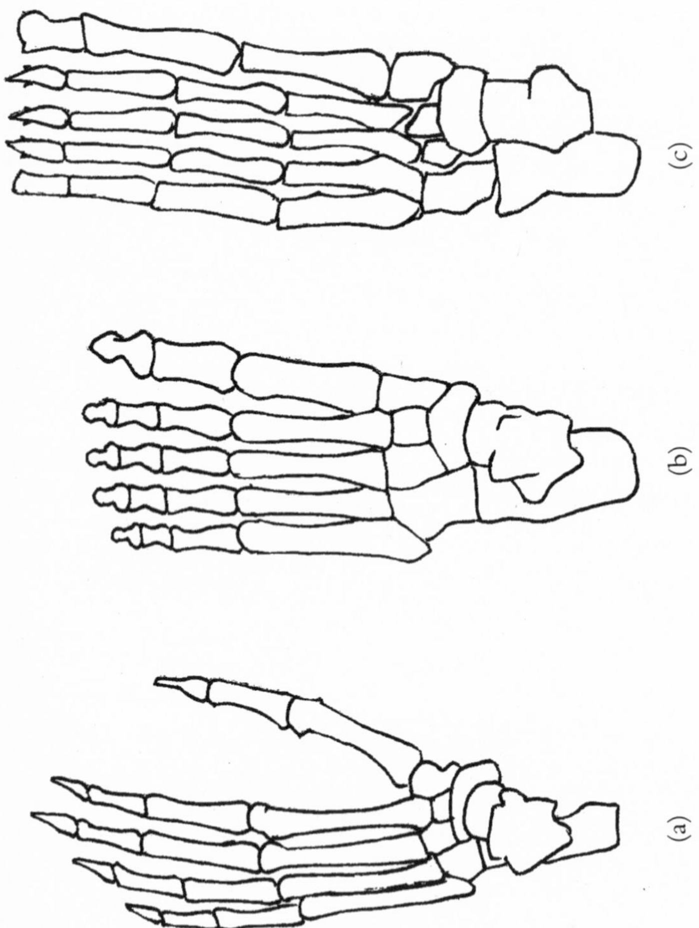

Figure 5.5 Comparison of foot skeletons (after Campbell, 1974; Wyss, 1988). (a) chimpanzee (*Pan troglodytes*); (b) man (*Homo sapiens*); (c) Steller's sea-lion (*Eumetopias jubatus*).

DISCUSSION

The morphological, physiological and molecular study of *living* animals is the richest source of evidence about our evolutionary history. Hitherto, much of the discussion of the AAT has been based on morphological and physiological rather than palaeontological data. But the fossil hominid record, although its findings are meagre prior to 4 million years ago (Pickford, 1986, p. 125), is well documented compared with that of many other mammals. A fresh look at the evidence suggests some possible new interpretations.

Australopithecine ancestors for all African hominoids?

From the researches of molecular biologists a few conclusions may be drawn (see also Gribbin and Cherfas, 1983, pp. 180–5; Hasegawa, Kishino and Yano, 1985, 1987; Diamond, 1988):

(1) Humans and chimpanzees are more closely related than either one of them is to the gorilla.
(2) The splitting time between the lineage leading to the gorilla and that leading to man and chimpanzee may be situated between 10 to 6 million years ago.
(3) That between man and chimpanzees may be situated between 8 and 4 million years ago (Figure 5.1 (a)).

Palaeontologists sometimes contest this chronology, and retain their conviction that the man/ape split occurred earlier. But when molecular and palaeontological data appear to be in conflict, the molecular evidence is the more reliable. Morphological characters (*a fortiori* of fragmentary fossil bones) are too much subject to the pitfalls of parallel and convergent evolution, as the *Ramapithecus* controversy of the 1970s illustrated.

One widespread assumption is that *Australopithecus* was closer to man than to the African apes because it has a smaller anterior dentition, thicker molar enamel and shorter iliac bones than chimps and gorillas, a more human orientation of the distal femoral and tibial articulations, and a univertebral articulation of the first rib. (The thicker molar enamel is no real argument, since the ancestors of the African apes are known to have had thick enamel (Martin, 1987).)

Other australopithecine features, however, more closely resemble *Pan* or *Gorilla*. For the cranial features, see Table 5.15. The human-like features of australopithecine limb bones also tend to have been exaggerated in the literature (Lewis, personal communication). Understandably, palaeontologists first notice resemblances with man, but more comprehensive comparisons afterwards also reveal the ape-like features. Most Hadar postcranials are different from both man and apes, but scapula, humerus, ulna, knee, hand and foot bones are more ape-like (Stern and Susman, 1983). The shoulder blade of *A. africanus* is rather chimp-like (Vrba, 1979). Arm and foot bones of robust Australopithecines are intermediate morphologically, with *A. robustus* being closer to man than *A. boisei* in this respect (Lewis, 1977, 1980; Feldesman, 1982; Susman, 1987). In *A. afarensis*, the ilia were short as in man, which is the chief reason why Lucy is thought to have been bipedal. But though they were short, they were orientated like an ape's (Stern and Susman, figure 6).

Table 5.15 Some cranial resemblances between apes and Australopithecines

- Brain size and sulcal pattern of the australopithecine endocasts appear to be ape- rather than human-like (Falk, 1985)
- The reconstructed skull from Hadar (mostly AL–333) is reminiscent of a female gorilla (Johanson and Edey, 1981, p. 351); that of *A. africanus*, of a female pygmy chimp (Zihlman *et al.*, 1978); already in 1925, A. Hrdlicka wrote that the Taung skull approached that of chimpanzees (Howells, 1985; see also Bromage, 1985)
- *A. boisei* WT–17000 had extremely convex infero-lateral margins of the orbits, such as found in some gorillas (Walker *et al.*, 1986)
- The nasal bone arrangement in some chimpanzees resembles that of robust Australopithecines (Eckhardt, 1987)
- The incus (ear ossicle) of *A. robustus* resembles *Pan* and perhaps *Homo* more than *Gorilla* (Rak and Clarke, 1979)
- Intra-palatal extension of the maxillary sinus has only been reported in Taung, robust Australopithecines and chimps (see Table 5.10)
- The australopithecine dentition was closer to apes in morphology (*A. afarensis*, Johanson and White, 1979; Johanson and Edey, 1981), molar microwear (Poirier, 1987, pp. 126, 179), enamel growth rate (Beynon and Wood, 1987), and development pattern (Conroy and Vannier, 1987, 1988; Bromage and Dean, 1985; Smith, 1987)

In sum, the impression is that most E. African Australopithecines (the larger specimens of *A. afarensis* and all *A. boisei*) were closer to the *Gorilla* lineage, and the South African *A. africanus* and *A. robustus* to the *Homo* and/or *Pan* lineages. This impression is strengthened by the postcranial evidence.

The question at issue is whether Lucy – or whatever fossil hominid – was evolving away from or towards an ape-like condition (Verhaegen, 1990). In the palaeo-anthropological literature, 'primitive' is sometimes used instead of 'ape-like', 'chimp-like' or 'gorilla-like' and 'advanced' instead of 'human-like'. It is not impossible that the African apes' ancestors were *more* bipedal than their descendants today (Gribbin and Cherfas, 1983, p. 125; Hasegawa, Kishino and Yano, 1985; Edelstein, 1987). Chimpanzees often walk bipedally on muddy ground (Nishida, 1980). The pygmy chimpanzee frequently practises ventro-ventral copulation, often believed to occur in *H. sapiens* as a consequence of bipedalism. If this concept is accurate, the African apes' pelves could have evolved from a Lucy-like pelvis by re-elongation of the iliac blades. Two possibly relevant facts derive from foetal development in the apes. One is that chimpanzee embryos have very human-like feet, with very long and adducted first digital rays (Coon, 1954). The other was recorded by Huxley:

> During most of the latter half of the prenatal life the human embryo, like the ape's, is covered all over with a coat of short, downy hair; so is an ape embryo of corresponding age. Before birth both ape and man shed this short hair and develop long hair on the head while remaining almost hairless on the body. Man retains this condition throughout life, while the newborn ape soon acquires its thick permanent garment. (Wells, Huxley and Wells, 1929.)

Taken in conjunction, these facts suggest a new scenario. It is possible that all African hominoids descended from an ancestor partly arboreal and partly aquatic, and bipedal in shallow water and on land. While the line leading to *Homo* became more aquatic (littoral), the *Pan* and the *Gorilla* lineages – probably independently – returned to a more arboreal existence and redeveloped some simian features suitable for that habitat, such as longer ilia, larger anterior teeth and thinner molar enamel, perhaps opposable big toes and even a slightly smaller brain.

African hominoids have limited hand and finger dorsiflexion, but increased supinatory motility of the forearm as compared with monkeys. These features are also found in seals and other marine mammals. If they were an inheritance of their semi-aquatic past, they could have hindered their becoming branch-runners again, like monkeys, and could have promoted their branch-hanging habits and very long arms. Indeed, it is only *after* birth – late in ontogeny – that an ape's arms become disproportionately long. Lucy did not show very long arms: its humerus was even shorter than in a female human pygmy, and much shorter than in a female pygmy chimpanzee. But one or two million years later, *A. boisei* displayed arms of gorilla length (Omo L–40–19 ulna). The branch-hanging adaptations – very long arms with limited hand dorsiflexion and hooked hands – could then become a preadaptation for terrestrial knuckle-walking in the African apes. (Also, some New World monkeys walk on the ground with 'tucked-under' phalanges (Zwell and Conroy,

1973).) To be sure, it is not suggested here that gorillas and common chimpanzees have descended from *robust* Australopithecines, although that possibility may not be fully excluded.

That molecular biology forces us to accept several parallel adaptations in the chimp and the gorilla lineages is only apparently a problem, since similar forms tend to develop similar adaptations in response to similar environmental or climatic changes; and parallel, convergent, reverse and even fluctuating evolution of morphological characters is extremely widespread, and often even more remarkable (Darwin, 1903, p. 171; White and Harris, 1977; Sheldon, 1988; Seger, 1987) than a parallel evolution of knuckle-walking in semi-erect, long-armed, hook-handed apes with limited hand dorsiflexion.

A. afarensis: some *Nasalis*-like locomotion features

The clearest evidence for australopithecine bipedality is that afforded by the Laetoli site A and G footprints. It is not known whether one of these sets of prints – and if so, which one – was made by a hominid of the same species as Lucy. And although it is evident that some of the early hominids walked on two legs for at least part of the time (Latimer and Lovejoy, 1989), it is not clear from the fossilised bones how well they were adapted to this mode of locomotion. Resemblances with man in iliac reduction, valgus knee, perpendicular distal tibial articulation and adducted first metatarsal bone are thought to represent adaptations for a bipedal stance and gait; but other explanations are possible, and the resemblance between Lucy and ourselves in respect of pelvis, knee and foot is far from complete.

The most obvious differences are the ape-like orientation of Lucy's ilia, the small femoral head (but long neck), the absence of a posterior insertion for the lateral meniscus, the short legs, and the curved toes. If these hominids were bipedal on the ground, their bipedality was different from ours. Susman (1987) states: 'The conception of the earliest hominids as savannah-dwelling, terrestrial bipeds does not account for the small size, relatively short lower limb, mobile ankle, long forefoot, curved toes, and ape-like toe-joints of *A. afarensis*'. The inference is that the early Australopithecines did not spend all their time on the ground, but had a habitat only partly terrestrial. Susman maintains that the non-terrestrial aspect of Lucy's environment was arboreal, and the evidence for (semi-)arboreality in the Hadar hominids is strong: orang-like features of the shoulder blades, with upward orientation of the glenoid fossae, curved hand and foot bones, negative tibial torsion, mobile ankle and knee, relatively short legs, monkey-like lumbo-sacral angle.

Another possible combination is terrestrial/aquatic. There are several indications that at least the early Australopithecines were semi-aquatic: distally reduced legs, with centrally placed tibiae, long and adducted big toes, short pelvis, broad trunk, loose rib articulation, and perhaps extensive skull pneumatisation and guttered nasal aperture. The mobile knees and ankles would be compatible with either climbing or swimming. If the early hominids were semi-aquatic, there is insufficient evidence to establish whether they originally lived in fresh or salt water, and whether they dived or only swam on the surface. The strong pneumatisation suggests frequent floating or swimming on the water surface, especially in fresh or weakly saline water habitats (Pickford, 1975; Bishop *et al.*, 1975; Bonnefille, 1976; Brain, 1981, p. 189).

It would be a mistake to assume that the arboreal and aquatic explanations are mutually exclusive. Perhaps the best available model for Lucy's modes of locomotion is to be found in the proboscis monkey, *Nasalis larvatus*. This monkey, which lives in the mangroves of Borneo, swims and dives very well, walks bipedally in shallow waters across the water courses of the estuary and on muddy ground, and climbs and even hangs from the branches with its arms (Ellis, 1986, 1991; Napier and Napier, 1967, p. 232). It has a protruding nose, a relative body enlargement and forelimb lengthening compared with other colobine monkeys. Detailed correlation is not to be expected, since taxonomically *Nasalis* belongs to the monkeys and Lucy to the hominoids; but the ways in which they diverge from their respective archetypes (see, e.g., figure 2 of Feldesman, 1982) show points of convergence which could well indicate comparable habitat and locomotor behaviour.

One million years later, the robust Australopithecines, like the giant panda, showed extremely broad and thick-enamelled cheek teeth. If they ate bamboo at the riverside, they often swam (but seldom dived) and waded, climbed and sat with erect trunks.

Fossil *Homo*: probably semi-aquatic

Fossil *Homo* shows much stronger signs of aquatic adaptation than *A. afarensis*. Evidence of this from the fossil record includes body and brain enlargement, Broca's area in the brain, ear exostoses, possible platycephaly, short iliac bone, flat femur, broad feet and hands with relatively long and robust first and fifth digital rays, and the use of pebble stone tools (like sea-otters). In the case of *H. erectus*, arguments for a salt-water habitat are the dense bones, and possibly his 'fast' dispersal to South East Asia and the East Indies (in an overland journey through the forests a terrestrial/arboreal primate would have encountered enough geographical obstacles to slow down or even stop this dispersal, as compared with a migration along the Indian Ocean). Presumably, different lineages from an ancestral coast-dwelling stock followed the rivers inland. *H. erectus* shows no clear adaptations for an arboreal habitat; although his tibiae were somewhat shorter than ours, his bipedal gait on the ground must have resembled our own.

Some Neanderthals are discovered near sea coasts, but most are found in river valleys. They share with *H. erectus* the large body and (even larger) brain, the platycephaly and the (slightly less) massive bones. They may have been descended from some *erectus* populations that moved up the rivers, since the less dense bones and the strongly enlarged frontal sinuses suggest a freshwater milieu. The Neanderthal broad arms and feet, and especially the ear exostoses, clearly indicate frequent diving (in cold water). The very protruding mid-face and nostrils and the large frontal sinuses suggest frequent floating on the back: the anterior air-filled sinuses and the posterior dense skull would have stabilised the head in the water with the nose upwards – the standard at-rest position adopted by the sea-otter.

The best available model for the kind of life led by *H. erectus* and *H. neanderthalensis* must be the still existing human communities where one or more sexes dive for seaweeds or shellfish (Hong, 1988; Kennedy, 1986; see also Verhaegen, 1991).

CONCLUSION

Palaeontological data do not rule out the possibility of semi-aquatic ancestors. There is some evidence for aquatic features in the Australopithecines, and they may not have been fully adapted for bipedality; there are indications that the gracile Australopithecines were at least partly arboreal.

There is a stronger case for assuming aquatic adaptations in fossil *Homo. H. erectus* had a very dense skeleton, which is found otherwise only in littoral bottom-feeders. The most unequivocal piece of evidence concerns Neanderthal man. Ear-canal exostoses are virtually pathognostic of frequent diving in colder water. Their abundance in the Neanderthals establishes beyond reasonable doubt the semi-aquatic nature of these people.

ACKNOWLEDGEMENTS

This survey has only been possible thanks to the numerous detailed anatomical descriptions and comparisons of fossil hominids by so many palaeontologists. I have to thank M. Pickford, J. de Vos, O.J. Lewis, S.J. Edelstein, S.C. Cunnane, M. Hasegawa, J. Wind, D. Ellis, W.M.A. De Smet, and especially C.J. van Nie, J.M. Patrick, D. Falk, Machteld Roede and Elaine Morgan for invaluable discussions, corrections and comments, and Morien Morgan for typing the manuscript.

REFERENCES

Abitbol, M.M., 1987, Evolution of the lumbosacral angle. *American Journal of Physical Anthropology*, **72**, 361–72.

Armstrong, E., 1983, Relative brain size and metabolism in mammals. *Science*, **220,** 1302–4.

Behrensmeyer, A.K. and Laporte, L.F., 1981, Footprints of a Pleistocene hominid in Northern Kenya. *Nature*, **289**, 167–9.

Ben-Itzhak, S. and Smith P., 1988, A radiographic study of fossil and recent humeri. *American Journal of Physical Anthropology*, **75**, 186–7.

Ben-Itzhak, S., Smith, P. and Bloom, R.A., 1988, Radiographic study of the humerus in Neanderthals and *Homo sapiens sapiens*. *American Journal of Physical Anthropology*, **77**, 231–42.

Berge, C. and Kazmierczak, J.B., 1986, Effects of size and locomotor adaptations to the hominid pelvis: evaluation of australopithecine bipedality with a new multivariate method. *Folia Primatologica*, **46**, 185–204.

Beynon, A.D. and Wood, B.A., 1987, Patterns and rates of enamel growth in the molar teeth of early hominids. *Nature*, **326**, 493–6.

Bishop, W. W., Pickford, M. and Hill, A., 1975, New evidence regarding the Quaternary geology, archaeology and hominids of Chesowanja, Kenya. *Nature*, **258**, 204–8.

Blaney, S.P.A., 1986, An allometric study of the frontal sinus in *Gorilla*, *Pan* and *Pongo*. *Folia Primatologica*, **47**, 81–96.

Blanton, P.L. and Biggs, N.L., 1968, Eighteen hundred years of controversy: the paranasal sinus. *American Journal of Anatomy*, **124**, 135–48.

Bonnefille, R., 1976, Implications of pollen assemblage from the Koobi Fora Formation, East Rudolf, Kenya. *Nature*, **264**, 4030–7.

Brain, C.K., 1981, *The Hunters or the Hunted?* (Chicago: University of Chicago Press).

Bromage, T., 1985, Taung facial remodelling: a growth and development study. In *Hominid Evolution*, ed. P.V. Tobias (New York: Liss), 239–45.

Bromage, T.G. and Dean, M.C., 1985, Re-evaluation of the age at death of immature fossil hominids. *Nature*, **317**, 525–7.

Brown, F.H., Harris, J.M., Leakey, R.E. and Walker, A., 1985, Early *Homo erectus* skeleton from West Turkana, Kenya. *Nature*, **316**, 788–92.

Bush, E., 1980, The thumb of *Australopithecus afarensis*. *American Journal of Physical Anthropology*, **52**, 210.

Cabanac, M., 1986, Keeping a cool head. *News in Physiological Sciences*, **1**, 41–4.

Calvin, W., 1983, A stone's throw and its launch window. *Journal of Theoretical Biology*, **104**, 121–35.

Campbell, B.G., 1974, *Human Evolution* (Chicago: Aldine), 2nd ed.

Carney, J., Hill, A., Miller, J.A. and Walker, A., 1971, Late Australopithecine from Baringo District, Kenya. *Nature*, **230**, 509–14.

Choukroun, M. L., Kays, C. and Varène, P., 1989, Effects of temperature on pulmonary volumes in immersed human subjects. *Respiration Physiology*, **76**, 255–66.

Churchill, S.E. and Trinkaus, E., 1988, Neanderthal scapular glenoid fossa morphology. *American Journal of Physical Anthropology*, **75**, 196.

Clark, J.D., Asfaw, B., Assefa, G., Harris, J.W.K., Kurashina, H., Walter, R.C., White, T.D. and Williams, M.A.J., 1984, Palaeoanthropological discoveries in the Middle Awash Valley, Ethiopia. *Nature*, **307**, 423–8.

Clutton-Brock, T.H. and Harvey, P.H., 1977, Primate ecology and social organization. *Journal of Zoology, London*, **183**, 1–39.

Conroy, G.C., Jolly, C.J., Cramer, D. and Kalb, J.E., 1978, Newly discovered fossil hominid skull from the Afar depression, Ethiopia. *Nature*, **276**, 67–70.

Conroy, G.C. and Vannier, M.W., 1987, Dental development of the Taung skull from computerized tomography. *Nature*, **392**, 625–7.

Conroy, G.C. and Vannier, M.W., 1988, The nature of Taung dental maturation continued. *Nature*, **333**, 808.

Coon, C.S., 1954, *The Story of Man* (New York: Knopf).

Coon, C.S., 1962, *The Origin of Races* (New York: Knopf).

Corruccini, R.S. and Ciochon, R.L., 1979, Primate facial allometry and interpretation of australopithecine variation. *Nature*, **281**, 62–4.

Darwin, C., 1903, *On the Origin of Species by Means of Natural Selection* (London: Watts).

Day, M.H., Leakey, R.E.F., Walker, A.C. and Wood, B.A., 1974, New hominids from East Rudolf, Kenya. *American Journal of Physical Anthropology*, **42**, 461–76.

Day, M.H. and Napier, J.R., 1964, Fossil foot bones. *Nature*, **201**, 969–70.

Deloison, Y., 1985, Comparative study of calcanei of primates and *Pan–Australopithecus–Homo* relationship. In *Hominid Evolution*, ed. P.V. Tobias (New York: Liss), 143–7.

Delson, E., 1987, Evolution of palaeobiology of robust *Australopithecus*. *Nature*, **327**, 654–5.

Diamond, J.M., 1988, Relationships of humans to chimps and gorillas. *Nature*, **334**, 656.

Eckhardt, R.B., 1987, Hominid nasal region polymorphism and its phylogenetic significance. *Nature*, **328**, 333–5.

Eckhardt, R.B., 1988, Primate phylogenetic patterns preserve persistent polymorphism. *American Journal of Physical Anthropology*, **75**, 207.

Edelstein, S.J., 1987, An alternative paradigm for hominoid evolution. *Human Evolution*, **2**, 169–74.

Ellis, D., 1986, Proboscis monkey and aquatic theory. *Sarawak Museum Journal,* **XXXVI** new series, **57**, 251–62.

Ellis D., 1991, Is an aquatic ape viable in terms of marine ecology and primate behaviour? (This volume, chapter 4.)

Falk, D., 1983, Cerebral cortices of East African early hominids. *Science*, **221**, 1072–5.

Falk, D., 1985, Hadar AL 162–28 endocast as evidence that brain enlargement preceded cortical reorganization in hominid evolution. *Nature*, **313**, 45–7.

Falk, D., 1986, Evolution of cranial blood drainage in hominids: enlarged occipital/marginal sinuses and emissary foramina. *American Journal of Physical Anthropology*, **70**, 311–24.

Falk, D., 1987, Hominid paleoneurology. *Annual Review of Anthropology*, **16**, 13–30.

Falk, D., and Conroy, G.C., 1983, The cranial venous system in *Australopithecus afarensis*. *Nature*, **306**, 779–81.

Feldesman, M.B., 1982, Morphometric analysis of the distal humerus of some Cenozoic catarrhines: the late divergence hypothesis revisited. *American Journal of Physical Anthropology*, **59**, 73–95.

Ferguson, W.W., 1987a, Revision of the subspecies of *Australopithecus africanus* (Primates: Hominidae), including a new subspecies from the late Pliocene of Ethiopia. *Primates*, **28**, 258–65.

Ferguson, W.W., 1987b, Reconstruction and re-evaluation of the skull of *Homo antiquus* (Hominoidea: Homininae) from Hadar. *Primates*, **28**, 377–91.

Fialkowski, K.R., 1986, A mechanism for the origin of the human brain: a hypothesis. *Current Anthropology*, **27**, 288–90.

Folkow, L.P. and Blix, A.S., 1987, Nasal heat and water exchange in gray seals. *American Journal of Physiology*, **253**, R833–9.

Foster, K., 1987, Evolution of cranial thickness: a consequence of cranial capacity? *American Journal of Physical Anthropology*, **72**, 198.

Franciscus, R.G. and Trinkaus, E., 1988a, The Neanderthal nose. *American Journal of Physical Anthropology*, **75**, 209–10.

Franciscus, R.G. and Trinkaus, E., 1988b, Nasal morphology and the emergence of *Homo erectus*. *American Journal of Physical Anthropology*, **75**, 517–27.

Geissman, T., 1986, Length estimate for KNM–ER 736, a hominid femur from the Lower Pleistocene of East Africa. *Human Evolution*, **1**, 481–93.

Gribbin, J. and Cherfas, J., 1983, *The Monkey Puzzle* (London: Triad, Paladin).

Harrison, R.J., 1958, *Man the Peculiar Animal* (Harmondsworth: Penguin Books).

Hasegawa, M., Kishino, H. and Yano, T., 1985, Dating of the human/ape splitting by a molecular clock of mitochondrial DNA. *Journal of Molecular Evolution*, **22**, 160–74.

Hasegawa, M., Kishino, H. and Yano, T., 1987, Man's place in Hominoidea as inferred from molecular clocks of DNA. *Journal of Molecular Evolution*, **26**, 132–47.

Hempleman, H.V. and Lockwood, A.P.M., 1978, *The Physiology of Diving in Man and other Animals* (London: Edward Arnold).

Henneberg, M., 1988, Decrease of skull size in the Holocene. *Human Biology*, **60**, 395–405.

Hildebrand, M., 1974, *Analysis of Vertebrate Structure* (New York: Wiley).

Hong, S.K., 1988, Man as a breath-hold diver. *Canadian Journal of Zoology*, **66**, 70–4.

Howells, W.W., 1985, Taung: a mirror for American anthropology. In *Hominid Evolution*, ed. P.V. Tobias (New York: Liss), 19–24.

Ivanhoe, F., 1985, On the neanderthal pubis and acromegaly. *Current Anthropology*, **26**, 526–9.

Johanson, D.C., 1985, The most primitive *Australopithecus*. In *Hominid Evolution*, ed. P.V. Tobias (New York: Liss), 203–12.

Johanson, D.C. and Edey, M.A., 1981, *Lucy, the Beginnings of Mankind* (London: Granada).

Johanson, D.C., Masao, F.T., Eck, G.G., White, T.D., Walter, R.C., Kimbel, W.H., Asfaw, B., Manega, P., Ndessokia, P. and Suwa, G., 1987, New partial skeleton of *Homo habilis* from Olduvai Gorge, Tanzania. *Nature*, **327**, 205–9.

Johanson, D.C. and Taieb, M., 1976, Plio-Pleistocene hominid discoveries in Hadar, Ethiopia. *Nature*, **260**, 293–7.

Johanson, D.C., Taieb, M. and Coppens, Y., 1982, Pliocene hominids from the Hadar formation, Ethiopia (1973-1977). *American Journal of Physical Anthropology*, **57**, 373–402.

Johanson, D.C. and White, T.D., 1979, A systematic assessment of early African hominids. *Science*, **203**, 321–30.

Jungers, W.L., 1982, Lucy's limbs: skeletal allometry and locomotion in *Australopithecus afarensis*. *Nature*, **297**, 676–8.

Jurmain, R., Nelson, H., Kurashina, H. and Turnbaugh, W.A., 1981, *Understanding Physical Anthropology and Archeology* (St Paul: West Publishing Co.).

Kennedy, G.E., 1985, Bone thickness in *Homo erectus*. *Journal of Human Evolution*, **14**, 699–708.

Kennedy, G.E., 1986, The relationship between auditory exostoses and cold water: a latitudinal analysis. *American Journal of Physical Anthropology*, **71**, 401–15.

Kimbel, W.H., White, T.D. and Johanson, D.C., 1984, Cranial morphology of *Australopithecus afarensis*, a comparison study based on a composite reconstruction of the adult skull. *American Journal of Physical Anthropology*, **64**, 337–88.

Kratzing, J.E., 1984, Anatomy and histology of the nasal cavity of the koala (*Phasolarctus cinereus*). *Journal of Anatomy*, **138**, 55–65.

Latimer, B.M., Lovejoy, C.O., Johanson, D.C. and Coppens, Y., 1982, Hominid tarsal, metatarsal and phalangeal bones recovered from the Hadar Formation: 1974–1977 collections. *American Journal of Physical Anthropology*, **57**, 701–19.

Latimer, B.M. and Lovejoy, C.O., 1989, The calcaneus of *Australopithecus afarensis* and its implications for the evolution of bipedality. *American Journal of Physical Anthropology*, **78**, 369–86.

Latimer, B., Ohman, J.C. and Lovejoy, C.O., 1987, Talocrural joint in African hominoids: implications for *Australopithecus afarensis*. *American Journal of Physical Anthropology*, **74**, 155–75.

Leakey, M.D., Clarke, R.J. and Leakey, L.S.B., 1971, New hominid skull from Bed I, Olduvai Gorge, Tanzania. *Nature*, **232**, 308–9.

Leakey, M.D. and Hay, R.L., 1979, Pliocene footprints in the Laetolil beds at Laetoli, Northern Kenya. *Nature*, **278**, 317–23.

Leakey, M.D., Hay, R.L., Curtis, G.H., Drake, R.E., Jackes, M.K. and White, T.D., 1976, Fossil hominids from the Laetolil Beds. *Nature*, **262**, 460–6.

Leakey, R.E.F. and Walker, A., 1988, New *Australopithecus boisei* specimens from East and West Turkana, Kenya. *American Journal of Physical Anthropology*, **76**, 1–24.

Lewis, O.J., 1977, Joint remodelling and the evolution of the human hand. *Journal of Anatomy*, **123**, 157–201.

Lewis O.J., 1980, The joints of the evolving foot, Part III. The fossil evidence. *Journal of Anatomy*, **131**, 275–98.

Loeffler, K., 1981, *Anatomie und Physiologie der Haustiere* (Stuttgart: Eugen Ulmer).

Martin, L., 1987, Significance of enamel thickness in hominoid evolution. *Nature*, **314**, 260–3.

Martyn, J. and Tobias, P.V., 1967, Pleistocene deposits and new fossil localities in Kenya. *Nature*, **215**, 476–80.

McFarland, W.M., Pough, F.H., Cade, T.J. and Heiser, J.B., 1979, *Vertebrate Life* (London: Collier Macmillan).

McHenry, H.M., 1982, The pattern of human evolution: studies on bipedalism, mastication and encephalization. *Annual Review of Anthropology*, **11**, 151–73.

McHenry H.M., 1986, The first bipeds: a comparison of the *A. afarensis* and *A. africanus* postcranium and implications for the evolution of bipedalism. *Journal of Human Evolution* **15**, 177–91.

McHenry, H.M. and Skelton, R.R., 1985, Is *Australopithecus africanus* ancestral to *Homo*? In *Hominid Evolution*, ed. P.V. Tobias (New York: Liss) 221–6.

Moerman, P., 1977, *In het spoor van de Neanderthal-mens* (Baarn: Boekerij).

Morden, J., 1988, Towards a hominid taphonomy: carnivore consumption of human carcasses. *American Journal of Physical Anthropology*, **75**, 251.

Morgan, E., 1982, *The Aquatic Ape* (London: Souvenir Press).

Morgan, E., 1984, The aquatic hypothesis. *New Scientist*, **1405**, 17–19.

Morgan, E. and Verhaegen, M., 1986, In the beginning was the water. *New Scientist*, **1498**, 62–3.

Napier, J.R., 1962, Fossil hand bones from Olduvai Gorge. *Nature*, **196**, 409–11.

Napier, J.R. and Napier, P.H., 1967, *A Handbook of Living Primates* (New York: Academic Press).

Nie, C.J. van, 1983, A comparative study of the morphology and the topography of the heart of the *Arctocephalus australis* (fur or ursine seal) and the heart of the *Phoca vitulina vitulina* (common or harbour seal) in their relation to the type of locomotion. *Aquatic Mammals*, **10**, 79–82.

Nie, C.J. van and Roede, M.J., 1991, Some cardiac topographic and morpho-physiological observations of the common seal and of man. (This volume, pages 290–3).

Ninkovich, D. and Burckle, L.H., 1978, Absolute age of the base of the hominid-bearing bed in Eastern Java. *Nature*, **275**, 306–8.

Nishida, T., 1980, Local differences in reactions to water among wild chimpanzees. *Folia Primatologica*, **33**, 189–209.

Ohman, J.C., 1986, The first rib of hominoids. *American Journal of Physical Anthropology*, **70**, 209–29.

Olson, T.R., 1985, Taxonomic affinities of the immature crania from Hadar and Taung. *Nature*, **316**, 539–40.

Oxnard, C.F., 1975, *Uniqueness and Diversity in Human Evolution* (Chicago: University of Chicago Press).

Pickford, M., 1975, Late Miocene sediments and fossils from the Northern Kenya Rift Valley. *Nature*, **256**, 279–84.

Pickford, M., 1986, Geochronology of the Hominoidea: a summary. In *Primate Evolution*, ed. J.G. Else and P.C. Lee (Cambridge: Cambridge University Press), 123–8.

Poirier, F.E., 1987, *Understanding Human Evolution* (Englewood Cliffs: Prentice-Hall).

Potts, R., 1988, Contexts of *Homo erectus/Homo sapiens* at Kanjera and Olorgesailie, Kenya. *American Journal of Physical Anthropology*, **75**, 258.

Pugh, L.G.C. and Edholm, O.G., 1955, The physiology of Channel swimmers. *Lancet*, **6893**, 761–8.

Radosevich, S.C. and Retallack, G.J., 1988, Paleoecology of hominids from the site AL–333, Hadar, Ethiopia. *American Journal of Physical Anthropology*, **75**, 258.

Rak, Y., 1986, The Neanderthal face: a new look to an old face. *Journal of Human Evolution*, **15**, 151–64.

Rak, Y. and Arensburg, B., 1987, Kabara 2 Neanderthal pelvis: first look at a complete inlet. *American Journal of Physical Anthropology*, **73**, 227–31.

Rak, Y. and Clarke, R.J., 1979, Ear ossicle of *Australopithecus robustus*. *Nature*, **279**, 62–3.

Romer, A.S. and Parsons, T.S., 1977, *The Vertebrate Body* (Philadelphia: Saunders).

Russell, M.D., 1985, The supraorbital torus: 'a most remarkable peculiarity'. Replies of Garn, S.M., Shea, B.T., Girgis, F., Turkel, S. and Zivanović, S. *Current Anthropology*, **26**, 337–60.

Sarmiento, E.E., 1987, Long bone torsions of the lower limb and its bearing upon the locomotor behavior of australopithecines. *American Journal of Physical Anthropology*, **72**, 250–1.

Seger, J., 1987, El Niño and Darwin's finches. *Nature*, **327**, 461.

Sheldon, P., 1988, Making the most of the evolution diaries. *New Scientist*, **1596**, 52–4.

Sickenberg, O., 1934, *Beiträge zur Kenntnis Tertiärer Sirenen* (Brussels: Koninklijk Natuurhistorisch Museum van België).

Simpson, G.G., 1959, *The Meaning of Evolution* (New Haven: Yale University Press).

Slijper, E.J., 1979, *Whales* (London: Hutchinson).

Smith, B.H., 1987, Maturational patterns in early hominids. *Nature*, **328**, 674–5.

Smith, R.J., 1984, Allometric scaling in comparative biology: problems of concept and method. *American Journal of Physiology*, **246**, R152–R160.

Stern, J.T. and Susman, R.L., 1983, The locomotor anatomy of *Australopithecus afarensis*. *American Journal of Physical Anthropology*, **60**, 279–317.

Steudel, K., 1978, A multivariate analysis of the pelvis of early hominids. *Journal of Human Evolution*, **7**, 583–95.

Stringer, C.B., 1978, Some problems in Middle and Upper Pleistocene hominid relationships. In *Recent Advances in Primatology*, ed. D.J. Chivers and K.A. Joysey (London: Academic Press).

Susman, R.L., 1987, Pygmy chimpanzees and common chimpanzees; models for the behavioral ecology of the earliest hominids. In *The Evolution of Human Behavior; Primate Models* (Albany: State University New York Press), 72–86.

Susman, R.L. and Stern, J.T., 1982, Functional morphology of *Homo habilis*, *Science*, **217**, 931–4.

Tague, R.G. and Lovejoy, C.O., 1986, The obstetric pelvis of AL 288–1 (Lucy). *Journal of Human Evolution*, **15**, 237–55.

Tardieu, C., 1986, The knee joint in three hominid primates: application to Plio-Pleistocene hominids and evolutionary implications. In *Current Perspectives in Primate Biology*, ed. D.M. Taub and F.A. King (New York: Van Nostrand Reinhold), 182–92.

Tobias, P.V., 1983, Recent advances in the evolution of the hominids with especial reference to brain and speech. In *Pontifical Academy of Sciences*, Scripta Varia **50**, 87–140.

Tompkins, R.L., Heller, J.A., Franciscus, R.G., 1988, Hominid femoral neck angle and biomechanical neck length. *American Journal of Physical Anthropology*, **75**, 279.

Trinkaus, E., 1976, A functional interpretation of the axillary border of the Neanderthal scapula. *Journal of Human Evolution*, **6**, 231–4.

Trinkaus, E., 1987, The Krapina hominid postcrania. *American Journal of Physical Anthropology*, **72**, 264.

Trinkaus, E. and Churchill, S.E., 1988, Neanderthal radial tuberosity orientation.

American Journal of Physical Anthropology, **75**, 15–21.

Tuttle, R.H., 1985, Ape footprints and Laetoli impressions: a response to the SUNY claims. In *Hominid Evolution*, ed. P.V. Tobias (New York: Liss), 129–33.

Verhaegen, M., 1985, The aquatic ape theory: evidence and a possible scenario. *Medical Hypotheses*, **16**, 17–32.

Verhaegen, M., 1987a, The aquatic ape theory and some common diseases. *Medical Hypotheses*, **24**, 293–300.

Verhaegen, M. 1987b, Vertonen de fossiele hominiden tekens van wateraanpassing? *Marswin*, **8**, 142–51.

Verhaegen, M., 1988, Aquatic ape theory and speech origins: a hypothesis. *Speculations in Science and Technology*, **11**, 165–71.

Verhaegen, M., 1990, African ape ancestry. *Human Evolution,* **5**, 295–7.

Verhaegen, M., 1991, Aquatic Ape Theory and fossil hominids. *Medical Hypotheses* (in press).

Vrba, E., 1979, A new study of the scapula of *Australopithecus africanus* from Sterkfontein. *American Journal of Physical Anthropology*, **51**, 117–30.

Walker, A., Leakey, R.E., Harris, J.M. and Brown, F.H., 1986, 2.5–myr *Australopithecus boisei* from west of Lake Turkana. *Nature*, **322**, 517–22.

Ward, S. and Hill, A., 1987, Pliocene hominid partial mandible from Tabarin, Baringo, Kenya. *American Journal of Physical Anthropology*, **72**, 21–37.

Washburn, S.L. and Moore, R., 1980, *Ape into Human* (Boston: Little, Brown).

Wells, H.G., Huxley, J. and Wells, G.P., 1929, *The Science of Life* (London: Amalgamated Press), vol. 1: 264.

Wheeler, P. 1985, The loss of functional body hair in man, *Journal of Human Evolution,* **42**, 12–27.

White, T.D. and Harris, J.M., 1977, Suid evolution and correlation of African hominid localities. *Science*, **198**, 13–21.

White, T.D. and Suwa, G., 1987, Hominid footprints at Laetoli: facts and interpretations. *American Journal of Physical Anthropology*, **72**, 485–514.

Wilson, J.A., 1979, *Principles of Animal Physiology* (New York: Macmillan).

Wind, J., 1976, Human drowning: phylogenetic origin. *Journal of Human Evolution*, **5**, 349–63.

Wood, B.A., 1974, Evidence on the locomotor pattern of *Homo* from early Pleistocene of Kenya. *Nature*, **251**, 135–6.

Wood, B.A., 1978, Classification and phylogeny of East Arican hominids. In *Recent Advances in Primatology*, ed. D.J. Chivers and K.A. Joysey (London: Academic Press), vol. 3: 350–72.

Wyles, J.S., Kunkel, J.G. and Wilson, A.C., 1983, Birds, behavior, and anatomical evolution. *Proceedings of the National Academy of Science, USA*, **80**, 4394–7.

Wyss, A.R., 1988, Evidence from flipper structure for a single origin of pinnipeds. *Nature*, **334**, 427–8.

Zihlman, A.L., Cronin, J.E., Cramer, D.L. and Sarich, V.M., 1978, Pygmy chimpanzee as a possible prototype for the common ancestor of humans, chimpanzees and gorillas. *Nature*, **275**, 744–6.

Zwell, M. and Conroy, G.C., 1973, Multivariate analysis of the *Dryopithecus africanus* forelimb. *Nature*, **244**, 373–5.

Part II

REACTIONS TO THE AQUATIC APE THEORY: FOR AND AGAINST

6 The Refutation that Never Was: The Reception of the Aquatic Ape Theory, 1972–1987

Graham Richards

SUMMARY

Elaine Morgan's work has been rejected or ignored by scientific researchers in the human evolution field since the publication of her first book on the subject, *The Descent of Woman*, in 1972. This chapter considers the reasons for this rejection, which persisted in the absence of any adequate refutation of the Aquatic Ape Theory (AAT). It is argued that no refutation was forthcoming because there was a lack of consensus among the scientific workers themselves regarding the central issues of bipedalism and hairlessness. The rejection of Morgan's work is considered to be primarily due to her outsidership, a position exacerbated by the barriers which human evolution researchers had understandably erected in the face of the speculative, outlandish and amateur attentions which the topic, by its very nature, tends to attract. On examination, her work does not fall into this category. It conforms to current theories of speciation better than the savannah-origins model, and accounts for a number of diverse phenomena hitherto not seen as connected – which is also generally considered to be a major virtue in a scientific theory. Finally, it is argued that the behavioural and psychological aquatic affinities of modern humans are sufficiently marked to require an evolutionary explanation, at least as much as other behaviours well established on the evolutionary research agenda.

INTRODUCTION

Between 1972, when Elaine Morgan's reformulation of Sir Alister Hardy's Aquatic Ape Theory (AAT) first appeared in her best-selling book *The Descent of Woman*, and the convening of the Valkenburg meeting in 1987, the hypothesis received no serious academic attention. The references to it in the academic literature were at best patronising (e.g., Isaac, 1983) and at worst contemptuous (e.g., Gowlett, 1984). A review by Pfeiffer in *Time* magazine (1972a) equating *The Descent of Woman* with 'another largely fictional work' – Clifford Irving's discredited biography of Howard Hughes – came close to eliciting a libel suit from the publishers Stein & Day. The same reviewer, writing a week later in the *New York Times Book Review* (1972b), noted 'Pseudoscience marches on'. Non-academic reviewers, by contrast, found the work logical, exciting, provocative and liberating. The ensuing silence was deafening. In spite of repeated pressure, the academic establishment failed to state publicly in clear terms the grounds on which the AAT was unsustainable, while assuring everybody that it was. A letter from C.O.

Lovejoy (1979) to one of Elaine Morgan's most indefatigable lay advocates, Chuck Milliken, typifies the posture adopted: 'the preponderance of evidence is so overwhelmingly contrary to the "aquatic theory" that no one found it necessary to consider a published reply'.* This is unconvincing; faced with widespread popular acceptance of such an allegedly false theory, scientists have a public responsibility to refute it as firmly as possible – a responsibility they usually show no reluctance in discharging, especially given the financial rewards of doing so via the US media!

Following the publication in 1982 of Morgan's *The Aquatic Ape*, the academics continued, in the main, to turn a blind eye to the theory. Lowenstein (1984) published a scornful attack in the journal *Oceans*, and in 1986 co-authored with A. Zihlman a two-page restatement of this in *BBC Wildlife*, the editors of the latter refusing Elaine Morgan the right to a detailed reply. The Lowenstein and Zihlman posture is typified by their statement that 'the only evidence for an aquatic phase in human evolution is a television script patched together from a scrapbook of unrelated anatomical and physiological snippets'. In their few public statements on the issue since 1972, academics have persistently assured the general reader that the reasons for hairlessness and bipedalism are well understood. They have never said what they are.

LACK OF CONSENSUS AMONG THE EXPERTS

In this chapter I will argue that, regardless of the ultimate evaluation of the AAT, its treatment by the academic establishment during the period 1972–86 was patently inadequate and needs explanation. A major factor in the situation in 1972 was that the academic debate on human evolution was itself in a crucial phase. Human evolution research had had a fairly disastrous first century, in which everything that could have gone wrong did; from forgeries like Piltdown Man to accidents like the loss of the Peking Man and Mikulov Castle material, from erroneous theoretical

* Responses of other leading figures to Milliken's inquiries include Mary Leakey (30 March 1980): 'I regard Mrs Morgan's theory as nothing more than the outcome of an over-fertile imagination without any possible bearing on the research on human evolution'; Robert Ardrey (5 November 1978): 'while Elaine Morgan's book is marvelous entertainment, it is not good science'. Stephen Jay Gould (14 November 1980) gives two reasons for rejecting the AAT, both of which were subsequently dealt with in Morgan (1982): (1) the evolution of strong legs is the reverse of what usually happens in aquatic mammals; (2) all the features cited are better explained by neoteny (however, as Morgan points out, this may be the mechanism, but it does not explain why the features had adaptive value – the ghost of 'orthogenesis' seems to be faintly hovering behind Gould's argument here). It should be noted, though, that all these attacks are directed at the case as presented in *The Descent of Woman* rather than in the more recent *The Aquatic Ape*.

presuppositions (brain-first and eastern origins models) to personality problems (Virchow, Dubois). Following the Second World War, with the discoveries in Olduvai and South Africa of further Australopithecines and *Homo habilis*, the situation had improved, and the possibility of settling down to 'normal science' seemed to be on the agenda at last. By 1972 something approaching a consensus was on the verge of emerging. But it was very fragile, and already under pressure from within the scientific community, most awkwardly from molecular biologists. The solid closing of ranks by human evolution researchers in the face of *The Descent of Woman* masked the fact that the solid, reliable, 'scientific' knowledge of the facts of human evolution, which so assuredly disproved the AAT, was a fiction, and that internal dissensus was mounting. In the event it transpired that most of the key features of the 1972 consensus – in so far as it existed – were to be rejected over the following decade. These included the beliefs that:

(1) *Ramapithecus* was probably the earliest hominid.
(2) The hominid and pongid lineages split approximately 15 million years ago.
(3) Hunting was a major feature of early hominid lifestyle.
(4) Bipedalism was directly associated with brain enlargement.
(5) Bipedalism was directly linked to stone-artefact manufacture.
(6) Hairlessness was sexual in function (facilitating display of secondary sexual characteristics).
(7) Although the initial adaptive value of bipedalism was unknown, facilitation of hunting was a likely candidate.

On the vital questions of the timing of the origin of bipedalism and the similarity of australopithecine walking to that of modern humans, there was heated contention. Pilbeam (1972, p. 71) can only vaguely talk about 'the Middle to Late Pliocene', and has doubts about the efficiency of australopithecine gait; he notes (Pilbeam, 1970) that the issue is puzzling and that 'The combination of circumstances which led to the emergence of hominid bipedalism two million or more years ago was clearly unique' (p. 95). There was in fact a major controversy between those who saw the *Australopithecinae* as very human-like and those who saw them as very different, even having evolved bipedalism independently (Napier, cited in Pilbeam, 1970, p. 142). (See Zuckerman, 1973, for key papers in this dispute centring on the interpretation of the Sts–5 pelvis.)

Every single one of the above beliefs is now either rejected, or adhered to by only a small minority of scientific authorities. Given that the AAT focused particularly on hairlessness and bipedalism, it is clear that the establishment position on these matters in 1972 was entirely devoid of the reliability that it claimed. Since its own theories on these issues were either false or matters of controversy within the discipline, it was actually in no position to refute alternative ones definitively.

SAVANNAH ORIGINS – THEORY OR AXIOM?

There is only one tenet from the 1972 consensus that is still preserved – namely, the savannah-origins theory. However, on closer examination the status of this proves to be less secure than it initially appears to be. The notion that hominids originated on the savannah is less a theory than an axiom. It was never formally arrived at by a process of rigorous empirical evaluation of its merits against other 'theories'. Rather, it slowly established itself as an axiomatic assumption on the grounds that, since our nearest relatives are forest dwellers and the earliest known fossil hominids were savannah dwellers, the crucial factor in hominid-pongid divergence was a move of hominids from forest to savannah. This is reasonable yet hardly watertight, since it leaves open the question of whether such a transition alone is sufficient to account for the manifest morphological and physiological differences between two such genetically similar groups. This question has rarely been explicitly addressed by mainstream human evolution theorists, who, treating the savannah origins account as axiomatic, frame their explanations of such differences within its parameters.

This has resulted in a proliferation of feature-specific explanations – as if we need one for bipedalism, another for hairlessness, another for fattiness, a fourth for vocal channel dominance, a fifth for ventro-ventral copulation and so on – the overall ensemble of distinctively human features being the result of a happy coincidence of a variety of adaptive responses to numerous separate selection pressures. With the exception of Wheeler's recent formulations (see chapter 13, this volume), evolutionary theorists have rarely attempted to offer an integrated explanation of how the forest–savannah transition could have had such dramatic sequelae for hominids, given that it is a move which numerous mammals have made without evolving any hominid traits. What is needed, then, is a serious appraisal of the explanatory adequacy of the savannah-origins model, an appraisal which takes on board the whole suite of hominid features incorporated in the AAT in addition to the 'big three' of bipedalism, hairlessness and subcutaneous fat. The academic establishment was thus guilty of misrepresenting an axiom as an empirically based theory.

HOW RELEVANT ARE FOSSILS?

A third respect in which the palaeontological establishment in particular has overstated the firmness of its knowledge claims is the assumption that the kinds of aquatic adaptation proposed by Sir Alister Hardy and Elaine Morgan are amenable to refutation on the basis of fossils alone. If hominid pelvic reorganisation is not, *per se*, evidence of an aquatic adaptation but is equally construable in terms of, for instance, vertical climbing, we are left with serious problems in identifying a skeletal trait which would be acceptable as unambiguously aquatic in its implications. The majority of the physiological traits with which the AAT is concerned are soft-tissue ones. This brings us to the regularly played-down problem of the identifiability of species from skeletal material alone; many extant mammalian species (such as lion and tiger) are known to be virtually undifferentiable at the skeletal level. We are bound to ask, then, how many proto-hominid subspecies were at large in East Africa between, say, 8 and 4 million years ago. What proportion of them have we so far identified? The recently discovered OH–62 (Johanson *et al.*, 1987), for example, is causing considerable problems, as it has relatively shorter legs than *Australopithecus afarensis* but has a habiline skull. So must we revise our image of *Homo habilis*, or suppose this to be a more arboreal subspecies – '*H. habilis sylvestris*' perhaps? This, one should note, could let the 'terrestrialists' off the hook even if an unambiguously aquatic hominid fossil were found – it would be perceived as a subspecies unrelated to the main hominid line.

The presence of early hominid fossils in one area (for instance, Java) has no *a priori* bearing on the probability of finding them in another area (for instance, South Africa), and hence the AAT is untouched by the discoveries to date – since no human palaeontological work has actually been done in the regions, such as the Danakil area, identified by the AAT proponents as crucial for their theory (LaLumiere, chapter 3, this volume). If fossils are to have any relevance to this debate at all, then both sides must state clearly what kinds of feature they would consider to be either characteristic of, or fundamentally incompatible with, the theses they are proposing. Since the relevance of fossils to the issue is in a sense far more central to the palaeontological establishment's case than to Elaine Morgan's – which is primarily formulated in terms of quite different kinds of data – the onus in this respect falls on them, perhaps, rather more than on the aquaticists.

Finally, it must be said that it is far from clear why the AAT is considered as intrinsically far-fetched, implausible or outlandish. Marsh-dwelling and wading primates are well known (including extinct ones like *Oreopithecus* (Azzaroli *et al.*, 1986)), and most classes of mammals have at least one aquatic member. As a scenario the AAT would seem to be perfectly compatible with current evolutionary theory; speciation is generally portrayed as involving the isolation of a small sub-population and its exposure to novel selection pressures (e.g., Gould and Eldredge, 1977). Such conditions typically occur when populations become isolated, as they might be on islands. The ATT thus fits this approach far better than the savannah-origins model, in which it is far from obvious how the ancestral population could have become isolated or subjected to the intensity of novel selection pressures required to bring about such a massive divergence from the pongids (though see Malone, 1987). One criterion frequently proposed as a characteristic of a 'good' theory is that it economically accounts for and unifies a range of phenomena that have previously not been seen as related; the AAT seems to do precisely this. To refer to it as consisting of 'unrelated anatomical and physiological snippets', as Lowenstein and Zihlman (1986) do, is simply to beg the question.

THE REJECTION OF ELAINE MORGAN'S IDEAS

In the light of the above, the academic response to the AAT requires further diagnosis. We have seen that its appearance in 1972 came at a particularly delicate time for mainstream theorising, and the ensuing silence can only legitimately be construed as arising from a genuine embarrassment at being unable convincingly to refute it. It was as if the scientific establishment was saying to itself, 'It cannot be true because if it was one of us would have thought of it first'. They all seemed to be awaiting the knock-down refutation from one of their colleagues, only to discover that none of them could actually provide one. Since human evolution research was in a state of internal turmoil throughout the late 1970s and early 1980s, any extensive attempted refutation would in any case have been rejected by a substantial body of the writer's fellow scientists, for it could not fail to commit the writer on matters which were still bones of contention. But why the need to reject Morgan's work quite so categorically?

There are two suggestions one could make as to why the theory met with this peculiar combination of vehement rejection and absence of coherent refutation. The first would be to blame it on Elaine Morgan's feminist identification. Undoubtedly this was a major factor in the initial reception of *The Descent of Woman*, but the *Zeitgeist* was on her side here, and few contemporary human evolution theorists have failed to make concessions to the feminist perspective, accepting that females as much as males have played a role in human evolution. Furthermore, there are now a number of eminent women in the area, in addition to Mary Leakey: for example, Dean Falk, Sarah Blaffer Hrdy, Jane Lancaster, Sue Parker, Brigitte Senut, Pat Shipman, Elizabeth Vrba and, indeed, Adrienne Zihlman. Nancy Tanner's *On Becoming Human* (1981) is explicitly feminist in orientation, but received a hearty endorsement from F. Clark Howell and the cooperation of people like John Pfeiffer and

Don Johanson. It includes the definitely *outré* assumption that Pliocene hominids constituted a single interbreeding gene-pool. Nevertheless, no wrath descended on her head on this account (though not all reviewers were very impressed: e.g., Wind, 1983).

The second line would be to focus on Elaine Morgan's 'outsider' status (Tanner, by contrast, is a Professor of Anthropology at the University of California, Santa Cruz). This was frequently stressed in reviews of *The Descent of Woman*, and has remained her most serious handicap. Modern sciences, particularly the hard sciences such as physics, chemistry and astronomy, are generally so specialised that an outsider has little hope of making a serious contribution to them. At the opposite end of the spectrum is psychology, my own discipline, where perennial mayhem reigns and theorists can, given sufficient fervour and energy, establish some kind of following within the discipline, however bizarre their position. Human evolution studies are somewhere between. It is a topic which has frequently attracted speculation by amateurs, von Däniken (1971) and Oscar Kiss Maerth (1973) being recent examples. Although the data on human evolution are in some respects 'hard', the topic itself is psychologically highly salient, since accounts of origins inevitably serve as cultural creation myths (see Richards, 1987, chapter 1).

Given the internal problems of the disciplines concerned, it is not surprising that human evolution theorists have sought to erect a particularly impermeable boundary between their 'science' and speculative amateur nonsense. Their initial, and broadly sensible, response to outsiders has been to ignore them for fear of encouraging them and getting embroiled in time-wasting public controversy (a tactic not always successful when dealing with powerful ideologically rooted opponents such as Creationists). The same routine was triggered by the publication of Elaine Morgan's first book on the topic, and those most adamantly opposed to her appear to be continuing to try to pigeon-hole her position in this way. The journal *New Scientist*, having treated the AAT sympathetically for some years, now seems to have fallen into line. Nevertheless it is clear, especially since *The Aquatic Ape* (1982), that this policy of intellectual isolation is inadequate and badly judged. Informally one knows that some authorities are covertly sympathetic, while the theory itself does not belong in the realms of bizarre speculation. To many academics in other disciplines who have read Elaine Morgan's work its rejection appears to require far more detailed arguments than it has so far received. Vague accusations that it is too speculative or 'unscientific' carry little weight among those of us aware how high the speculative content of human evolution theorising is in general (the 1972 'consensus' turned out to be virtually entirely so!) and that what counts as 'scientific' is far from clear in the wake of post-Kuhnian philosophy of science.

THE NEED FOR HUMAN AQUATICISM TO BE ON THE EVOLUTIONARY AGENDA

The final curious feature about the reception of the AAT is not only that it was rejected but that the issues it raised were not even placed on the agenda as topics requiring examination from the evolutionary perspective. As a psychologist looking at human evolution, I believe that the level of affinity with water of modern *Homo sapiens sapiens* asks for some kind of evolutionary attention, regardless of the fate of Elaine Morgan's particular theory. Leaving aside the physiological features as such, what of the behavioural ones? We are the only land mammal, as far as I am aware (other than elephants, for whose aquatic ancestry Elaine Morgan also makes out a case in Appendix 2 of *The Aquatic Ape*), that uses water for grooming, putting great energy into the associated technology of bathrooms, showers, saunas and the like! Any extraterrestrial ethologist watching us would surely be struck by our tendencies to migrate to beaches during the summer, to build swimming-pools, to adorn our dwellings with aquaria and images of lakes and seascapes, and to locate our settlements primarily in association with rivers and lakes or by the sea. Add to all this the not inconsiderable swimming and diving skills possessed by many species members, and the major role of both marine and freshwater foods in many of our diets. Although human boat-making skills were probably developed only within the last forty millennia, they again testify to our ability to adapt rapidly to marine and lacustrine environments (see Johnstone, 1980, for an account of the evolution of sea-craft).

Now it may be objected that one is here dealing with facultative rather than obligatory behaviours. This is true, but the notion of a distinction between the two is problematical in relation to human behaviour in general. Even our bipedalism has a substantial learned component (Devine, 1985), heterosexuality is not universal, and neither is any particular domestic or social structure. In short, it is hard to identify any human behaviour which is strictly obligatory. This has not prevented researchers and theorists seeking evolutionary origins for much of it, such as Lovejoy (1981) on monogamy, Lorenz (1966) on our alleged aggression, or Thornhill and Wilmsen (1983) on rape. Exception would not be taken to the identification of extant behavioural legacies of arboreality. We are, furthermore, fascinated by the drinking of liquids of all kinds, and a high proportion of our food intake can be in liquid form (for example, the Kenyan Masai traditionally subsisted largely on milk and blood from their cattle). This seems to go way beyond what would be necessary to meet the physiological needs for water which we share with all other living creatures. We also enjoy wallowing, gaze meditatively at breaking waves, and incorporate ritual immersion and washing into our religions. Although perhaps not too much should be made of some of these inclinations – we do also gaze at trees, mountains and even savannahs – my general feeling is that the only phenomenon exerting a comparable overall effect is fire (for which a quite different analysis would be required). The AAT does not, for most of its advocates anyway, pretend to apply to events much beyond 5 million years ago. It is not surprising, then, that some current features of human physiology are maladaptive for aquatic behaviour, having evolved since the hypothesised aquatic phase. The argument is that there is an identifiable stratum of our current behaviour and physiology that is best explained as a legacy from a distant aquatic phase, and that the 'scrapbook of unrelated anatomical and physiological snippets', to which we may add some behavioural ones, adds up to a suite of typically aquatic features. My present point, however, is only that current levels of human aquaticism appear, on the face of it, to deserve at least as much evolutionary consideration as some of the behavioural traits which have been so favoured, such as monogamy, aggression, rape and non-verbal communication (e.g., Eibl-Eibesfeldt, 1973).

It must be noted that an emerging difficulty with this whole area is that there is a lack of detailed information available regarding the ontogenetic plasticity of certain human physiological features of relevance to the AAT (such as subcutaneous fat levels and distribution); how variable *is* the phenotypic expression of human genotypes under different environmental conditions? (For broader theoretical discussions of the genes/environment issue, see Lewontin, 1982, 1983.)

I would like to end by stressing the theoretical importance of the case of the recently extinct Agaiumbu tribe of New Guinea, to which I drew attention in Richards (1987). This well documented lake-dwelling tribe exhibited clear physiological adaptations to their primarily aquatic environment, particularly in the musculature of their lower limbs. Walking on dry land was painful and awkward for them (Monckton, 1920). They had presumably only been living in this environment for at most a few millennia, and possibly for a far shorter period. As wives were taken from neighbouring land tribes, they were not entirely genetically isolated. (Darlington (1969) overlooked this in his passing mention of them.) The 'aquatic' adaptations of the Agaiumbu either resulted from some change at the genetic level or represent a physiological response to their peculiar maturational circumstances. If the former, they testify to the rapidity with which humans can evolve in the aquatic direction; if the latter, they testify to the human genetic potential for water-adaptive phenotypic expression, given the right environment. The latter seems on balance more plausible, given that they were not genetically isolated. (See also Schagatay, this volume, chapter 15).

CONCLUSION

1 The reaction of traditional human evolution researchers to the 1972 statement of the AAT involved adopting a false posture of scientific certainty and within-discipline consensus. Yet, in so far as there was a consensus at that time, its central hypotheses on the critical issues of the evolutionary significance of bipedality and hairlessness have all been subsequently abandoned, dissensus remaining the norm ever since.

2 The presentation of the savannah-origins model as a 'theory' or well established fact was misleading, since it actually functioned as an axiom, an *a priori* assumption setting the parameters within which theory-construction proper was conducted. This resulted in a proliferation of feature-specific explanations.

3 The direct relevance of fossil evidence for the AAT is unclear, since most of the features it seeks to explain are soft-tissue ones, while pelvic changes are indecisive as they can result from vertical climbing as well as swimming. The respective merits of the AAT and the savannah-origins model cannot be fully evaluated as long as the search for hominid fossils is restricted to areas predicted by the latter.* The number of proto-hominid subspecies flourishing in the late Miocene cannot be deduced from the present fossil evidence and may be difficult to establish, even in principle, given the difficulty of differentiating closely related species on skeletal anatomy alone.

4 The perception that the AAT is outlandish is unwarranted, since there is nothing intrinsically unusual about a mammalian lineage producing an aquatic species. Several extant primate species are marsh-dwelling, sea-wading and/or have aquatic behaviour in their repertoires (see Ellis, this volume, chapter 4). The speciation scenario proposed by the aquaticists is also in some respects more in line with current speciation theories than the savannah-origins model.

5 The reaction of the scientific establishment to the AAT can be understood better in terms of the perceived 'outsidership' of Elaine Morgan than in terms of its feminist component or scientific short-

* It would be an extraordinary find indeed which could unambiguously falsify either the AAT or the savannah-origins model. Nevertheless, we do seem to have a situation where the AAT proponents are making a specific prediction that, given favourable geological conditions, hominid fossils will be found in contexts where proponents of the savannah-origins model do not expect to find them. Should they be proved right, then the probability of the AAT being correct would at any rate be enhanced. But since, *a priori*, the probability of finding such fossils is considered so low (by virtue of the dominance of the savannah-origins model), the likelihood of raising the resources to test the AAT prediction is minimal. Although out of place here, it would be an interesting intellectual exercise to analyse the implications of every possible outcome of such a fossil hunt (no fossils because of absence of fossil beds, hominid fossils without aquatic features, hominid fossils with aquatic features, fossil beds but no hominids, stone tools but no hominid fossils and so on) for the respective probabilities of the two positions.

comings. It was miscategorised as belonging to a genre of amateur, speculative theorising, to which the subject of human evolution remains perennially prone. This reaction was understandable, but mistaken. It was probably exacerbated by the fact that nobody in the field could formulate a comprehensive refutation during a phase in which, even within the scientific establishment, there was controversy (often quite heated) on a number of relevant issues.

6 Finally, it was argued that current levels of human aquaticism are as much a legitimate topic for the evolutionary theorist's agenda as, for example, monogamy, aggression and rape, which are already on it. The distinction between obligatory and facultative is unhelpful when considering human behaviour, and there are surely more swimmers in the world than there are rapists.

ACKNOWLEDGEMENTS

The author is grateful to Elaine Morgan for access to her files on the reception of *The Descent of Woman* and to Chuck Milliken for photocopies of, and permission to quote from, correspondence.

REFERENCES

Azzaroli, A., Boccaletti, M., Delson, E., Moratti, G. and Torre, D., 1986, Chronological and palaeogeographical background to the study of *Oreopithecus bamboli*. *Journal of Human Evolution*, **15**, 533–40.

Däniken, E. von: 1971, *Chariots of the Gods* (London: Souvenir Press).

Darlington, C.D., 1969, *The Evolution of Man and Society* (London: Allen & Unwin).

Devine, J., 1985, 'The versatility of human locomotion'. *American Anthropologist*, **87** (3), 550–70.

Eibl-Eibesfeldt, I., 1973, *Love and Hate: on the Natural History of Basic Behaviour Patterns* (London: Methuen).

Ellis, D., 1991, Is an aquatic ape viable in terms of marine ecology and primate behaviour? (This volume, chapter 4).

Gould, S.J. and Eldredge, N., 1977, Punctuated equilibria: the tempo and mode of evolution reconsidered. *Paleobiology*, **3**, 115–51.

Gowlett, J., 1984, *Ascent to Civilization: The Archaeology of Early Man* (London: Collins).

Isaac, G.Ll., 1983, Aspects of human evolution. In *Evolution from Molecules to Men*, ed. D.S. Bendall (Cambridge: Cambridge University Press), 509–45.

Johanson, D.C., Masao, F.T., Eck, G.G., White, T.D., Walter, R.C., Kimbel, W.H., Asfaw, B., Manega, P., Ndessokia, P., and Suwa, G., 1987, New partial skeleton of *Homo habilis* from Olduvai Gorge, Tanzania. *Nature*, **327**, 205–9.

Johnstone, P., 1980, *The Sea-craft of Prehistory* (London: Routledge & Kegan Paul).

LaLumiere, L.P., 1991, The evolution of genus *Homo*: Where it happened. (This volume, chapter 3).

Lewontin, R.C., 1982, Organism and environment. In *Learning, Development and Culture: Essays in Evolutionary Epistemology*, ed. H.C. Plotkin (Chichester: John Wiley).

Lewontin, R.C., 1983, Gene, organism and environment. In *Evolution from Molecules to Men*, ed. D.S. Bendall (Cambridge: Cambridge University Press).

Lorenz, K., 1966, *On Aggression* (London: Methuen).

Lovejoy, C.O., 1979, letter to Chuck Milliken dated 9.5.79.

Lovejoy, C.O., 1981, The origin of man. *Science*, **211**, 341–50.

Lowenstein, J., 1984, The leaky logic of the aquatic ape. *Oceans* (July/ August), 72.

Lowenstein, J. and Zihlman, A., 1986, The wading ape: a watered down version of human evolution. *BBC Wildlife*, April, 182–3.

Maerth, O.K., 1973, *The End was the Beginning* (London: Michael Joseph).

Malone, David, 1987, Mechanisms of hominoid dispersal in Miocene East Africa. *Journal of Human Evolution*, **16**, 469–81.

Monckton, C.A.W., 1920 (repr. Penguin, 1936), *Some Experiences of A New Guinea Resident Magistrate, Second Series* (Harmondsworth: Penguin Books).

Morgan, E., 1972, *The Descent of Woman* (London: Souvenir Press).

Morgan, E., 1982, *The Aquatic Ape* (London: Souvenir Press).

Pfeiffer, J., 1972a, Book Reviews. *Time* magazine (19 June), 91.

Pfeiffer, J., 1972b, Book Reviews. *New York Times Book Review* (25 June), 6.

Pilbeam, D., 1970, *The Evolution of Man* (London: Thames & Hudson).

Pilbeam, D., 1972, *The Ascent of Man: an Introduction to Human Evolution* (New York: Macmillan).

Richards, G., 1987, *Human Evolution: an Introduction for the Behavioural Sciences* (London: Routledge & Kegan Paul).

Schagatay, E.K., 1991, The significance of the human diving reflex. (This volume, chapter 15).

Tanner, N.M., 1981, *On Becoming Human* (Cambridge: Cambridge University Press).

Thornhill, R. and Wilmsen, N., 1983, Human rape: an evolutionary analysis. *Ethology and Sociobiology*, **4**, 137–73.

Wheeler, P., 1991, Body hair reduction and tract orientation in man: hydrodynamics or thermoregulatory aerodynamics? (This volume, chapter 13).

Wind, J., 1983, Book Reviews: *On Becoming Human* by N.M. Tanner. *Journal of Human Evolution*, **12**, 319–20.

Zuckerman, S., (ed.), 1973, *The Concepts of Human Evolution* (London: Academic Press/ Zoological Society of London).

7 Does the Geological Evidence Support the Aquatic Ape Theory?

Martin Pickford

SUMMARY

After a short discussion of the *Zeitgeist* associated with Hardy's introduction of the Aquatic Ape Theory, the use of analogy rather than of homology of features to support the AAT, as well as the lack of time dimension in the discussion by AAT advocates, is criticised in this chapter. An examination of the geological record appears to provide little support for a (semi-) aquatic phase in hominid evolution.

INTRODUCTION

The Aquatic Ape Theory (AAT) emerged during the 1960s and 70s, more or less at the same time that tremendous quantities of well packaged publicity concerning human origins were being offered to the general public and to scientists alike, from the East African hominid mines. At that time, the common perception of the East African Hominid Origins School (EAHOS) (and the South African one, one may add) was that humans originated during the Pliocene drought (cf. Ardrey, 1967), a sort of testing-ground through which mankind was supposed to have passed with flying colours, while the apes shrank primitively off to their permanently humid forest refuges. A tenet of this story was that into this Pliocene drought went a population of Miocene apes, small-brained, acultural, quadrupedal arborealists living predominantly on fruits and celery gathered in small home ranges, while out of the other end of the parched Pliocene evolutionary forge emerged a smart, larger-brained, cultured, bipedal, terrestrial hominid, eating animal proteins and ranging far and wide over the African savannah, with head held high.

It is no coincidence, in my opinion, that Hardy (1960) proposed the AAT at more or less the time that the publicity mills were blaring forth the EAHOS message at its loudest. He was apparently dissatisfied with much of the evidence being put forward, especially the absence of evidence concerning the Pliocene drought. In fact, if one searches the literature, no evidence was ever offered in support of such a drought. It was simply a prerequisite of the Pluvial Theory that the preceding period must have been dry, because by definition it could not have been as wet or wetter. But with the discarding of the Pluvial Theory in the late 1950s, the Pliocene drought concept persisted, initially vaguely voiced but oft repeated, until it came to have a life of its own – just as did the Pluvial Theory – and reached its acme in Ardrey's book *African Genesis* (1967). Hardy was, in my view, merely raising an alternative hypothesis, perhaps with tongue in cheek, although the message itself was serious enough. The EAHOS message might just be wrong, and scientists ought to take a closer look at the evidence offered by the EAHOS, rather than blindly accepting (almost reverently) what has subsequently turned out to be wishful thinking and self-delusion on rather a daunting scale.

It is also no coincidence that at about the same time that the general public, particularly in America, was being bombarded with the Wall Street version of Human Origins, there was a re-emergence of Creation Science in America. Creation Scientists had every reason to be dissatisfied with the evidence put forward by the EAHOS; equally dissatisfied were many palaeontologists and geologists, as any perusal of the scientific literature will show. Different sectors of society reacted differently to their bewilderment; Creation Scientists took one course of action – a return to fundamental principles as revealed in the Bible; geologists and palaeontologists asked for more evidence and better accountability from EAHOS, while the Aquatic Ape School apparently plunged for the opposite of 'aridity' as a moulder of humanness, and so was born the concept of the watery past in human evolution.

DISCUSSION OF THE AQUATIC APE THEORY

In common with the drought theory, the watery hypothesis has these essential elements: a primitive ape goes through a 'trying time' in a 'strange' environment, in the process being transformed into a hominid. Instead of drought, the strange environment is a surfeit of water.

Most of the evidence put forward by Hardy and subsequent champions of the AAT, such as Morgan (1982) and Verhaegen (chapter 5, this volume), consists of anatomical and behavioural features, every one of which is an *analogue* of features found in a variety of distantly related mammals and other vertebrates, whose only commonality is their aquatic or amphibious lifestyle. The core of their argument seems to be that 'analogy' equates with 'commonality of selection pressure'. Wings, be they of birds, bats or bumble-bees, for example, suggest selection for locomotion through air regardless of relatedness among these winged creatures. Morgan and Verhaegen follow this kind of logic throughout their published work, pointing out one or another analogy between humans and one or another aquatic animal, until quite an impressive list of features has emerged. Differences between humans and the same set of animals seldom feature in their studies, similarity evidently outweighing differences on a constant basis. *Homology* has seldom, if ever, entered any of their scenarios.

Furthermore, virtually all the evidence supposedly supporting the AAT comes from the neontologic record. Very little solid evidence emerges from the fossil record, although Verhaegen appears to observe aquatic adaptations in Neanderthal man. (This evidence, though, is far too late to have a bearing on the ape–human transition.) It is unfortunate for the AAT that the bulk of the evidence thought to support it lacks the time dimension. Evolution, after all, occurs over time, which means that any source of data lacking that dimension is incomplete as far as evolution studies are concerned. The lack of the time dimension is the greatest drawback of the molecular phylogenetic method. All phylogenies produced using neontological data alone are nothing more nor less than *scala naturae*.

The possession of the time dimension is the palaeontologist's strongest point. The discovery of the depth of geologic time during the early part of the nineteenth century was the great contribution to science and humanity made by the founders of palaeontology. Without this discovery and what it means, we might still be saddled with the Aristotelian 'ladder of life' concept which was based mainly on what people observed in the extant biosphere, to which was added a modicum of religion and myth. The Aristotelian *scala naturae* lacked the time dimension, as does most molecular phylogeny and the AAT.

However, before we dismiss the AAT out of hand, we ought to examine the fossil record, as have Verhaegen and LaLumiere (this volume, chapters 5 and 3, respectively), to see if indeed there is any evidence which might be interpreted in such a way as to yield support for it. Verhaegen considers that there is taphonomic evidence from the East African, and anatomical evidence from the European, fossil record, which supports the AAT. LaLumiere sees no evidence as yet, but predicts that such evidence will be forthcoming if only we look in the right place; and in order to lend weight to his vision, he provides us with quite a detailed view of where to look, evidently being a supporter of the 'island biogeography' approach to speciation. It is strange that none of the known numerous hominoid and hominid localities discovered in Africa and Eurasia fulfils the requirements of LaLumiere. He apparently preferred to base his arguments on evidence that does not exist (but which might), rather than on evidence that has already been gathered.

Let us examine the geological evidence to see whether any of it can be interpreted in such a way as to provide support for the AAT. Whether one takes a long-term view of human origins, as did LaLumiere and as Verhaegen used to (that is, the transition from ape to man took place during the upper Miocene), or the short-term view that Verhaegen now seems to champion (aquatic analogues in Neanderthal man, millions of years after the ape–human transition), the geological record does not provide convincing evidence from which the AAT could benefit.

The early scenario

Of all the pre-hominid fossils recovered in the Old World, now totalling more than 3,000 specimens from hundreds of localities ranging in age from the lower Miocene (18 million years ago) to the Holocene, scattered through three continents, only a minute proportion of specimens has, to my knowledge, been found in fully lacustrine sediments or in marine (including littoral) strata. And this is despite the fact that an aquatic ape would have been living in the very environment most likely to lead to its preservation as a fossil.

In East Africa, for example, where fully lacustrine sediments abound, only a few specimens have been recovered, although the sediments yield a profusion of other fossils. The only lacustrine strata to have yielded such specimens in Kenya are those at Nachola, a *Kenyapithecus* site, from which postcranial evidence indicated an arboreal lifestyle rather than an aquatic one. At this site, *Kenyapithecus* may well have lived in the trees which grew in the area, the fossil trunks of which are a common feature of the sediments.

On the contrary, the richest concentrations of hominoid fossils occur in sediments which accumulated subaerially, well away from lakes (Pickford, 1986).

In the Siwalik Hills of Pakistan and India, all the fossil hominoids now totalling several hundred specimens from many different sites, the environment of the hominoids was a wooded to forested plain bordering the precursors of the Ganges and Indus Rivers. The various European and Chinese hominoids were also found in non-lacustrine settings; the closest that any of the sites gets to being lacustrine are the lignites which accumulated in swamp forests. Among these, even the enigmatic *Oreopithecus* was not aquatic, being instead an arborealist.

The late scenario

In Plio-Pleistocene strata of the Old World which have yielded hominids, the story repeats itself. None of the specimens occurs in fully lacustrine strata, nor in marine sediments. Instead, they occur in subaerial strata such as commonly accumulate in flood plains, volcanic slopes, palaeosols and cave systems. That many of these sediments were formerly misinterpreted as representing 'lake beds' and as such were used as evidence in support of the Pluvial Hypothesis of Wayland (1934) and others, is a historical fact that in no way provides support for the AAT. For many years any sediment in East Africa was erroneously called 'lake beds', regardless of its origin. For example, the type section of the Kamasian pluvial is an ignimbrite (a volcanic rock deposited as a super-hot ash which remelts under its own weight and temperature) which was deposited on dry land. We estimate that only about 5 per cent of the volume of sediment in the Gregory Rift Valley accumulated under fully lacustrine conditions. For the Nyanza Rift, the figure is even less (0.01 per cent). In contrast, about 70 per cent of the volume of sediment in the Albert Basin of the Western Rift is lacustrine, yet only a single ape tooth has been found in these highly fossiliferous strata.

If the geological evidence is to be a source of support for the AAT, then all the positive evidence as to palaeo-environments that is currently available has to be discarded or discounted, and recourse taken to what the geological record 'might' yield. It is true that fossils of upper Miocene apes and/or hominids are rare (Pickford, 1988), and it could be argued that, during the critical period, the fossil record supports neither the AAT nor any other hypothesis concerning ape–human transitions. Search as we might in appropriately aged (upper Miocene to lower Pliocene) the lacustrin strata, of which there are vast sequences rich in fossils in Kenya (Mpesida, Samburu, Lukeino and Chemeron) and Uganda (Albert and Edward Basins), fossil hominoids continue to evade us.

CONCLUSION

The only conclusion to be drawn on the basis of available evidence (that is not to be derided for its quantity and quality), is that apes and hominids avoided lakes and seas throughout the Miocene and Plio-Pleistocene, just as they do today.* Any other conclusion, including the suggestion that we have not looked in the right place, must come under the heading of 'special pleading'. Under this category of reasoning, I place both LaLumiere's and Verhaegen's geological results.

REFERENCES

Ardrey, R., 1967, *African Genesis* (Glasgow: Collins).

Hardy, A.C., 1960, Was man more aquatic in the past? *New Scientist*, **7**, 642–5.

LaLumiere, L. P., 1991, Evolution of genus *Homo*: where it happened. (This volume, chapter 3.)

Morgan, E., 1982, *The Aquatic Ape* (London: Souvenir Press).

Morgan, E., 1991a, The origins of a theory. (This volume, chapter 1.)

Morgan, E., 1991b, Why a new theory is needed. (This volume, chapter 2.)

Pickford, M., 1986, Sedimentation and fossil preservation in the Nyanza Rift System, Kenya. In L. Frostick *et al.* (eds) *Sedimentation in the African Rifts* (Geological Society of London Special Publications), vol. 25: 345–62.

Pickford, M., 1988, From *Kenyapithecus* to *Australopithecus*. *Proceedings of the Vth Congress of the European Anthropological Association* (Lisbon), **1**, 7–11.

Verhaegen, M., 1991, Aquatic features in fossil hominids? (This volume, chapter 5.)

* Editors' comment: At least six species of primates have been recorded as swimming when free-ranging, and a further twelve swimming and wading in zoos; they represent all four primate major taxa (Ellis, this volume, p. 53).

Wayland, E.J., 1934, Rifts, rivers, rains and early man in Uganda. *Journal of the Anthropological Institute*, **64**, 333–52.

Author's note added at proof stage: The editors mention that there are several primates which swim and wade. I know about the cercopithecids which venture into the sea, and I know about the Orang which wades across narrow rivers. This is the reason why I was careful to confine my statement to hominoids and hominids, and to say that the Miocene to Pliocene forms tended to avoid lakes and seas. I still maintain this point of view, and the fact that six out of 172 species of extant primates enter water does not in my opinion greatly bolster the AAT, nor does it alter the fact that fossil primate remains seldom occur in lacustrine sediments.

8 Adaptation and the Aquatic Ape

Alan Turner

SUMMARY

The arguments for an aquatic ape phase during the course of human evolution represent a 'Just So Story' approach to explaining evolutionary development, and show little awareness of the current debate in evolutionary biology about the significance of apparent adaptations. The fact that aspects of our anatomy and physiology permit us to operate in water offers no insight into our recent evolutionary history, unless couched in the questionable terms of the adaptationist programme whereby origin is simply interpreted in terms of current utility. While the details remain to be established, the hominids appear to have evolved in the same manner as other members of the African terrestrial mammalian biota, and our aquatic 'adaptations' are adequately explained as part of our generalised mammalian ability to cope with a range of circumstances.

INTRODUCTION

The argument put forward by Morgan (1972, 1984, 1985, 1986; Morgan and Verhaegen, 1986) in favour of the Aquatic Ape Theory of human origins is presented as a fresh approach, unbiased by prior assumptions of the kind to be found in conventional writings on the subject of human evolution. But the sequence of Morgan's writings shows that the aquatic phase is itself taken as an established fact, with new fossil evidence simply fitted into the overall scenario. The result is that any resolution of the question, 'Did we or did we not go through an aquatic phase?', is rendered impossible. We simply get bogged down in disputes about whether hair loss, sweating, tears, diving ability, subcutaneous fat in babies and a host of other attributes necessitate a period of life in the water at some point in our past.

It is clear that most if not all of these attributes do not militate *against* an aquatic lifestyle of some sort or other, but that is scarcely the same as saying that they indicate an aquatic ape forebear. The arguments presented by Morgan, and by Hardy (1960, 1977), exemplify what may be termed the 'Just So Story' or *ad hoc* approach to explaining evolutionary development – a method of scientific inquiry that is of dubious validity (Clutton-Brock and Harvey, 1979). We might as well argue that the fine balance controls and other characteristics that enable us to ride bicycles must have been developed during a bicycle-riding phase in the Pliocene – perhaps with tandems as reinforcing devices for ensuring monogamous coupling (although not necessarily in transit). If bicycles are unknown from the Pliocene we obviously have to look harder for them, unblinkered by the academic status quo.

I do not intend to become involved in the discussion about specific details of morphology and physiology. Instead, I want to step back and examine the logic that underlies the development of the AAT, and then to examine some of the explanations offered by Morgan and Hardy as examples of the tenor of the argument.

THE ADAPTATIONIST SCENARIO

Evolution is the chief organising concept of modern-day biology, and a key aspect of that organisation is the notion of adaptation. But what is an adaptation? Williams (1966), Lewontin (1978), Gould and Lewontin (1979), Clutton-Brock and Harvey (1979) and Gould and Vrba (1982) have all pointed in recent years to the difficulties that beset the unwary who use the term in an unguarded manner. Gould and Vrba (p. 5) cite the early recognition of the problem by Darwin (1859, p. 197) and repeat his example: skull sutures in young animals may indeed assist parturition, but if their presence is due to the 'laws of growth' (in Darwin's words) then they cannot be termed adaptations towards ease of birth. But, to this day, the logic of Darwin's argument appears to have fallen on deaf ears among those who offer an adaptationist explanation for every trait of an organism in what Gould and Lewontin term the 'adaptationist programme'. As Gould and Vrba (p.13) express it, 'current utility carries no automatic implication about historical origin'. In making this point, the latter authors were particularly concerned to highlight flaws in the concept of preadaptations, but in the course of their discussion usefully illustrated the problems surrounding the entire issue of adaptation. In their view, only features promoting fitness *and built by selection for their current roles* may be termed adaptations, whereas the operation of other useful characters not built by selection for their current roles should be considered as effects. In the present context this may seen like rather rarefied academic hair-splitting, but it illustrates the essential point that one cannot simply assume that a given character was selected to perform a given function. And if one cannot make such an assumption, then it becomes very difficult indeed to use such characters to infer the precise course of evolutionary development and the detailed natural history of a species at given times.

Seen from this perspective, the AAT is a first-class example of the adaptationist programme taken to an extreme. For it interprets virtually every feature of human morphology, physiology and behaviour that does not positively indicate hydrophobia as the product of natural selection during an aquatic phase of hominid evolution. This procedure is, of course, unsound. No consideration is given to the role of incidental effects in the development of characters. No effort is made to distinguish between any likely effects and any possible true adaptations. The entire presentation is one of dubious scientific value, offered under the flimsy pretext of examining the supposedly competing 'hypotheses' of neoteny and a strictly savannah origin.

As Morgan (1982; p. 22) admits, neoteny is a mechanism. As such it cannot be set in comparison with theories of human origins in a savannah environment; yet although it is really irrelevant to the argument, it is forced to function as straw-man in the presentation of the AAT. As for shortcomings in the argument for human origins on the African savannahs, it is not particularly difficult to criticise as inadequate in one way or another some of the published efforts to produce a synthesised interpretation of human evolution. Many such efforts appear in the secondary literature, often written by people with no greater claim to expertise in current evolutionary theory (and its major points of debate) than familiarity with popular notions of Darwinian natural selection, survival of the fittest and adaptation as an overall outcome. The correlation between the first and last of these three is usually taken to be extremely close. Within- and between-species changes are often inextricably confused, leading to the assumption that major adaptive changes must correlate with speciation events. A new hominid species must, in such an interpretation, have exhibited locomotor and behavioural traits, as well as a level of intelligence, different from anything that went before. On the other hand, more specialist investigations often concentrate on particular features of hominid skeletal anatomy and the inferences that may be drawn about relevant details of the soft tissues. Over-emphasis on the possible adaptive significance of certain skeletal features is almost predictable in such circumstances. To judge by the examples quoted by Gould and Lewontin (1979), few such specialists are likely to be immune to the lure of the adaptationist programme, or to be able to distinguish true reasons for origin from interpretations of current utility. And although they are concerned with evolution in a particular family, few such specialists are really evolutionary biologists engaged in debate about the theoretical underpinnings of the subject. Rather, they are users of evolutionary theory as they currently understand it, and as Gould and Lewontin, and Gould and Vrba (1982), have pointed out, opportunities for misunderstanding are rife.

But all such interpretations, by synthesisers or by specialists, correct in their details or otherwise, set the hominids within a generalised woodland–savannah mosaic of the kind clearly indicated for eastern Africa during the Plio-Pleistocene. This is not surprising, because that is what the environmental evidence points to for the areas in which all the East African hominid fossils have so far been found. It is not as though the 'conventional' interpretations of hominid evolution are being forced into some inappropriate and wrong-headed palaeo-environmental mould. The Savannah Theory of human evolution does not stand in competition with one or other rival theories, as Morgan suggests. The pattern that we see and the evolutionary process that we infer takes place within a changing vegetational mosaic, in turn linked to environmental shifts (Vrba *et al.*, 1985). Abundant evidence is now emerging that macroevolutionary events in the African terrestrial biota are closely correlated with environmental changes, and the hominids do not appear to be unusual in this respect (Bonnefille, 1985; Delson, 1985; Vrba, 1985a, 1985b; Turner, 1985, 1986a, 1986b; Wesselman, 1985). That these environmental changes are likely to be a major causal factor in macroevolution has received strong support from recent developments in evolutionary theory (Vrba, 1985c, 1985d; Paterson, 1986), developments that stress the continued existence of a species while its normal habitat prevails. In other words, while we may quibble about details and adaptive scenarios, the terrestrial evolution of the hominids makes very good sense when assessed in conjunction with the palaeo-environmental evidence and the evolution of contemporaneous taxa, and is supported by a strong inference about the cause of speciation.

ON THE BEACH

What do Morgan and Hardy offer between them by way of a replacement for terrestrial origins of the hominids? The simple answer is a total explanation for every feature; but here I shall be necessarily selective. Three major points seem to lie at the heart of the AAT: first, the problem of our missing body hair; second, the implications of our apparent aquatic adaptations; and third, the significance of the fossil evidence.

The need to invoke an aquatic development phase in explanation for our absent body hair stems from a perceived evolutionary paradox: we have lost our hair but apparently gained subcutaneous fat. As viewed by Morgan and Hardy, this seems to make no sense in a savannah-living animal; yet the real problem lies in the perspective, and in the assumption that each feature can be tied to a specific, adaptive response. We are told by Morgan that presumed hair loss in humans may have resulted from selection pressure for faster swimming. The evidence is merely a claim by Hardy (1977) that members of the Sydney University swimming team saved one second in a one-hundred-yard swim by shaving off all their body hair. Hardy suggested that groups of our ancestors might have been better able to escape a shark attack by being less hairy. But while a fast-swimming species might benefit from a little fine-tuning of streamlining, are we really to believe that a swimming primate in a life-or-death contest with a superb swimmer such as a shark would achieve much by the loss of body hair?

Hardy followed his suggestion about body hair with a claim that the streamlined shape of the human body is further evidence for an aquatic past, a claim with which Morgan appears to agree. But both authors completely overlook the fact that our present-day body shape can have little to do with the matter if the intense selection for a streamlined body shape took place during the Pliocene, when hominid size, limb proportions and body shape were somewhat different and remained different. One might also note that the proboscis monkey, favoured by Morgan (1982) as an example of a primate with a generalised swimming ability, shows few obvious signs of the supposed characters strongly selected for in our own lineage. In other words, it can, like ourselves, get by very well in the water with its existing generalised abilities.

Hardy's article concluded with a suggestion concerning a 'recent' discovery (the diving reflex — see Patrick, this volume, chapter 14) — one which, in Hardy's words 'is almost as conclusive as the fossil evidence, I believe'. His suggestion concerned putting members of all known ape species in a bath with their faces submerged, to see if they, like other diving species and humans, exhibit a diving reflex. The presence of the reflex was to be determined by electrocardiographically monitored changes in the circulation of the blood. Morgan (1982) draws attention to the practical difficulties involved in such an experiment, but reiterates Hardy's belief in the importance of the phenomenon for the AAT. But the diving reflex, including both breath-holding and bradycardia, seems to be a much more generalised mammalian response than Morgan considers it to be (Zapol, 1987), and really offers little support for ideas about selection pressures during our relatively recent past.

It is quite legitimate to investigate the physiology of an animal that clearly has a major capacity for aquatic activity, to examine the features that permit it to dive deeply or to swim quickly, and to talk in terms of adaptations to such a mode of life (provided, of course, that one bears in mind the necessary caveats about historical origin in relation to current utility discussed above). But it is quite another thing to take human characteristics that *permit* aquatic activity and to construct from them an otherwise wholly unsupported evolutionary scenario of the kind presented by Morgan. The Weddell seal, *Leptonychotes weddelli*, for example, is obviously well adapted to life in deep, cold seas, and shows a remarkable range of physiological and anatomical refinements to this end (Zapol, 1987). Human 'adaptations' to aquatic life are by comparison rather feeble, among the range in animals able to cope in water rather than in those that have to exist in it permanently or for much of their time. Viewing human abilities in terms of intense selection pressures during an aquatic phase of development therefore appears a rather extreme explanation for what are no more than generalised mammalian abilities. To raise this objection is not to render human characteristics 'explanation-proof', as asserted by Morgan (1984, p. 12). The intention is, rather, to avoid raising what is no more than an *ad hoc*, Just So Story 'explanation' to the status of a 'proof', in the manner of the AAT.

The issue of the fossil evidence, or rather its absence, appears at a number of places in the argument. Hardy (1977) suggested that attention should be concentrated in those areas of the world where fossil proof of his theory might be forthcoming. It is hard to envisage precisely what form such proof might take, however, since simply finding hominid fossils in deposits close to the sea would hardly inform us about intense marine activities of the kind implied by the theory. In contrast, Morgan (1984, p. 12) attacks what she characterises as the 'we must wait for more evidence' school of palaeontological response to the AAT, claiming that such a stance 'tacitly assumes that fossil evidence is in some way intrinsically more valid than other kinds of evidence', and that 'many scientists are disputing this proposition'. In support of that latter point she cites a statement by Colin Patterson to the effect that fossils rarely overturn theories of relationships based on recent organisms. That citation reveals a degree of unfamiliarity with biological debate. Patterson was referring to systematics and to the question of the part to be played by fossil data in reaching decisions during cladistic analyses of relationships. His statement has nothing to do with the utility of fossil data in inferring past activities of a taxon, and Morgan has simply taken it out of context.

As to the question of whether fossil evidence is intrinsically more valid than other kinds, the answer depends on what it is one wants to know about. It would certainly be difficult to learn very much about Plio-Pleistocene hominids without the fossil evidence. And in the same paper that questions the supremacy of the fossils, Morgan still seems to find in the most recent finds considerable support for her ideas. For example, we read (Morgan, 1984, p. 13) that the bipedality of our putative ancestor *Australopithecus afarensis* may have been the result of an aquatically induced preadaptation towards bipedal locomotion. Fortunately for Aquatic Ape Theory supporters, the aquatic phase took place during the undocumented gap in the fossil record before 4 million years ago, presumably at the same time that they believe we were losing our hair in order to be able to swim faster than sharks. But if the selection pressure for swimming speed was so intense, then why, one might ask, did the process end up with hominids possessing a skeleton like Lucy's that lacks evident adaptations towards high-speed swimming? Morgan (1982, p. 78) offers the observation that 'no other aquatic mammal is descended from a primate. This would affect, for one thing, his style of swimming', and goes on to argue that apes can adopt a frog-like swimming action. That may be true, and *A. afarensis*, even with its relatively short legs (Susman, Stern and Jungers, 1985), may also have been quite adept at such a stroke, but that argument does little to clarify the need for hair loss in an animal moving through the water in such a manner. At this point the AAT starts to become entangled in its own adaptationist web: the only solution would be to discard elements of the adaptationist explanation – but which ones? If one adopts a rigorously adaptationist stance then how does one select from among the multitude of phenomena to be accorded such an explanation when the explanations begin to conflict?

The fact that we have a dearth of fossil evidence prior to 4 million years ago does not really mean that all options are open for guessing what happened in the late Miocene and early Pliocene. It serves no scientific purpose to set out hypotheses of 'preadaptations' for bipedality based on Just So Stories of an aquatic lifestyle. If one is forever going to argue about 'missing evidence' that might change our views, evidence that will be found if only we look in the right place unblinkered by conventional wisdom, then one might as well go the whole way and put everything down to unknown causes. Mio-Pliocene outings to the seaside by hominids are not ruled out, but they need hardly be invoked as causal mechanisms.

CONCLUSION

Ideas about evolution, both in overview and in relation to specific taxa and events, are constantly subjected to criticism from within the biological sciences. I have discussed here some of the criticisms levelled at the adaptationist programme in particular, as well as pointing to the shortcomings of many efforts to explain the evolution of the hominids. What is apparent from these in-house disputes, however, is the need for an awareness of the basic issues involved, the theoretical underpinnings of the subject. Evolution is not in dispute, but some of the details are being revised, and many working in the field are not fully aware of the details of the debate. In criticising from outside, one can be right (to criticise) for the wrong reasons if one is not aware of the larger problems – a trap that always awaits the non-specialist commentator in any field. Subjects like evolution in general, and human evolution in particular, seem to invite non-specialist attention (at least in the form of criticism) rather more than, say, physics and its more esoteric aspects like quantum mechanics. Perhaps it is because much of physics is largely impenetrable without the mathematical tools, whereas evolution gives more the appearance of an academic free-for-all indulged in by everybody from Creationists upwards. This is not a dismissal of critics (Creationists excepted), but it is an attempt to encourage an appropriate degree of caution on the subject. There is more to understanding evolution than a belief in natural selection and the construction of adaptationist scenarios, and if specialists can be shown to have fallen into that trap then the non-specialist may need to exercise great caution.

ACKNOWLEDGEMENTS

I am grateful to C.A. Gordon and A.C. Kemp for discussion of many of the points raised here, and for comments on an earlier version of the manuscript.

REFERENCES

Bonnefille, R., 1985, Evolution of the continental vegetation: the palaeobotanical record from East Africa. *South African Journal of Science*, **81**, 267–70.

Clutton-Brock, T.H. and Harvey, P.H., 1979, Comparison and adaptation. *Proceedings of the Royal Society of London*, **B205**, 547–65.

Darwin, C., 1859, *On the Origin of Species* (London: John Murray).

Delson, E., 1985, Neogene African catarrhine primates: climatic influence on evolutionary patterns. *South African Journal of Science*, **81**, 273–4.

Gould, S.J. and Lewontin, R.C., 1979, The spandrels of San Marco and the Panglossian paradigm. *Proceedings of the Royal Society of London*, **B205**, 581–98.

Gould, S.J. and Vrba, E.S., 1982, Exaptation–a missing term in the science of form. *Paleobiology*, **8**, 4–15.

Hardy, A., 1960, Was man more aquatic in the past? *New Scientist*, **7**, 642–5.

Hardy, A., 1977, Was there a *Homo aquaticus? Zenith*, **15**(1), 4–6.

Lewontin, R.C., 1978, Adaptation. *Scientific American*, **239**(3), 156–69.

Morgan, E., 1972, *The Descent of Woman* (London: Souvenir Press).

Morgan, E., 1982, *The Aquatic Ape* (London: Souvenir Press).

Morgan, E., 1984, The aquatic hypothesis. *New Scientist*, **102**, 11–13.

Morgan, E., 1985, Sweaty old man and the sea. *New Scientist*, **105**, 27–8.

Morgan, E., 1986, Lucy's child. *New Scientist*, **112**, 13–15.

Morgan, E. and Verhaegen, M., 1986, In the beginning was the water. *New Scientist*, **109**, 62–3.

Paterson, H.E.H., 1986, Environment and species. *South African Journal of Science*, **82**, 62–5.

Susman, R.L., Stern, J.T. and Jungers, W.L., 1985, Locomotor adaptations in Hadar hominids. In *Ancestors: The Hard Evidence*, ed. E. Delson (New York: Liss), 184–92.

Turner, A., 1985, Extinction, speciation and dispersal in African larger carnivores, from the Late Miocene to Recent. *South African Journal of Science*, **81**, 256–7.

Turner, A., 1986a, Some features of African larger carnivore historical biogeography. *Palaeoecology of Africa*, **17**, 237–44.

Turner, A., 1986b, Species, speciation and human evolution. *Human Evolution*, **1**, 419–30.

Vrba, E.S., 1985a, African bovidae: evolutionary events since the Miocene. *South African Journal of Science*, **81**, 263–6.

Vrba, E.S., 1985b, Ecological and adaptive changes associated with early hominid evolution. In *Ancestors: the Hard Evidence*, ed. E. Delson (New York: Liss), 63–71.

Vrba, E.S., 1985c, Environment and evolution: alternative causes of the temporal distribution of evolutionary events. *South African Journal of Science*, **81**, 229–36.

Vrba, E.S., 1985d, Introductory comments on species and speciation. In *Species and Speciation*, ed. E.S. Vrba (Pretoria: Transvaal Museum Monograph no. 4, ix–xviii.
Vrba, E.S., Burckle, L.H., Denton, G.H. and Partridge, T.C. (eds.) 1985, Palaeoclimate and Evolution I. *South African Journal of Science*, **81**, 224–75.
Wesselman, H.B., 1985, Fossil micromammals as indicators of climatic change about 2.4 myr ago in the Omo Valley, Ethiopia. *South African Journal of Science*, **81**, 260–1.
Williams, G.C., 1966, *Adaptation and Natural Selection* (Princeton, New Jersey: Princeton University Press).
Zapol, W.M., 1987, Diving adaptations of the Weddell seal. *Scientific American*, **256**(6), 80–5.

9 The Aquatic Ape Theory, Seen from Epistemological and Palaeoanthropological Viewpoints

Holger and Signe Preuschoft

SUMMARY

In this chapter the Aquatic Ape Theory is evaluated according to epistemological criteria and its explanative value is compared with that of what AAT proponents call the Savannah Theory. To that purpose, the fossil record is reviewed, while employing the strictest 'functional' explanations for the morphological characters of the fossils. The known stages of human evolution are found to form an uninterrupted sequence of functional adaptations to arboreal, semi-arboreal/terrestrial and cursorial modes of locomotion. In many cases the adaptive value can be defined semi-quantitatively as mechanical advantages for a given type of locomotion. Our comparison made it necessary to develop some testable hypotheses about the locomotor behaviour of presumed aquatic ancestors, something that so far has not been proposed by AAT advocates. The morphological adaptations advantageous for some possible aquatic forms of locomotion do not exist.

We find that the Aquatic Ape Theory:

- does not explain more findings than do the more traditional ideas;
- does not allow a more complete integration of accepted but unassociated facts;
- does not contain fewer contradictions, nor leave fewer gaps;
- does not allow more parsimonious explanations;
- does not allow for more precise or more correct predictions of new findings;
- does not yield hypotheses that can be tested in a more reliable, simpler or more convincing way than those deduced within the framework of the Savannah Theory. In fact, the weakest point of the new theory seems to be that its proponents do not develop hypothetical explanations that can be tested on the basis of known natural laws, or even on the basis of empirically well established rules.

It has to be admitted, though, that the promotion of the new AAT has stimulated a thorough reconsideration of what we believe to know, to investigate new facts, and to acquire new knowledge.

INTRODUCTION

The Aquatic Ape Theory was designed to explain morphological and physiological characteristics of man, and to contrast with what AAT proponents call the Savannah Theory. By emphasising the latter term, they refer to the widespread belief that the evolutionary steps which led to the present human body shape took place in woodland or gallery forests in savannah-like landscapes, and later in grasslands scattered with trees. In fact, the proponents of the Aquatic Ape Theory ascribe more uniformity and homogeneity to other current ideas on hominid evolution than we – and others – had attributed to them before. The traditional savannah scenario fits in fairly well with a large number of assumptions about the origins of important human traits (see p. 161), though admittedly it does not yield plausible explanations for all the features of our species.

The AAT postulates that human evolution has taken place in a completely different ecological scenario: namely, in or close to water. Consequently, the selective pressures assumed to have been responsible for the development of traits that distinguish human from non-human primates are different from those proposed by the majority of previous researchers. Therefore, we are confronted with two theories competing to offer better explanations of the same, uniquely human, features. Scientific seriousness demands an impartial judgement on the value of both theories. This is what is attempted in this chapter. Instead of trying to reach a decision on which theory is 'true' or 'false', we prefer to evaluate them on the basis of the following criteria:

- *explanative value*: the better theory is able to explain more findings than the other one;
- *integrative value*: the better theory allows for a more complete integration of commonly accepted but formerly unassociated facts;
- *extension and absence of contradictions*: a good theory does not imply contradictions and leaves few or no gaps between the partial explanations provided by it;
- *parsimony*: those explanations are to be preferred which are less complicated with respect to the causal mechanisms implied and the theoretical concepts referred to. A theory that embodies such explanations is more 'beautiful', or more 'elegant';
- *prognostic value*: the theory to be preferred is superior in its ability to make correct predictions of new findings;
- *testability*: to judge the prognostic value of a theory it must be possible to deduce testable hypotheses from that theoretical framework;
- *stimulus value*: a good theory should stimulate new approaches and research projects.

SURVEY OF THE FOSSIL RECORD

Although the possibility cannot be ruled out that important stages of hominid evolution remain to be discovered, we should work within the framework offered by the fossils available today when we attempt to reconstruct our ancestry, at least as long as we commit ourselves to the essentially empirical methods of natural science.

The evolution of man is now thoroughly documented (Vogel, 1974; Pilbeam, 1972; *National Geographic*, 1985; Johanson and Edey, 1982). We can trace back our ancestry through the stages of anatomically modern man of the Upper Palaeolithic (going back at least 40,000 years, perhaps even 80,000) and Neanderthal man of the middle Palaeolithic (about 150,000 years ago), to *Homo erectus* of the Early Palaeolithic (from 260,000 or 300,000 back to 1.6 million years ago; see Figure 9.1). The evolution of almost the entire skeleton is known, and there are few obvious differences that distinguish the body shape of Neanderthal man or *H. erectus* from that of modern man. Fossils of these forms have been found in Europe, Asia and Africa.

The probable ancestors of *H. erectus* were hominids called Australopithecines. In this context, it is not relevant to discuss the possible existence of a separate taxon, *H. habilis*. That discussion boils down to the question of whether there is a distinct evolutionary stage between *H. erectus* and *Australopithecus*. Certainly, the genus *Australopithecus* is split into robust and gracile forms and perhaps even into more than two species. Most parts of their skeletons are known, though unfortunately not all from the same sites. A conclusive analysis of australopithecine morphology is further hampered by the fact that essential skeletal parts are missing. At many sites remains of both forms, robusts and graciles, occur side by side. Australopithecine fossils date back to 3.5 million years ago and seem to be confined to East and South Africa. Some hominid-like fossils of greater age are known, but their taxonomical positions are not certain.

Those ancestors of the Australopithecines that we know are hominoids from the Miocene (more than 5.5 million years ago). They show dentitions and skull shapes very similar to those of modern apes. They have been found in several sites in Europe and Asia, in particular in the Siwalik foothills south of the Himalayas, and in Africa, east of the Rift Valley. The overall body shape and nearly all parts of the skeleton are known from a very complete find on Rusinga Island in Lake Victoria of a small species named *Proconsul africanus*. Nobody knows for sure whether it is representative of the entire group, because from other sites only fragments of the skeleton are known. Nevertheless, these fragments show no obvious differences from *P. africanus*. Surprisingly, the overall body shape of *Proconsul* resembles modern tree-living monkeys much more than modern apes. It is uncertain, however, whether the Miocene apes also possessed long tails. They are distinguished from modern apes by lacking their bulky trunk, short hind limbs and elongated forelimbs. Nor do they possess the typical features of modern gibbons (the 'lesser apes')

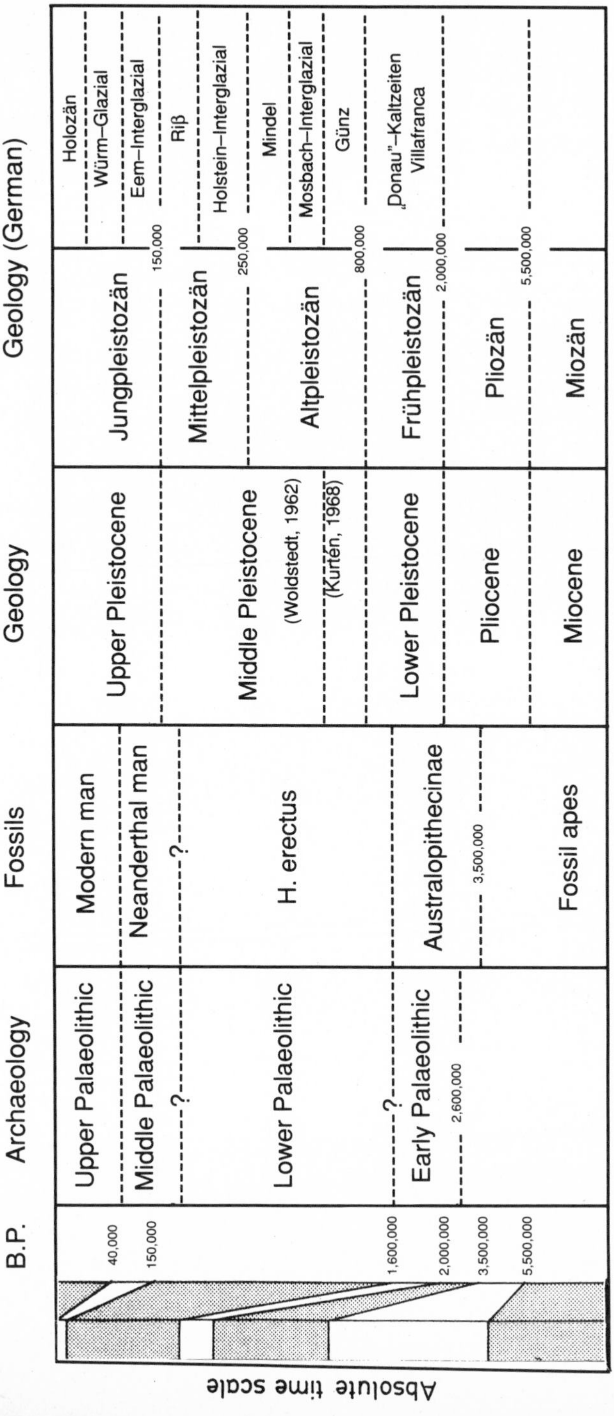

Absolute time scale

B.P.

40,000
150,000
1,600,000
2,000,000
3,500,000
5,500,000

Archaeology

Upper Palaeolithic
Middle Palaeolithic
?
Lower Palaeolithic
?
Early Palaeolithic
2,600,000

Fossils

Modern man
Neanderthal man
?
H. erectus
Australopithecinae
3,500,000
Fossil apes

Geology

Upper Pleistocene
Middle Pleistocene
(Woldstedt, 1962)
(Kurtén, 1968)
Lower Pleistocene
Pliocene
Miocene

Geology (German)

Jungpleistozän: Holozän; Würm–Glazial; Eem–Interglazial
150,000
Mittelpleistozän: Riß; Holstein–Interglazial
250,000
Altpleistozän: Mindel; Mosbach–Interglazial; Günz
800,000
Frühpleistozän: „Donau"–Kaltzeiten, Villafranca
2,000,000
Pliozän
5,500,000
Miozän

Figure 9.1 Chronology of hominid evolution.

such as the relatively slender trunk, the long hindlimbs and the extremely long forelimbs. Because of the similarity in their dentitions, but not in their body shapes, to those of modern pongids, the Miocene forms have been called 'dental apes'. We conclude that the bodily characteristics of both, lesser and great apes, are the result of more recent adaptations which have taken place roughly within the last 6 million years.

According to recent chronologies, the Miocene ended about 5.5 million years ago. That means that there is no longer a large gap in the known evolutionary history of hominids, as assumed until recently by palaeoanthropologists, who believed that the Miocene ended 10 million years ago. In fact, there are only some 2.5 or 3.5 million years that are without fossil records of our ancestry (see Figure 9.1). Hence, the starting-point for further considerations should be the known hominoids of the middle Miocene.

The environment in which the earliest of these evolutionary processes took place was, according to palaeo-ecological research (Pickford, 1986; Retallak, Dugas and Bestland, 1990), something between woodland and savannah, with gallery forests along rivers and freshwater lakes. The commonly used hypotheses imply a shift to bipedal locomotion and to a new diet because of the progressively dry, open grasslands which expanded during the late Miocene and early Pliocene. There are no known fossil documents to support the assumption that seashores were the habitats of these forms.

A SELECTION OF HOMINOID CHARACTERS THAT CAN BE EXPLAINED FUNCTIONALLY

General remarks on functional explanations of morphological characters

It is purely speculative to create, as do the AAT proponents, a system of presumed functional needs believed to be advantageous under hypothetical ecological conditions which have perhaps never existed among our ancestors. In order not to unduly restrict the chances of finding positive answers, one should avoid focusing exclusively on human traits which seem to be enigmatic. Instead, features should be considered which can be readily understood according to current ideas, or which can be traced through our known ancestry. Bearing this in mind, it is reasonable to concentrate on dentition, skull shape, trunk shape, pelvis, hindlimbs, feet, fingers and toes.

In the present era of neo-Darwinian thinking, it has become customary to refer by the term 'adaptation' to both the character and the use made of it – that is, its 'function'. If we use the term 'adaptation' we have to indicate precisely what a given trait is 'good for', or which traits are advantageous for fulfilling a given 'function'. Explanations for the acquisition or the loss of morphological traits can be given, according to Bock and von Wahlert (1965), on one of two levels: (a) that of biological role; (b) that of (mechanical) function. In this chapter, we restrict the use of the term 'function' to statements about how a feature works mechanically, depending on its physical properties. The use made of form characteristics during an animal's life history should be termed 'biological role'; in contrast to function, this can be ascertained only by observing animals in their natural environment.

The mechanical function must be fulfilled under all 'normally' occurring circumstances, enabling the structure not to fail in critical situations. The principle is now widely accepted that the body's shape must be such that its parts are suited to sustain the highest forces that can act on it under 'normal' conditions, while requiring a minimum of force or energy. The validity of that principle is underlined by the existence of a morphogenetic mechanism which causes an *intra vitam* remodelling of existing bones, tendons and ligaments. This leads to shape characteristics that fit optimally with the mechanical stresses induced by 'normal' locomotion or posture. Conversely, this means that the mechanical function can often be derived accurately from the shape of a fossil bone. It is this close connection between shape and function which leads us to put so much emphasis on the biomechanical approach to 'functions'.

'Biological roles' in the sense of Bock and von Wahlert (1965) are not tied so closely to morphology. In spite of this, most attempts to understand morphology are undertaken on the level of biological roles – as in the AAT debate. We prefer a strictly mechanical approach to function, because mechanical functions are more readily identifiable than biological roles (for further discussion, see Chivers *et al.*, 1984). In a terrestrial animal, the 'external' forces that can act on the body are limited by body weight (Preuschoft, 1985). These forces are usually concentrated on the hands or feet, or (while sitting) on the ischial callosities or equivalent structures.

Miocene Apes

The remains of *Proconsul africanus* from Rusinga Island probably belong to one individual (Figure 9.2). Forelimbs and hindlimbs are of equal length, which indicates quadrupedal locomotion. The limbs are long and rather strong relative to the slender trunk. Both traits are typical of modern monkeys as well, and relate to the great step lengths that characterise monkey locomotion (Vilensky, 1983; Reynolds, 1985a, 1985b) in contrast to other, more specialised, cursorial quadrupeds. The hands and feet are of an elongate and slender form. Their prehensile propensities are shown by the length of the metapodials and the length and curvature of the phalanges, as well as by the positions and the shapes of the joints. According to Preuschoft (1970, 1971a, 1971b, 1973a, 1973b), the

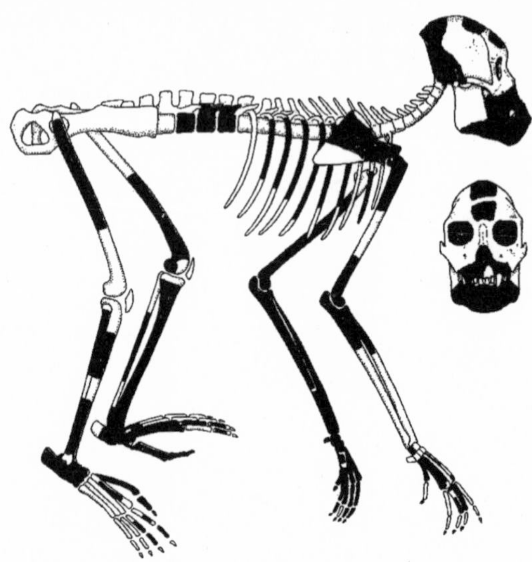

Figure 9.2 Reconstruction of *Proconsul africanus*, the best known among the potential forerunners of hominids (from Walker and Teaford, 1989).

curvature of the phalanges is an adaptation for grasping slim objects such as twigs. A phalanx (Figure 9.3) is exposed to bending moments caused by the action of the distal and proximal joint forces on one side, and to the pull of the flexor tendons and the force resulting from the redirection of the tendons running through the annular part of the tendon sheath. A curvature reduces bending moments by bringing the bone axis closer to the resultant force, which thus exerts more compression than bending. This alone gives strong evidence for an arboreal adaptation, as detailed by Preuschoft (1971b) for subfossil Madagascan lemuroids. The functional adaptation of other traits of *Proconsul* have been investigated by Preuschoft (1973b; see also Morbeck, 1972, for a different argument).

Australopithecines

Most features which characterise Australopithecines as the earliest hominids and distinguish them from Miocene apes are intermediate between modern great apes and modern man.

The most intriguing trait, the relatively large brain, yields no direct evidence about the environment in which australopithecine evolution took place. In gracile Australopithecines, which were of approximately the same size as modern chimpanzees (30–40 kg: Jungers, 1982), the braincase volume is estimated to be 380–600 cm^3, but for chimpanzees its volume is only 360–450 cm^3 (own data on *Pan troglodytes verus*, Frankfurt collection). In this context, it is important to recall that all primates, in

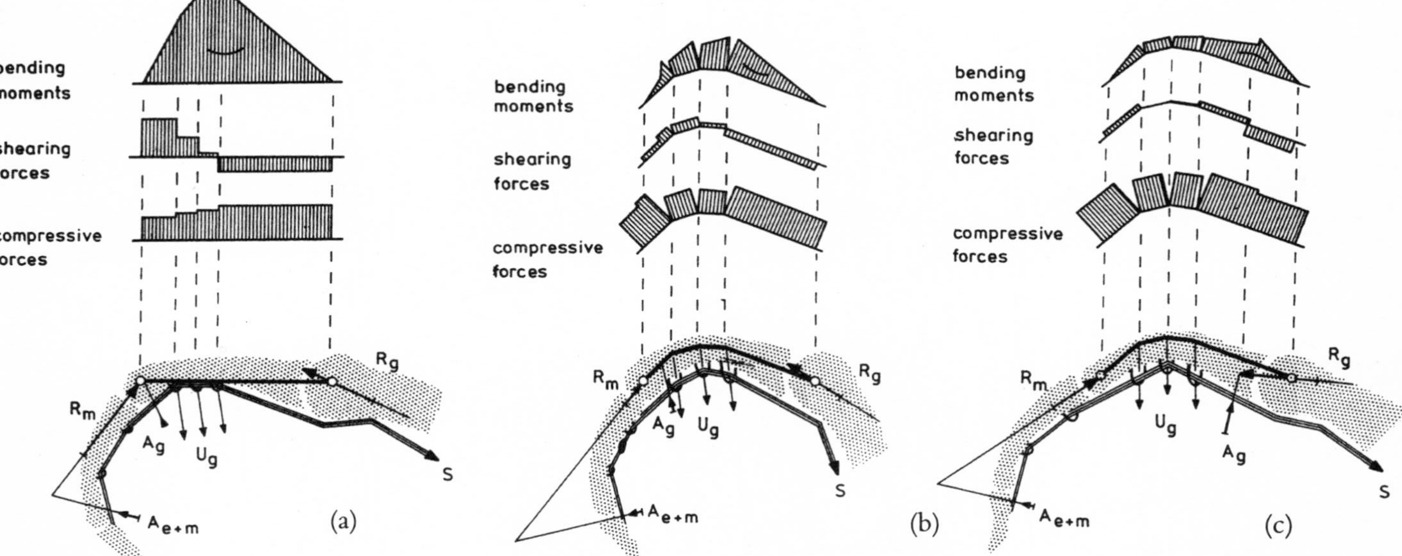

Figure 9.3 Stresses in finger bones of a primate present during a power grip, as used in climbing.
The curvature of the phalanges reduces bending stresses, and thus can be considered an adaptation to climbing. (a) straight phalanx; (b) curved phalanx, flexed joints; (c) curved phalanx, more extended joints. The arrows indicate forces which act on the finger bones: A = reaction forces exerted by the substrate against the terminal plus middle phalanx (Ae+m) or the proximal phalanx (Ag); S = muscle force on the flexor tendons. Both forces combine at the interphalangeal joint to form a resultant force Rm which pushes the middle phalanx against the proximal. The tendon force S is forced by the annular fibres of the tendon sheath to change its direction, and therefore exerts a force Ug, which is distributed over a part of the phalanx (illustrated as three partial forces at three points). All forces mentioned combine to a resultant Rg, which acts on the metacarpophalangeal joint.

particular the monkeys and apes, possess large brains relative to their body size; and within these large brains, the neocortex is the most progressively developed part (Stephan, 1967; Starck, 1982). Recently, the assumption has gained ground that brain size as well as the elaborate cognitive abilities of monkeys and apes are related to the fact that all of them are group-living animals with very complicated social systems. Thus, a progressive coevolution of the brain and the cognitive abilities necessary for living in these social systems is assumed. The evolution of the cognitive capacities is very likely to be closely tied to the development of a sophisticated communication system.

The sensory capabilities of humans are very similar to those of other higher primates. All diurnal primates are characterised by elaborate visual capacities, and to a large extent their communication relies on visual signals of subtle gradation and short-lasting quality. This also holds true for modern humans. It would be a waste of energy and a source of error to develop visual communicative systems and sensory organs of this quality under the conditions of poor visibility typical of an aquatic environment. In addition, the vocal communication of modern man lacks the elements and features of vocalisation and sound reception typical of aquatic animals.

The entire configuration of the skull and dentition changed in the period between the pongid-like forms of the Miocene and the early hominids of the Pliocene. Whereas in the former the long, narrow, U-shaped dental arcade (Figure 9.4) was situated *in front of* a fairly small braincase, the latter had a shorter, rather parabolic dental arch *below* an enlarged braincase (Figure 9.5). Simultaneously, a reduction in the size of the canines as well as an enlargement of the molars occurred, plus a change in the cusp shape. Traditional considerations of biological roles converged on the idea that large canines became superfluous because hand-use replaced them as 'weapons', and hands replaced the mouth as tools for the intake of food (small-object-feeding, hunting). In a recent paper, Preuschoft (1989a) has traced a direct mechanical interdependence that must have existed between the evolution of these traits: the reduction in size of the front teeth indicates changes in diet, leading to 'small object feeding ' (Jolly, 1970). The dome-shaped cusps are adapted to breaking down brittle and hard food items, like seeds and nuts – but also mollusc shells. According to Lucas, Corlett and Luke (1986a, 1986b), enlargement of the molar surfaces permits mastication of an equivalent amount of food if body size increases, but leads at the same time to a reduction in bite pressure. But the hardness of food items required an increase in bite pressure. Consequently, the muscles had to become enlarged and the load arms of the bite forces shortened. The latter was achieved by reducing snout length and increasing facial height. The characteristically flat or even concave face of robust Australopithecines (Robinson, 1972), or the pillar-like structures in

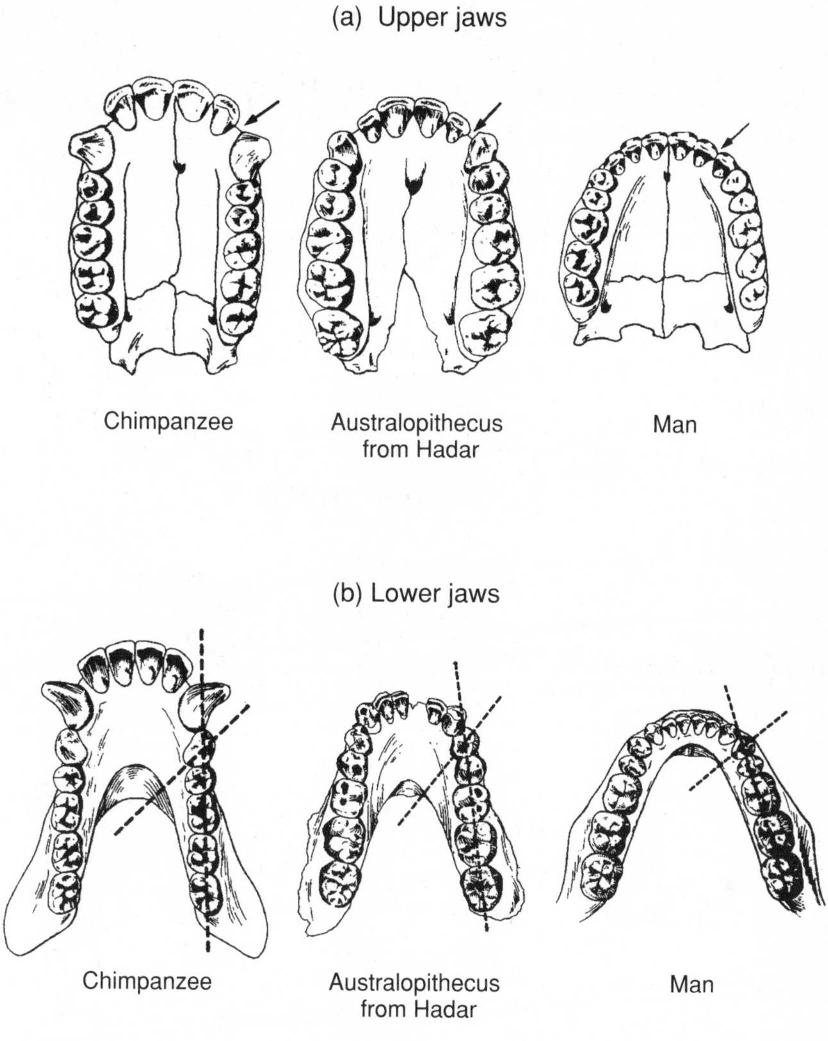

(a) Upper jaws

Chimpanzee

Australopithecus from Hadar

Man

(b) Lower jaws

Chimpanzee

Australopithecus from Hadar

Man

Figure 9.4 The long narrow dental arcade of Miocene (and modern) apes has been transformed during hominid evolution into a short, parabolic dental arcade without large canines.

(a) Upper jaws: the arrows show the gap between the lateral incisor and the canine; (b) Lower jaws: the broken lines indicate the angle of the tooth rows and the greatest diameter of the anterior premolar. (Not to the same scale; from Johanson and Edey, 1982.)

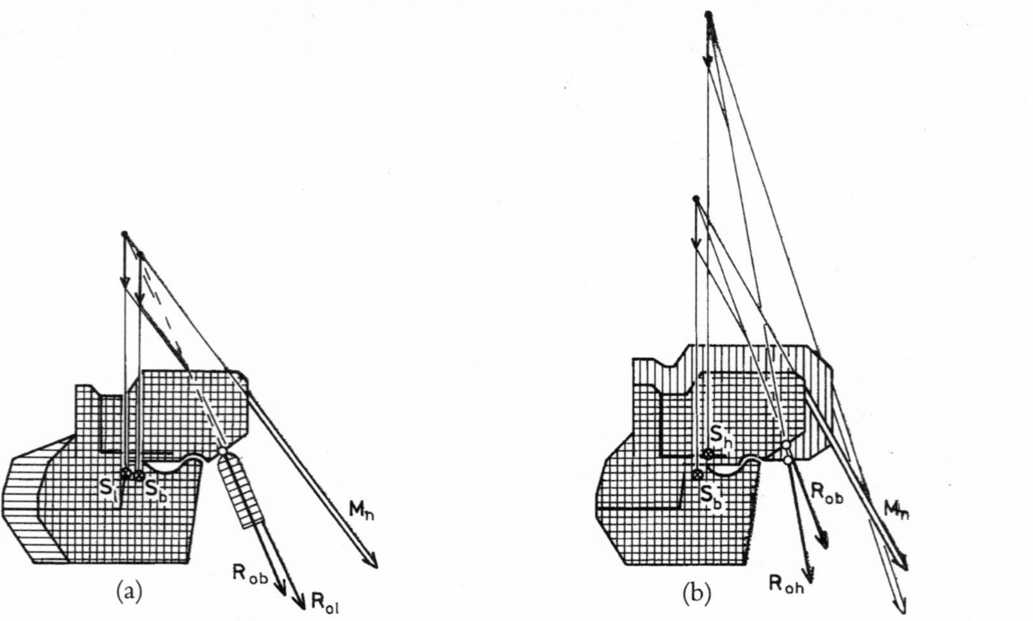

Figure 9.5 Schematic representation of the most marked changes of cranial shape during hominisation

Sl = centre of gravity, long snout; Sb = centre of gravity, short snout; Sh = centre of gravity, with increased vault height; Mn = nuchal musculature; Ro = resultant of muscle force and weight force, which passes through the occipital condyles, nearly perpendicular to the plane of the foramen magnum. The reduction of snout length as in (a), but not the enlargement of the braincase as in (b), shifts the centre of gravity dorsally. The resultant force which acts on occipital condyles and cervical vertebrae assumes a steeper direction in short-snouted skulls. Elevation of the vault (b) changes the direction of the nuchal muscles, so that the resultant Ro also assumes a steeper position. The higher face provides longer lever arms for the masticatory muscles.

graciles (Rak, 1983), served to give the upper jaw the strength necessary to sustain the increased bite forces (Preuschoft, 1989a).

This line of reasoning does not support the theory that Australopithecines were scavengers or hunters (as is assumed in other contributions to this volume), because the dentition of a meat-eater is exposed to different selective pressures. Rather, it favours the idea that early hominids tended towards open country and towards eating grass seeds or other hard objects. It would seem attractive (although it is not attempted here) to fit our argument into a scenario of hominids exploiting marine, coastal or benthic resources.

In non-human primates the head, which has its centre of gravity far in front of the condyles, must be balanced by considerable muscle force (Figure 9.5). The foramen magnum and the occipital condyles face backward in order to be perpendicular to the resulting force, as shown by Demes (1985). Given the short neck, so characteristic of primates, this seems to be inevitable for animals in the pronograde posture, because there is simply no possibility of moving the head above the level of the back. A major prerequisite for saving energy by balancing the head closer to its centre of gravity seems to be, in view of the short neck, upright posture of the trunk. Any enlargement of the brain, accompanied by increased vault height, moves the centre of gravity upward, in a cranial direction. This is not a disadvantage as long as the head is carried like humans carry it. The reduction of snout length contributes to shifting the centre of gravity of the head backward, in pronograde as well as orthograde posture. This reduces the load arm while increasing the power arms, thus reducing the muscular force necessary to keep the head balanced. The condyles, and with them the plane of the foramen magnum, tilt forward, following the swing of the resulting joint force.

Australopithecines apparently possessed a pronounced lordosis in a long lumbar spine of not less than six vertebrae (Robinson, 1972). This has been interpreted as evidence for upright body posture. Preuschoft, Hayama and Günther (1988) have investigated the mechanical conditions existing in long, slender-bodied Japanese macaques as a consequence of their acquisition of upright body posture (Figure 9.6). Under the influence of gravity (that is, without the help of buoyancy when submerged in water), a lordosis appears to offer an important advantage for an animal in an orthograde posture. It provides the erector spinae muscles with a longer lever arm, and moves the vertebral column towards the gravity vertical of the upper body. If a lordosis is present, shortening of the trunk is not necessary to keep the expenditure of muscle force low. Widening of the trunk in the frontal plane and a reduction of its dorso-ventral diameter are further traits which reduce the waste of energy connected with permanent, strong contraction of the erector spinae muscles. In fossils, the existence of these traits can be deduced from the shape of the ribs (Schmid, 1983.) The shallow trunk of modern man implies a dorsal position of the centre of gravity: that is, it is closer to the vertebral column as the supporting structure. The same result is achieved by the shoulder blades having moved dorsally from their original position, which is lateral to the thorax in pronograde animals.

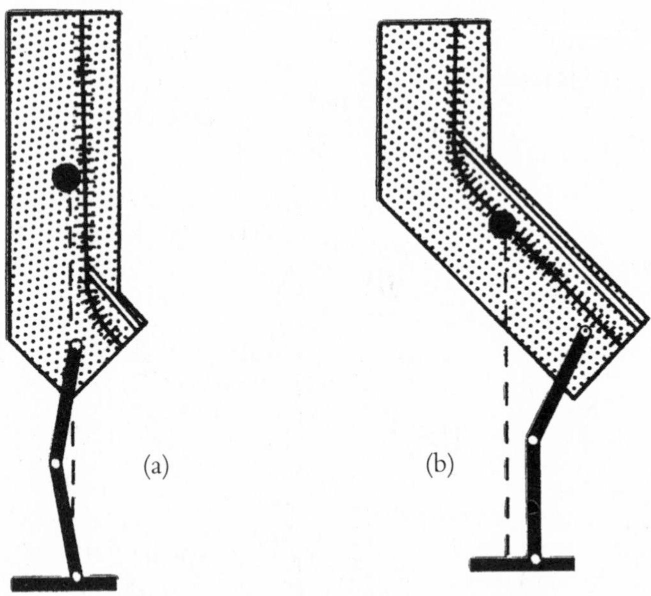

Figure 9.6 In upright trunk postures, a lordosis reduces the loadarm length of the more cranial sections of the body, while providing long power arms for the dorsal muscles.
In (a) the lordosis is shifted caudally into the pelvic region (i.e., to the iliac neck), so that the energy-saving effect is maximal (see also Preuschoft, Hayama and Günther, 1988).

The australopithecine pelvis (Figure 9.7) is commonly interpreted as being adapted 'to some degree' to an upright stance (Napier, 1967; Robinson, 1972; Preuschoft, 1971a; Lovejoy, 1973, 1975; Lovejoy, Heiple and Burstein, 1973). With regard to one detail, the length of the iliac neck, we can confirm this conclusion: the rearward shifting of the 'kink' in the trunk (shown in Figures 9.6 and 9.7) is limited by the length of the ilium. If its 'neck', the part between hip joint and ilio-sacral joint, is shortened, additional energy can be saved. This shortened iliac neck is one of the most characteristic features of the australopithecine pelvis as compared with the long ilium of modern pongids and the short one of

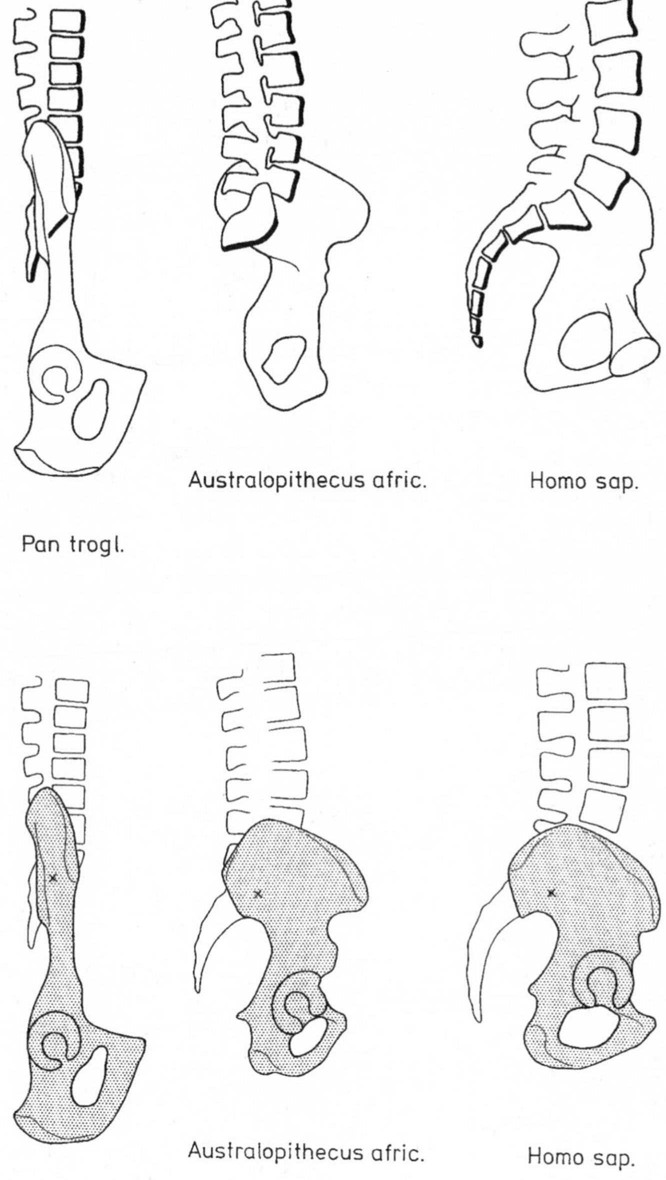

Figure 9.7 Side view of various primates' pelves to show the shortening and 'lordosising' of the iliac neck during hominid evolution.

modern humans. This will be worked out in detail by Preuschoft, Schmid and Berge in a forthcoming paper (in preparation).

In standing on one leg, or in the stance phase of walking, the human hindlimb is exposed to bending moments in the frontal plane (Figure 9.8 (a)). The well known valgus position of the knee joint causes a reduction of these bending moments at the knee joint and along the lower leg. This valgus position is apparent in the laterally open angle between the vertical and the femoral shaft, if placed upright on its condyles (Figure 9.9 (b)). The same trait already existed in Australopithecines (Preuschoft, 1971a), but is not present in modern pongids (Figure 9.8 (b)). As a consequence of this valgus position of the knee (Figure 9.9 (b)), the force produced by the quadriceps muscle and the force transmitted by the patellar ligament to the tibia also form a blunt, laterally open angle. This means that a laterally directed resultant acts on the patella. To prevent the patella from sliding, the lateral margin of the patellar facet (Figure 9.9(d)) is higher than the medial in *Australopithecus* and in later hominids (Lovejoy and Heiple, 1970; for additional details see Preuschoft, 1971a). In contrast, the knees of quadrupeds necessarily have a varus or neutral position, even in cases where an upright posture is assumed occasionally. Pongids (Figures 9.8 (b), 9.9 (a)) show the morphological characteristics favourable for climbing – namely, a marked varus position of the knee which allows strong abduction of the hip (see also Preuschoft, 1961, 1970) without placing the foot lateral to the gravity vertical.

Preuschoft (1971a) has shown that the metatarsals and the talus of the Australopithecine-like foot from Olduvai (OH–8) possess the shape characteristics of a rather rigidly built 'ground plate', well suited for walking on the ground (Figure 9.10). In this they resemble the respective elements in the human foot more closely than those in the foot of pongids (Figure 9.11). The anatomy of the australopithecine foot is known only incompletely (Davis, Day and Napier, 1964), but the toes are long and strong compared to those of modern man, and short compared to the toes of pongids. Stern and Susman (1983) have emphasised this in combination with other traits, and have argued that at least *A. afarensis* retained marked adaptations for climbing.

On the other hand, the conclusion that Australopithecines were bipedal is convincingly supported by the footprints and tracks found at Laetoli (Leakey, 1978, 1979; White, 1980). These documents of bipedal walking in a hominid are about 3.5 million years old and belong to the oldest known hominid fossils.

A lot of 'reasons' for the evolution of upright posture and locomotion in terms of biological role have been proposed: for instance, hunting, carrying of food or infants, use and transport of tools; better view over high grass, and higher speed (the latter seems doubtful). To these interpretations we can hardly contribute anything new. But all these traits make sense only if we imagine an animal which shifted from motor habitats similar to those of arboreal macaques or the versatile grey langurs (in forest areas) to bipedal travelling in more open landscapes. It may well be that the two-million-years' history of australopithecine bipedalism stretches from a still partly arboreal lifestyle to bipedal walking (Stern and Susman, 1983). The incompleteness of individual finds of early

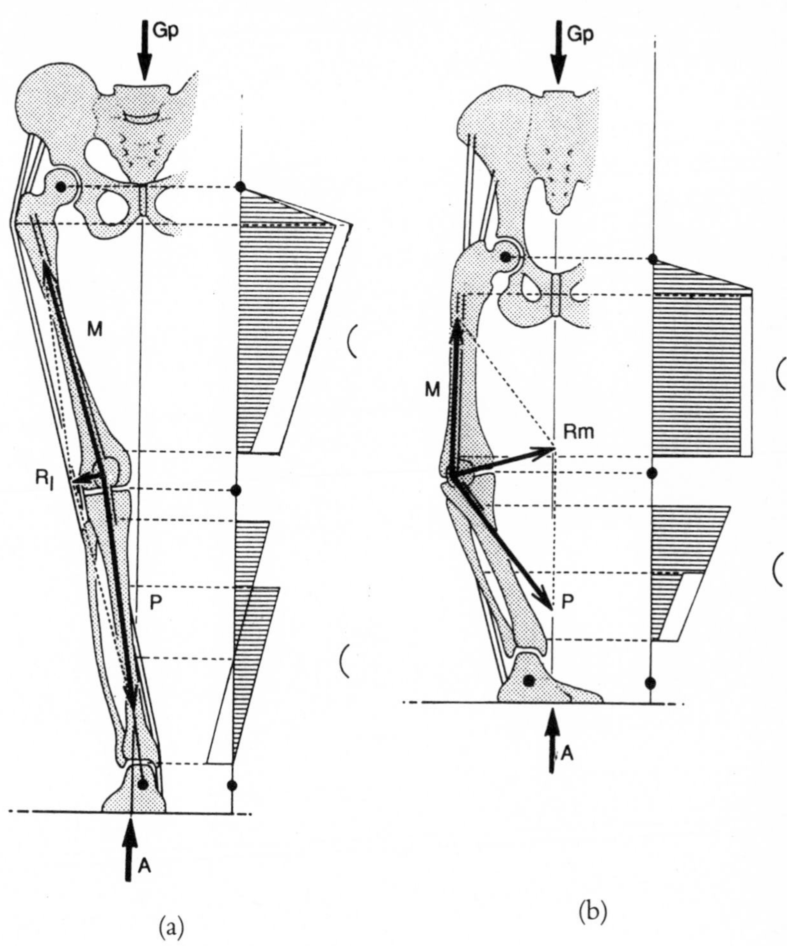

Figure 9.8 Right hindlimb under full body weight seen in frontal view.

(a) Human. The pulling forces of the quadriceps muscle (M) and of the patellar ligament (P) combine to form a laterally directed resultant (R_1).

(b) Gorilla. The resultant Rm applied to the patella is directed medially. Gp is the weight of the body above the pelvis; A is the ground reaction force. Note the difference of bending moments in both species.

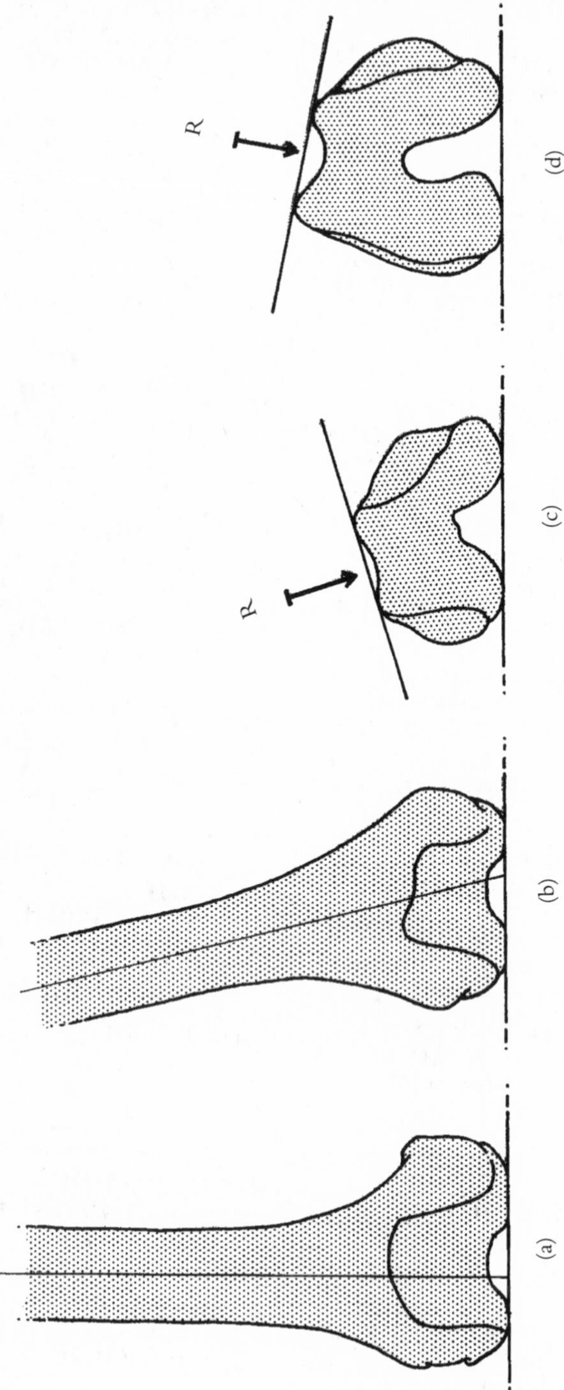

Figure 9.9 Valgus position of the right knee joint in *Homo sapiens* (b) compared to the varus position of the knee in *Gorilla* (a); and elevation of the medial margin in a pongid (*Gorilla*) (c) compared to the elevated lateral margin of the patellar facet, typical of *Homo* (and Australopithecines) (d).
The patellar facets in both species are orientated almost perpendicularly to the resultant forces (R) acting on the patella as shown in Figure 9.8.

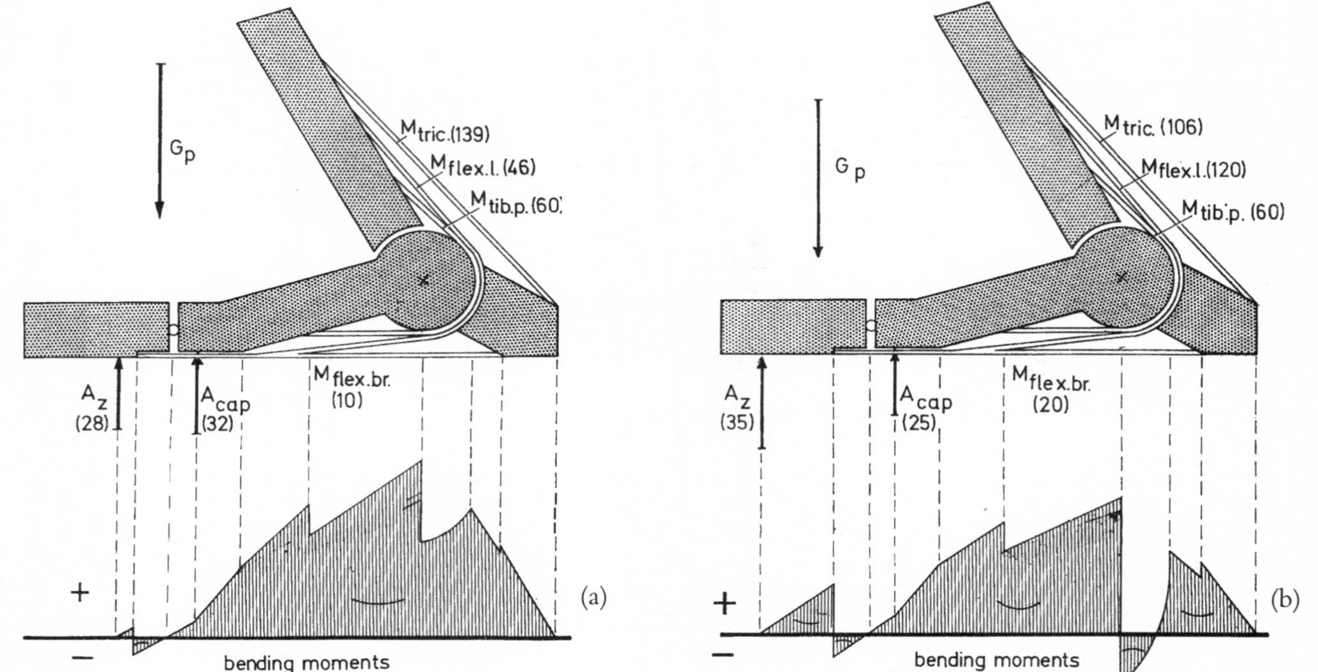

Figure 9.10 Stress patterns in the foot.

(a) A foot adapted to ground walking by having rather short toes (external force A_z close to metatarso-phalangeal joint), weak toe flexors, and a strong triceps muscle is under great bending stress. (b) A foot adapted to prehension by long toes (A_z far away from metatarso-phalangeal joint), necessarily strong toe flexors and consequently weak triceps, is exposed to smaller bending moments (from Preuschoft, 1970).

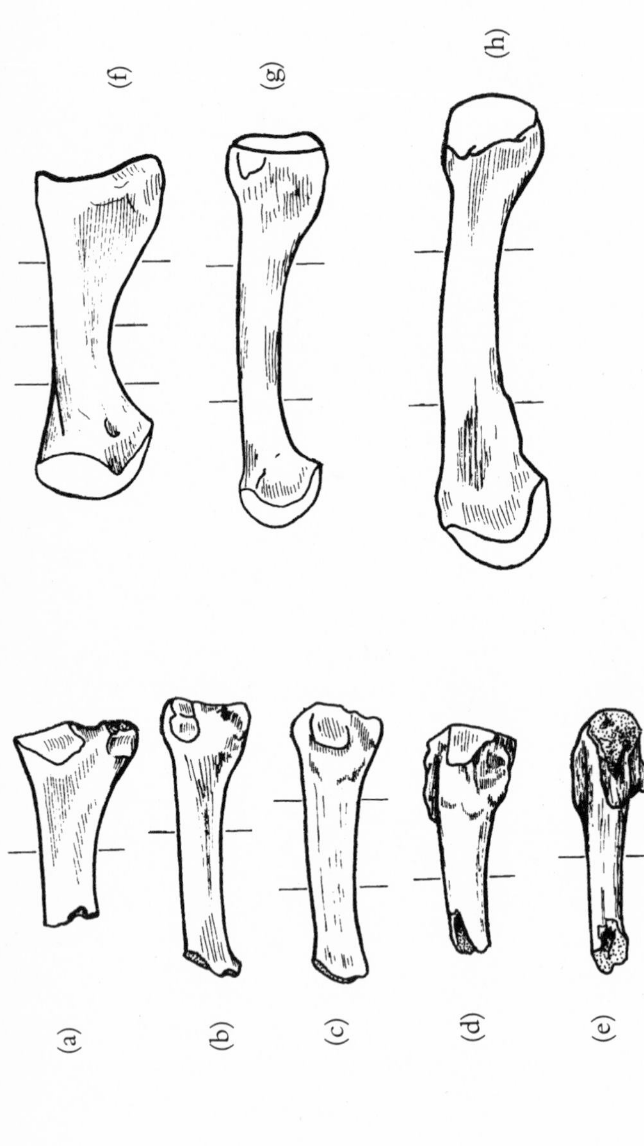

Figure 9.11 The metatarsals of the Olduvai foot OH–8 (a–e) posses relatively smaller diameters in their distal sections than a *Gorilla* (h), but are relatively 'high' in their proximal sections, thus resembling the shape typical of humans (f, g). Because bending resistance depends on the square of the diameters, a comparison with Figure 9.10 shows that the fossil metatarsals are less adapted to prehension than those of gorillas, but more so than those of humans. On the other hand, they are less adapted to serving as a ground plate than the feet of modern humans (from Preuschoft, 1971a).

Australopithecines (like Lucy), and of later stages of their evolution, does not yet allow us to spell out the development in detail.

Homo erectus and Neanderthal man

Fossils of both forms are very similar to modern man with regard to body shape, proportions and size. Aside from inconspicuous and only metrically and statistically discernible details, *H. erectus* differs only in skull shape from present-day humans. This holds true for Neanderthal man as well. A recent study by Demes (1987) has demonstrated that the absence of the canine fossa and the associated width of the maxillary cavity in Neanderthal man's skull were a consequence of biting forces acting on the canines and anterior premolars. Therefore, these characteristics are identified as adaptive and functional, which indicates a behaviour peculiar to this form.

Between *Australopithecus* and *H. erectus* important evolutionary changes took place. The brain enlarged from less than 600 cm^3 to at least 800 and up to 1200 cm^3. Bodily changes – that is, the elongation of the hindlimbs, the reshaping of the pelvis and the shortening of the vertebral column – conform to the acquisition of rather fast and endurant bipedal walking as the predominant mode of locomotion. Walking became faster and less energy-consuming in *H. erectus*, by comparison with former evolutionary stages. Seen from a biomechanical viewpoint, walking is a rhythmical exchange between potential and kinetic energy, as in a pendulum (Cavagna, Heglund and Taylor, 1977; Mochon and McMahon, 1980, 1981; Witte, 1991). The elongation of the hindlimbs as well as increased absolute body size offer means of increasing walking speed without additional input of energy. This has been evaluated for fossil hominids by Preuschoft and Witte (1991; Witte *et al.*, 1991). The same authors have shown that the proportions of arms and trunk must correlate to hindlimb length in order to compensate for undue rotational movements of the body caused by the forward and backward swinging of the long, heavy hindlimbs.

There is strong evidence that *H. erectus* knew how to use fire, and it is certain that he was able to produce a variety of tools. The 'cognitive' abilities of *H. erectus*, and even more those of later hominids, relaxed the selective pressure on what are normally called biological 'adaptations' by compensating for maladaptations which otherwise would have been subject to negative selection. Coevolution of cultural and biological traits seems to have started at this stage.

WHAT NEW INSIGHTS DOES THE AQUATIC APE THEORY OFFER?

In contrast to most palaeoanthropologists, the proponents of the Aquatic Ape Theory have neither attempted to clarify the chronology of the known fossil documents nor to interpret them in terms of their differences and similarities. Instead, they focus on the explanation of modern man's peculiarities as compared to modern apes and other mammals.

Among the features emphasised by the AAT are (1) some which are not at all peculiar to man, and (2) others which can be explained more satisfactorily within the framework of conventional ideas, which by no means imply an aquatic stage. Here, we will briefly discuss some examples of both categories.

1 Low hair-density is also found among modern large apes. According to Schultz (1936), gorillas, chimpanzees and orang-utans have about 300–500 hairs per cm^2 – in contrast to the lesser apes and some monkeys which possess 2000–3000. The arrangement of body hair, as well as the importance of sweat glands for a primate who exposes himself to full sunshine, is discussed by Wheeler (chapter 13, this volume). Also, it should be noted that all primates in tropical regions usually avoid direct sunshine. Subcutaneous fat is arranged in similar deposits in many mammals, including primates (Pond, this volume, chapter 12).

2 Bipedality should be considered in connection with the fact that most primates are 'hindlimb-dominated' and show a tendency to sit upright when resting or investigating things closely. While standing or walking, most primates carry a larger part of their body weight on the hindlimbs than on the forelimbs (Figure 9.12). This has been found experimentally by Kimura, Okada and Ishida (1979) in Japanese macaques, and was later confirmed in chimpanzees by Kimura (1985, 1987). The animals put their hindlimbs forward, close to their gravity vertical (see also Reynolds, 1985a, 1985b). In addition, primates possess short necks, so that their centre of gravity is shifted caudally in comparison with other, cursorial mammals like dogs and hooved animals. As a consequence, the amount of body weight resting on the hindlimbs is increased, and the forelimbs are relieved (Preuschoft, 1990; see also Figure 9.12). For leapers among the primates the same holds true (Peters and Preuschoft, 1984; see also Günther, 1989; Demes and Günther, 1989a, 1989b). If a primate puts its feet slightly forward – that is, exactly beneath its centre of gravity – it can lift its hands from the ground, because its full weight rests on the hindlimbs. In fact, a variety of bipedal postures is readily assumed by many non-human primates, often for extended periods. The mechanical requirements of *permanent* bipedality under terrestrial conditions, and the resulting selective pressures, have been discussed above.

The biological role of upright sitting and bipedal standing in non-human primates is not completely understood. So it is not surprising that the biological role of bipedality in early hominids is so much discussed. A

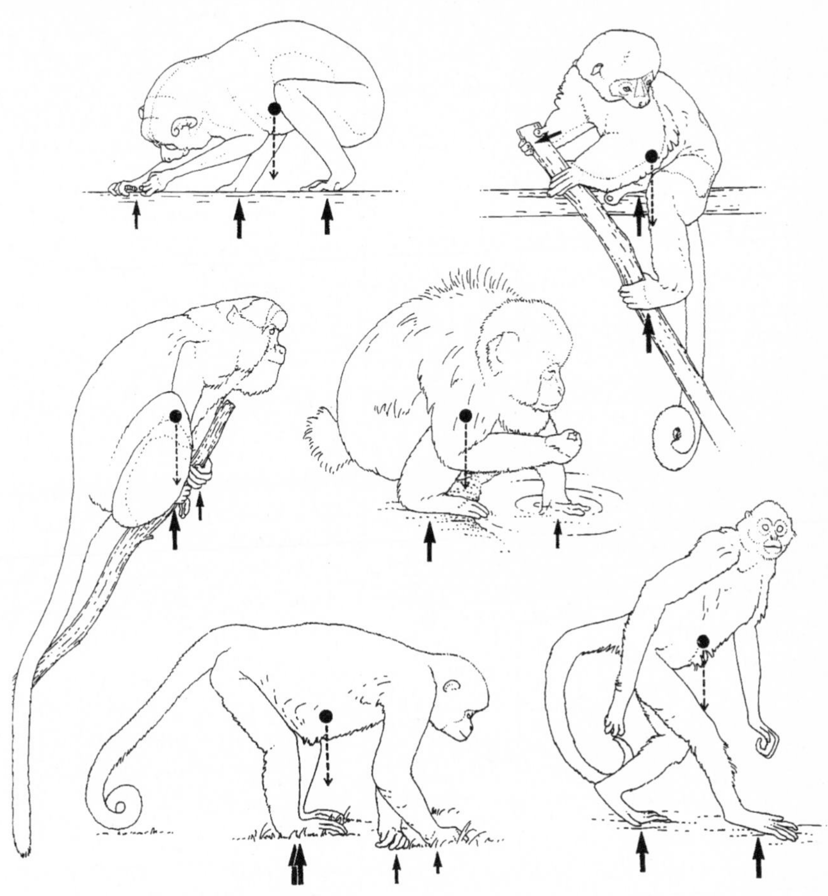

Figure 9.12 All primates carry a larger proportion of their body weight on the hindlimbs than other, cursorial, mammals do; primates are 'hindlimb-dominated', or 'preadapted' to bipedal posture and locomotion. The dots show the approximate positions of the centres of gravity, the broken arrows the direction of the weight force. The heavy arrows indicate the direction and sizes of the reaction forces to body weight.

promising new approach is contained in Wheeler's contribution to this volume (chapter 13). Undoubtedly, however, the tendency to carry much weight on the hindlimbs is related to the primates' characteristic mode of investigating and handling objects: they examine objects first by means of their hands, in contrast to most other mammals which use their lips, teeth, tongues and noses for exploration.

Interestingly, a mechanical investigation of bipedalism provides us with a hypothesis about the origin of another feature stressed by AAT adherents – namely, the 'diving reflex'. Experimental results (Nachemson, 1959, 1966; Nachemson and Elfström, 1970; Morris, Lucas and Bresler, 1961) indicate that the trunk is kept in equilibrium at the intervertebral discs not only by muscle contractions, but also by making use of the 'pneu' formed by the intestines in the abdomen and thorax, which are enclosed by the abdominal and thoracic wall muscles (see also Preuschoft, Fritz and Niemitz, 1979). Compression of the lungs requires the existence of a valve in the airways – that is, the larynx. Possibly this is the origin of the closing mechanism discussed by proponents of the AAT in the context of the 'diving reflex'.

Besides the features already emphasised, the AAT leaves open some important questions:

- When (in the chronological framework of Figure 9.1) would the pronounced aquatic phase of evolution have occurred?
- Which fossils in fact indicate an aquatic life?
- Which traits must be present in an aquatic primate to fulfil its immediate functional needs?

While the first and the second questions can be postponed until future finds provide us with the information that is lacking, the third requires the formulation of precise hypotheses that can be tested. The basis of any functional explanations of the morphological facts outlined above is empirical data, or at least precise hypotheses formulated in terms of biomechanics. Testable hypotheses of this kind, however, are usually missing in the AAT advocates' suggestions. Our attempts to obtain information from them about which of the evolutionary settings described below fits best with their theory, were unsuccessful. Apparently, they prefer raising questions to answering them. So, since testable hypotheses proposed by AAT defenders are lacking, we have ourselves tried to pin down the possibilities that exist for an 'aquatic' lifestyle. Concentrating on considerations discussed at the Valkenburg meeting, we can imagine only three variants that may serve as testable hypotheses:

(1) The aquatic stage of hominid evolution took place along seashores. The ancestral hominids waded – searching for food, or avoiding predators – in shallow water (*marsh waders*).

(2) Our aquatic ancestors lived in somewhat deeper waters, either swimming close to the surface or diving (*shallow-water swimmers*).
(3) Our ancestors were active, endurant swimmers, able to move rapidly in deep waters (*deep-water divers*).

Let us now try to investigate, for these three scenarios, the functional demands and their mechanical consequences.

If we assume variant (1), the *marsh wader* (Figure 9.13), we should expect the aquatic ape to have been equipped with long hindlimbs (which we indeed find in humans). Since water resistance will unduly slow down the forward swing of the limb, it is essential to raise the hindlimbs above the surface. This means that the wader has to avoid water more than knee-deep. Adaptation to wading will inevitably produce short femora and long tibiae. The locomotor mode shown in Figure 9.13 is admittedly expensive from an energetic point of view, but still more efficient than moving the swinging leg against water resistance. The proportions of femur to tibia as shown in Figure 9.13 are not present in the fossil record.

Regardless of the limb proportions, long extremities protect the trunk against becoming wet, which would lead to loss of body heat. The hindlimbs are immersed in water, which reduces their weight. Even partial immersion of the trunk, however, would greatly increase water resistance and make locomotion energetically very expensive and fleeing slow. In addition, the buoyancy of the trunk would relieve the vertical ground foot force to such an extent that wading became difficult because ground contact would be lost.

In humans and other primates the ratio of length of thigh to length of lower leg plus foot is commonly 1:1. This ratio leads to minimal angle displacement in walking movements, since the necessary lifting of the body's centre of gravity is combined with the smallest possible angle of excursion of the knee joint. Because mechanical work W is defined not only by

$$W = F \cdot s, \text{ but also by } W = M \cdot \text{phi}$$

(where F is the force, s the distance covered, M the muscular force, and phi the excursion of the knee joint in degrees), the 'work' required for these movements is also minimised. Therefore, the 1:1 length ratio minimises the energy required for terrestrial walking (Witte, 1991). In addition, soft substrates – as found frequently on the bottom of lakes or sea – favour a large area of support, which means long, wide feet. The 'rolling-off' of the human foot under these conditions implies a disadvantage, since it begins (heel strike) and ends (push-off by toes) with a load concentration on a reduced area of support. Everybody who has walked on soft ground knows its energy-consuming effect.

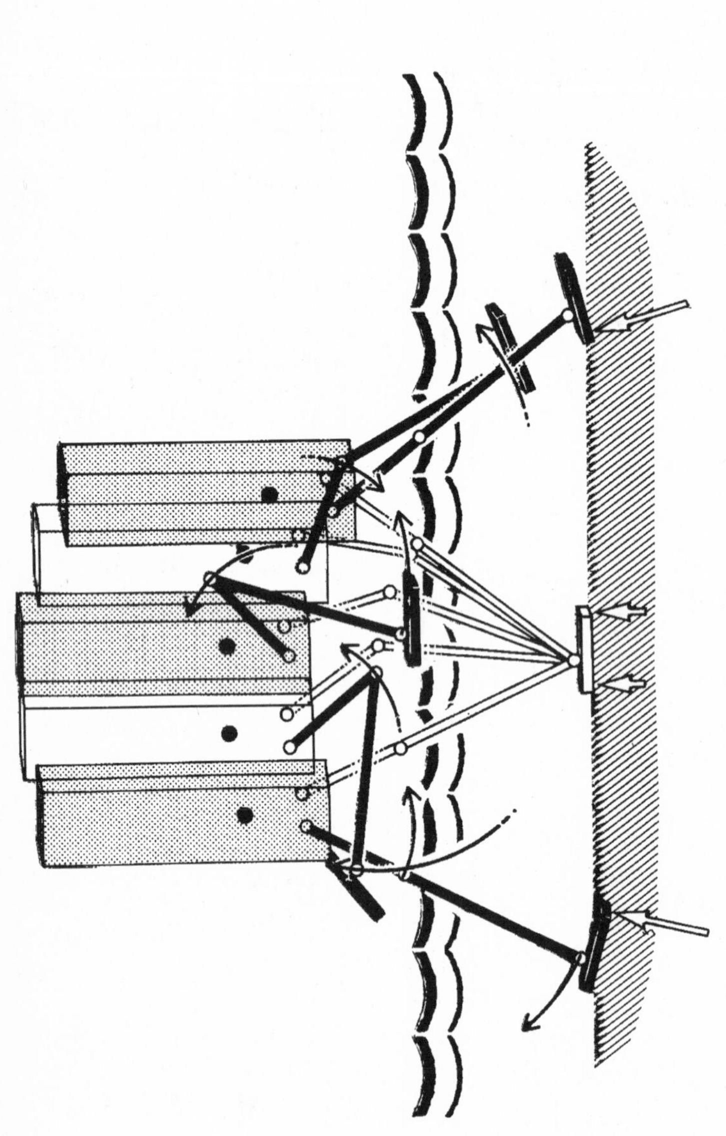

Figure 9.13 A 'marsh wader' has to keep its trunk, and swing its hindlimbs forward, *above* the water level. For the latter function, short thighs and long lower legs are advantageous. Note the reaction forces acting between ground and foot, varying with the shifting of the centre of gravity.

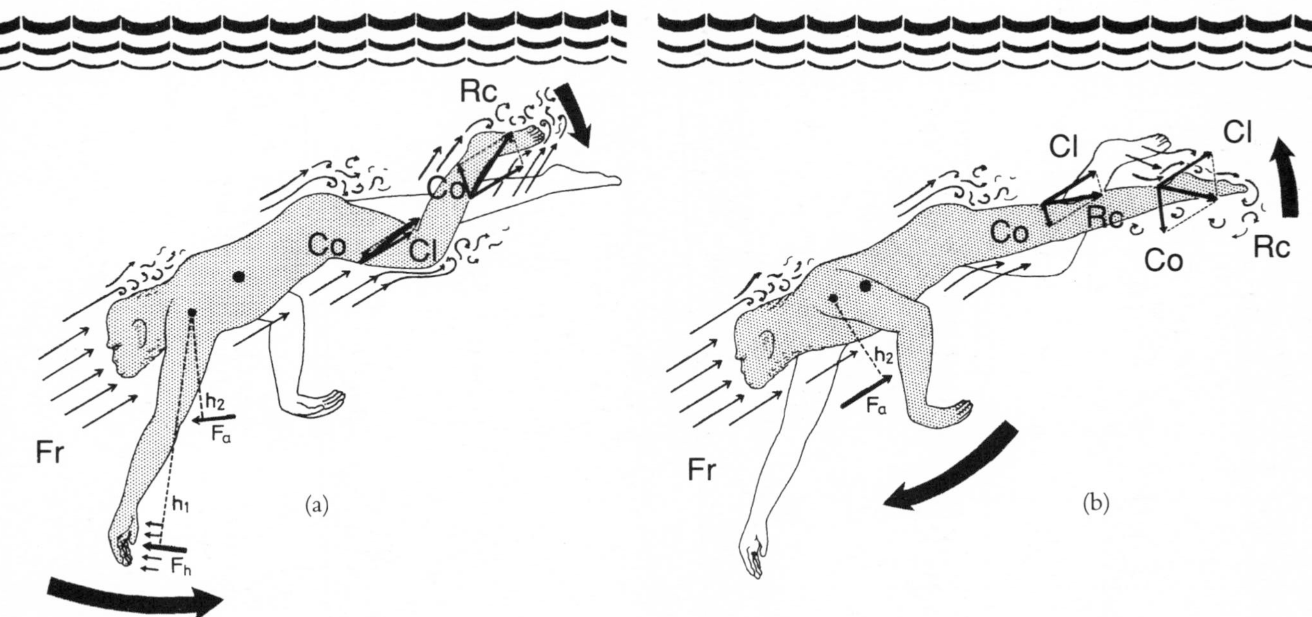

Figure 9.14 Forces (arrows) acting against the body of a swimming hominid.
(a) left arm moving backward during the propulsive stroke and left hindlimb moving ventrally; (b) left arm moving forward in the recovery stroke and left hindlimb moving dorsally. The propelling forelimb creates a moment (force Fa or Fh, multiplied by lever arm h2 or h1, respectively) that rotates the head dorsally, towards the surface. At the moving hindlimbs, the water flow produced by locomotion (Cl) combines with the flow evoked by the up-and-down movement of the limbs (Co) to form a resultant water current (Rc). At the joints, as well as at the heels, turbulences are created that increase drag and make this animal's swimming slow and energetically expensive. To our knowledge, long scalp hair and a beard do not exclude water turbulence in the neck region.

Variant (2), the *shallow-water swimmer*, and (even more) variant (3), the *deep-water diver*, require the body density to be similar to that of water (Figure 9.14). This seems to hold true for most mammals, depending on the volume of air in their lungs and fur (Wind, 1976). One problem is the intake of air. The nostrils in all known primates are positioned frontally in the mid-face. So it is difficult for them to raise their nostrils above the water level, particularly since the neck is so short that head movements are limited.

The weight of a swimming body becomes negligible, and the forces that have to be exchanged between the body and its environment in order to cause propulsion are distributed over large areas of the body's surface. In animals not suspended in a dense, heavy fluid, body weight leads to a reaction force concentrated on the contact areas between body and ground. While swimming, all tetrapods maintain their usual pronograde orientation of the trunk axis, and their limbs move forwards and backwards as they do on the ground. The backward movements of the limbs serve to propulsion. In anteversion of the same limbs (recovery stroke), a smaller surface must be exposed to the resistance of the water to make the locomotion efficient (Wind, 1976). In the backward-directed power stroke, water resistance against the moving limb causes, as a side effect, a moment that rotates about the body's centre (Figure 9.14(a)). This increases with arm length. As long as the swimming animal remains at the surface, the backward rotation contributes to keeping the head above the water level. As soon as the animal starts diving, the ventral position of the limbs (the arms in Figure 9.14) below the trunk, which is inevitable for terrestrials, becomes a disadvantage. In fact, most tetrapods adapted to swimming have reduced limb length and the limbs are laterally placed or 'sprawled', so that (horizontal) rotation caused by one side is compensated for by the other. Enlargement of hands and feet provides them with larger paddles to make propulsion more efficient. These traits have never been found in fossil hominids. Neither in fossil nor in living primates do we find the shortened stylopodia or the broadened, elongated feet and hands which are the most obvious adaptations of habitually swimming tetrapods. Wide excursions, which include abduction to assume a 'sprawling' position, are admittedly possible in the shoulder and hip joints of many primates. But this is more probably connected with their climbing habits. Webs between the fingers and toes, which increase the surface in the power stroke while being folded in the recovery stroke, may have occurred in fossil forms – we just cannot recognise them on the skeleton. But they exist also in the indisputably non-aquatic modern apes, where they are even better developed than in humans.

Let us imagine that already orthograde hominoids took to a swimming mode of life – as shown in Figure 9.14. Because of the position of the lower limbs behind rather than ventral of the trunk, the balance of propulsive external forces would have posed no problem. But this presupposes what AAT proponents claim to explain: why these ancestors changed their body position from pronograde to orthograde on land before colonising the water.

Anyway, the body shape of modern humans is poorly adapted to swimming. The length of the hindlimbs as well as that of the forelimbs increases load-arm length without yielding more propulsion during swimming. This trait, therefore, clearly implies a waste of energy and hence a disadvantage. The existence of few joints between long segments leads to a disturbance of the water flow along the propulsive extremity, which results in a disadvantageous drag. This holds true not only for the thigh and the lower leg, but also for the metapodia and phalanges. A simple means often employed to increase the efficiency of a limb as a propulsive organ in water is to use it as a hydrofoil in both directions, up and down. This is only possible if joint excursions are possible in both directions, and if the segments are largely symmetrical. As emphasised by Wind (1976; this volume, chapter 17), in most or even all primates this holds true for the shoulder and carpal movements, but not at all for the elbow and finger joints, nor for the joints of the hindlimbs. In living as well as fossil primates, movements of the knee and ankle joints and finger and toe joints are limited at full extension, and at least the phalanges, and sometimes also the tibia, are curved, which makes them asymmetrical.

On the level of biological roles, we believe that the human affection for water depends on fashion. Today everybody seems fond of bathing, but a hundred years ago this was far less common. Another argument, just as attractive as the affectionate relationship of humans to water, should not be ignored: from the early stages of human history, on through all centuries, the wealthy classes have chosen to build their homes in places that exhibit a clear preference for open, diverse landscapes, with grassland interspersed with patches of woodland or individual trees, often embellished by flowing water or lakes: the parkland savannah. Man's evident dislike of dense forest may be illustrated by the extent of its intended total destruction.

CONCLUSION

Current palaeoanthropological explanations do not satisfy AAT proponents. This is because current ideas do not (yet?) yield plausible reasons for *all* human characteristics, and AAT proponents insist that other questions about hominisation have to be raised. Therefore, the current ideas are rejected and new ones proposed.

A final evaluation of the AAT is impeded by the fact that it is vague in several respects. It leaves open the relative and absolute dating of the presumed aquatic phase. It stresses some arbitrarily selected 'enigmatic' features of *Homo sapiens* and provides purely hypothetical explanations for them – without any attempt to give detailed, causal explanations for the origins of these traits. Because hitherto the AAT has been discussed only at the level of biological roles, not at the level of the mechanical functions fulfilled by the morphological structures that are found in fossils, the theory suffers from a lack of precision. The reason for, as well as the consequence of, this flaw is the absence of testable hypotheses and predictions deduced from them.

If not only the enigmatic characteristics, but others as well, are taken into account, it becomes evident that the AAT contains large *gaps*; its proposals are insufficiently *integrated* and by no means free from *contradictions*. Also, the *parsimony* of the AAT has to be questioned, because of the lack of explanations for less conspicuous traits. In its present form, the AAT is not able to produce satisfying *hypotheses that can be tested empirically*. One of its few *predictions* postulates the extension of the search for fossils into areas which have not yet yielded any finds. To be sure, by refusing to accept common opinions, the AAT has *stimulated* a reconsideration of ideas already available. Unfortunately, the AAT does not provide us with a more *complete understanding* of the facts about human evolution than we have got already.

On the other hand, detailed investigations of the mechanical function of several traits of modern humans, as well as of our fossil precursors, have been carried out. The results of these studies fit together, and are in accordance with, or even support, the traditional palaeoanthropological ideas which assume the evolution of hominids in a terrestrial, savannah-like habitat.

Although we feel attracted and, more so, challenged by some of the arguments derived from the Aquatic Ape Theory, we regret to conclude that we cannot offer any support to it. We do not agree that there is a need to postulate an aquatic phase in the evolution of man.

REFERENCES

Bock, W.J. and von Wahlert, G., 1965, Adaptation and the form-function complex. *Zoomorphologie*, **91**, 49–61.

Brown, F., Harris, J., Leakey, R. and Walker, A., 1985, Early *Homo erectus* skeleton from West Lake Turkana, Kenya. *Nature*, **316**, 788–92.

Cavagna, G.A., Heglund, N.C. and Taylor, C.R., 1977, Mechanical work in terrestrial locomotion: two basic mechanisms for minimizing energy expenditure. *American Journal of Physiology*, **233**, 233–61.

Chivers, D.J., Andrews, P., Preuschoft, H., Bilsborough, A. and Wood, B.A., 1984, Food acquisition and processing in primates: concluding discussion. In *Food Acquisition and Processing in Primates*, ed. D.J. Chivers, B.A. Wood and A. Bilsborough. (London: Plenum Press), 545–65.

Davis, P.R., Day, M.H. and Napier, J.R., 1964, Hominid fossils from bed I, Olduvai

Gorge, Tanganyika. *Nature*, **201**, 967–70.

Demes, B., 1985, Biomechanics of the primate skull base. *Fortschrift d. Zoologie*, **30**, 139–42.

Demes, B., 1987, Another look at an old face: biomechanics of the neanderthal facial skeleton reconsidered. *Journal of Human Evolution*, **16**, 297–303.

Demes, B., Creel, N. and Preuschoft, H., 1986, Functional significance of allometric trends in the hominoid masticatory apparatus. In *Primate Evolution*, ed. J.G. Else and P.C. Lee. (Cambridge: Cambridge University Press), 229–37.

Demes, B. and Günther, M.M., 1989a, Wie die Körpermasse den Springstil von Halbaffen und deren Proportionen bestimmt. *Zeitschrift Morph. Anthropologie*, **77**, 209–25.

Demes, B. and Günther, M.M., 1989b, Biomechanics and allometric scaling in primate locomotion and morphology. *Folia Primatologica*, **53**, 125–41.

Günther, M.M., 1989, Funktionsmorphologische Untersuchungen zum Sprungverhalten an mehreren Halbaffenarten. Unpublished dissertation, Berlin.

Johanson, D. and Edey, M., 1982, Lucy: Die Anfänge der Menschheit. (Munich, Zürich: R.Piper). English original: *Lucy: The Beginnings of Humankind* (New York: Simon and Schuster).

Jolly, C. J., 1970, The seed eaters: a new model of hominid differentiation based on a baboon analogy. *Man*, **5**, 5–26.

Jungers, W.L., 1982, Lucy's limbs: skeletal allometry and locomotion in *Australopithecus afarensis*. *Nature*, **297**, 676–8.

Kimura, T., 1985, Bipedal and quadrupedal walking of primates: comparative dynamics. In *Primate Morpho-physiology, Locomotor Analyses and Human Bipedalism*, ed. S. Kondo. (Tokyo: University of Tokyo Press), 81–104.

Kimura, T., 1987, Development of chimpanzee locomotion on level surfaces. *Human Evolution*, **2**.

Kimura, T., Okada, M. and Ishida, H., 1979, Kinesiological characteristic of primate walking: its significance in human walking. In *Environment, Behavior, and Morphology: Dynamic Interactions in Primates*, ed. M.E. Morbeck, H. Preuschoft and N. Gomberg. (New York: G. Fischer), 297–311.

Leakey, M.D., 1978, Pliocene footprints at Laetoli, Northern Tanzania. *Antiquity*, **52**,133.

Leakey, M.D., 1979, 3.6 million year old footprints in the ashes of time. *National Geographic*, **155**, 446–57.

Lovejoy, C.O., 1973, The gait of *Australopithecus*. *Yearbook of Physical Anthropology*, **17**, 147–61.

Lovejoy, C.O., 1975, Biomechanical perspectives on the lower limb of early hominids. In *Primate Functional Morphology and Evolution*, ed. R.H. Tuttle (The Hague, Paris: Mouton), 291–326.

Lovejoy, C.O., Burstein, A.H. and Heiple, K.H., 1972, Primate phylogeny and immunological distance. *Science*, **176**, 803–5.

Lovejoy, C.O. and Heiple, K.G., 1970, A reconstruction of the femur of *Australopithecus*. *American Journal of Physical Anthropology*, **32**(1), 33–40.

Lovejoy, C.O., Heiple, K.G. and Burstein, A.H., 1973, The gait of *Australopithecus*. *American Journal of Physical Anthropology*, **38**(3), 757–79.

Lucas, P.W., Corlett, R.T. and Luke, D.A., 1986a, Postcanine tooth size and diet in anthropoid primates. *Zeitschrift Morph. Anthropologie*, **76**, 253–76.

Lucas, P.W., Corlett, R.T. and Luke, D.A., 1986b, A new approach to postcanine tooth size applied to Plio–Pleistocene hominids. In *Primate Evolution*, ed. J.G. Else and P.C. Lee (Cambridge: Cambridge University Press), 191–201.

Mochon, S. and McMahon, T.A., 1980, Ballistic walking. *Journal of Biomechanics*, **13**, 49–57.

Mochon, S. and McMahon, T.A., 1981, Ballistic walking: an improved model. *Math.*

Bioscience, **52**, 241–60.
Morbeck, M.E., 1972, A re–examination of the forelimb of the Miocene Hominoidea. Unpublished PhD thesis, Berkeley. University of California.
Morris, J.M., Lucas, D.R. and Bresler, B., 1961, Role of the trunk in the stability of the spine. *Journal Bone Jt. Surg.* **43**a, 327–51.
Nachemson, A., 1959, Measurement of intradiscal pressure. *Acta orthop. scandinavica*, **28**, 269–89.
Nachemson, A., 1966, The load on lumbar disks in different positions of the body. *Chir. Orthop.* **45**, 107–22.
Nachemson, A. and Elfström, G., 1970, *Intravital Dynamic Pressure. Measurements in Lumbar Disks* (Stockholm: Almqvist & Wiksell).
Napier, J., 1967, The antiquity of human walking. *Scientific American*, **216**, 4, 56–66; also in *Vertebrate Adaptations, Readings from Scientific American*, ed. N.K. Wessells, 38–48.
National Geographic, 1985, The search for early man. **168** (5).
Peters, A. and Preuschoft, H., 1984, External biomechanics of leaping in *Tarsius* and its morphological and kinematic consequences. In *Biology of Tarsiers*, ed. C. Niemitz, (Stuttgart: G. Fischer) 227–55.
Pickford, M., 1986, Geochronology of the Hominoidea: a summary. In *Primate Evolution*, ed. J.G. Else and P.C. Lee (Cambridge: Cambridge University Press), vol. 1: 123–8.
Pilbeam, D., 1972, *The Ascent of Man* (New York: Macmillan).
Pond, C. M., 1991, Adipose tissue in human evolution. (This volume, chapter 12.)
Preuschoft, H., 1961, Muskeln und Gelenke der Hinterextremität des Gorilla. *Morpholog. Jahrbuch*,**101**, 432–540.
Preuschoft, H., 1964, Die Nerven der Vorderextremität des Gorilla. *Anatomischer Anzeiger*, **115**, 313–34.
Preuschoft, H., 1970, Functional anatomy of the lower extremity. In *The Chimpanzee*, ed. G.H. Bourne (Basel, Munich and New York: Karger–Verlag),**3**, 221–94.
Preuschoft, H., 1971a, Body posture and mode of locomotion in Early Pleistocene Hominids. *Folia Primatologica* **14**, 209–40.
Preuschoft, H., 1971b, Mode of locomotion in subfossil giant lemuroids from Madagascar. *Proc. 3rd. int. Congr. Primat., Zürich 1970* (Basel, New York: Karger–Verlag), **1**, 79–90.
Preuschoft, H., 1973a, Functional anatomy of the upper extremity. In *The Chimpanzee*, ed. G.H. Bourne (Basel, Munich and New York: Karger–Verlag), **6**, 34–120.
Preuschoft, H., 1973b, Body posture and locomotion in some East African Miocene Dryopithecinae. In *Human Evolution*, ed. M.H. Day (London: Taylor & Francis), **11**, 13–46.
Preuschoft, H., 1985, On the quality and magnitude of mechanical stresses in the locomotor system during rapid movements. *Zeitschrift Morphologie u. Anthropologie* **75**(3), 245–62
Preuschoft, H., 1989a, Biomechanical approach to the evolution of the facial skeleton of hominoid primates. *Fortschrift d. Zoologie*, **35**, 421–31.
Preuschoft, H., 1989b, Body shape and differences between species. *Journal of Human Evolution*, **4** (2–3), 145–56.
Preuschoft, H., 1990, Gravity in primates and its relation to body shape. In *Gravity in Primates*, ed. F.K. Jouffroy, H. Stack and C. Niemitz (Florence: Il Sedicesimo), 109–27.
Preuschoft, H., Fritz, M. and Niemitz, C., 1979, The biomechanics of the trunk in primates and problems of leaping in tarsius. In *Environment, Behavior and Morphology: Dynamic Interactions in Primates*, ed. M.E. Morbeck, H. Preuschoft and N. Gomberg (New York: G. Fischer), 327–45.
Preuschoft, H., Hayama, S. and Günther, M., 1988, Curvature of the lumbar spine during acquisition of bipedalism in Japanese macaques. *Folia Primatologica*, **50**, 42-58.
Rak, Y., 1983, *The Australopithecine Face* (New York: Academic Press).

Retallack, G.J., Dugas, D.P. and Bestland, E.A., 1990, Fossil soils and grasses of a Middle Miocene East African grassland. *Science*, **247**, 1325.

Reynolds, T.R., 1985a, Mechanics of increased support of weight by the hindlimbs of primates. *American Journal of Physical Anthropology*, **67**, 335–49.

Reynolds, T.R., 1985b, Stresses on the limbs of quadrupedal primates. *American Journal of Physical Anthropology*, **67**, 351–326.

Robinson, J.T., 1972, *Early hominid posture and locomotion* (Chicago: University of Chicago Press).

Schmid, P., 1983, Eine Rekonstruktion des Skelettes von A.L. 288–1 (Hadar) und deren Konsequenzen. *Folia Primatologica*, **40**, 283–306.

Schultz, A.H., 1933a, Die Körperproportionen der erwachsenen catarrhinen Primaten, mit spezieller Berücksichtigung der Menschenaffen. *Anthrop. Anzeiger*, **10**, 154–85.

Schultz, A.H., 1933b, Observations on the growth, classification and evolutionary specialization of gibbons and siamangs. *Human Biology*, **5**, 212–55, 385–428.

Schultz, A.H., 1936, Characters common to higher primates and characters specific for man. *Quarterly Review of Biology*, **11**, 259–83, 425-55.

Starck, D., 1982, *Vergleichende Anatomie der Wirbeltiere* (Berlin: Springer–Verlag), vols. I–III.

Stephan, H., 1967, Quantitative Vergleiche zur phylogenetischen Entwicklung des Gehirns der Primaten mit Hilfe von Progressionsindices. *Mitt. der Max–Planck–Gesellschaft*, **2**, 63-86.

Stern, J.T. jr. and Susman, R.L., 1983, The locomotor anatomy of *Australopithecus afarensis*. *American Journal of Physical Anthropology*, **60**, 279–317.

Vilensky, J.A., 1983, Gait characteristics of two macaques, with emphasis on relationships with speed. *American Journal of Physical Anthropology*, **61**, 255–65.

Vogel, C., 1974, *Biologie in Stichworten. V: Humanbiologie–Menschliche Stammesgeschichte–Populationsdifferenzierung* (Kiel: F. Hirt).

Walker, A.C., and Teaford, M., 1989, The hunt for Proconsul. *Scientific American*, **260**(1), 76–82.

White, T.D., 1980, Evolutionary implications of Pliocene hominid footprints. *Science*, **208**, 175-6.

Wind, J., 1976, Human drowning: phylogenetic origin. *Journal of Human Evolution*, **5**, 349–63.

Wind, J., The non-aquatic ape: the Aquatic Ape Theory and the evolution of human drowning and swimming. (This volume, chapter 17.)

Witte, H., 1991, *Über mechanische Einflüsse auf die Gestalt des menschlichen Körpers*. Dissertation Bochum.

Witte, H., Preuschoft, H. and Recknagel, S., 1990, Biomechanics of walking and adaptation of hominid body shape. *Zeitschrift Morphologie u. Anthropologie* (in press).

10 What Constitutes an Aquatic Mammal?

Paul Leyhausen

SUMMARY

The Aquatic Ape hypothesis claims, among other things, to provide a better explanation of human near-nakedness than any other proffered so far. Morgan (1972, 1984), for instance, has stated cursorily that during evolution all aquatic mammals tend to lose their pelt and become hairless.

About half of the mammalian orders have produced at least one aquatic or semi-aquatic species. The members of two orders have lost their terrestrial faculties completely and are unable to leave the water even temporarily: the Cetacea and the Sirenia. These have indeed lost almost all their body hair. Of those mammalian species which spend a great deal of their time in the water but are not permanently bound to it, only the hippopotamuses and the Great Indian rhinoceros have lost almost all their hair. But the vast majority, from platypus and water-opossum to polar bear and elephant seal, have not only retained their pelt but have greatly improved it, with the result that many of them have been, and some still are, threatened with extinction because of their valuable fur. This includes even those who come to shore only for the business of reproduction but lead a pelagic life for the rest of the year.

But perhaps the pre-hominid ape who took to the water to escape predation by the leopard, as Morgan has graphically described, had, like the extant anthropoid apes, already lost the soft underlayer of wool so essential to a protective fur. Did he, then, shed the coarse covering hair as well, since it was now useless? But mammals like the capybara, whose case is similar, did not.

Mammals who spend a considerable proportion of their life in the water, even tropical water, have to safeguard themselves against losing body heat too rapidly. They are characterised by a shortening of the limbs, and also of the tail where it is not used as a means of propulsion. The need for this safeguard is greater, the smaller the animal.

In short, a closer look at aquatic and semi-aquatic mammals does not support the Aquatic Ape hypothesis; nor does this become any more plausible when we consider that, at the time when the epic flight from the impact of over-powerful terrestrial predators to the shores of the Indian Ocean is supposed to have taken place, these same shores were still infested by *Crocodylus porosus* and its likes.

THE HYPOTHESIS

The Aquatic Ape hypothesis mainly rests on three sets of arguments:

(1) Reasoning purporting to show why the 'traditional' explanations of human hairlessness and bipedalism are unsatisfactory.

(2) The assumption that the loss of body hair had already occurred in the prehominid stage of human evolution.

(3) Claims that bipedalism could easily be acquired by an ape wading in shallow water, and that nakedness is of advantage to an aquatic or, rather, semi-aquatic mammal.

TESTING THE HYPOTHESIS

This chapter is primarily concerned with some aspects of argument (3), but a few remarks on (1) and (2) will be made first.

1 Morgan (1972) argued that anthropoid apes, when on the ground, prefer quadrupedal locomotion because their bipedal walk is ungainly and slow. But chimpanzees are able to run very fast on two legs, though perhaps not for any great distance (Leyhausen, 1954). However, the more extreme brachiators, the gibbons, must have acquired bipedalism while in the trees: very often they swing off a branch, land feet-first on another, and run along it for a while before launching themselves again into brachiatory swings. Often they walk along a branch on their hind legs, while simultaneously stabilising themselves by pro-forma brachiation with their hands along a branch extending over their heads. Now, gibbons have not developed knuckle-walking to the same perfection as did gorillas and chimpanzees, and when down on the forest floor they are able to run much faster bipedally than quadrupedally. Although there has been some discussion of the possibility that man bypassed brachiation in the course of his evolution, there can be no serious doubt that some of our prehuman ancestors were knuckle-walkers. This is a method of locomotion solely adopted by brachiators coming down to earth again – the gorilla and the chimpanzee in particular. The gibbon example may even point to the possibility that some early prehominids were more advanced brachiators than the immediate ancestors of chimpanzees and gorillas. However this may be, the gibbons show that bipedal locomotion in a brachiator need not be slow. Their case also casts doubt on the so far undisputed tenet that bipedalism must have evolved on the ground. It may well have started in the trees.

2 Etchings of human forms on reindeer antlers seem to show that even as late as the Aurignacian the body of palaeolithic man was well covered with terminal hair. Morgan quotes Hardy (1960): 'on the human body the vestigial hairs follow precisely the lines that would be followed by the flow of water over a swimming body'. This is incorrect (Figure 10.1). At the very top of the shoulders, where they strike against the onflowing water, the hairs strain against the current, thus offering maximum resistance to it. No aquatic mammal shows a similar flow of the hair. The human pattern is indeed unique even among primates, apes included. In all aquatic mammals the hair runs straight and even down from the head, over the neck and shoulders and along the body, and nowhere does it turn against the direction of the water flowing along the swimming body (Leyhausen, 1969).

Figure 10.2 presents a reconstruction of what human hair would have looked like at a stage of hominid evolution when it still covered the body more or less completely. It shows the owner (a) in a calm and (b) in

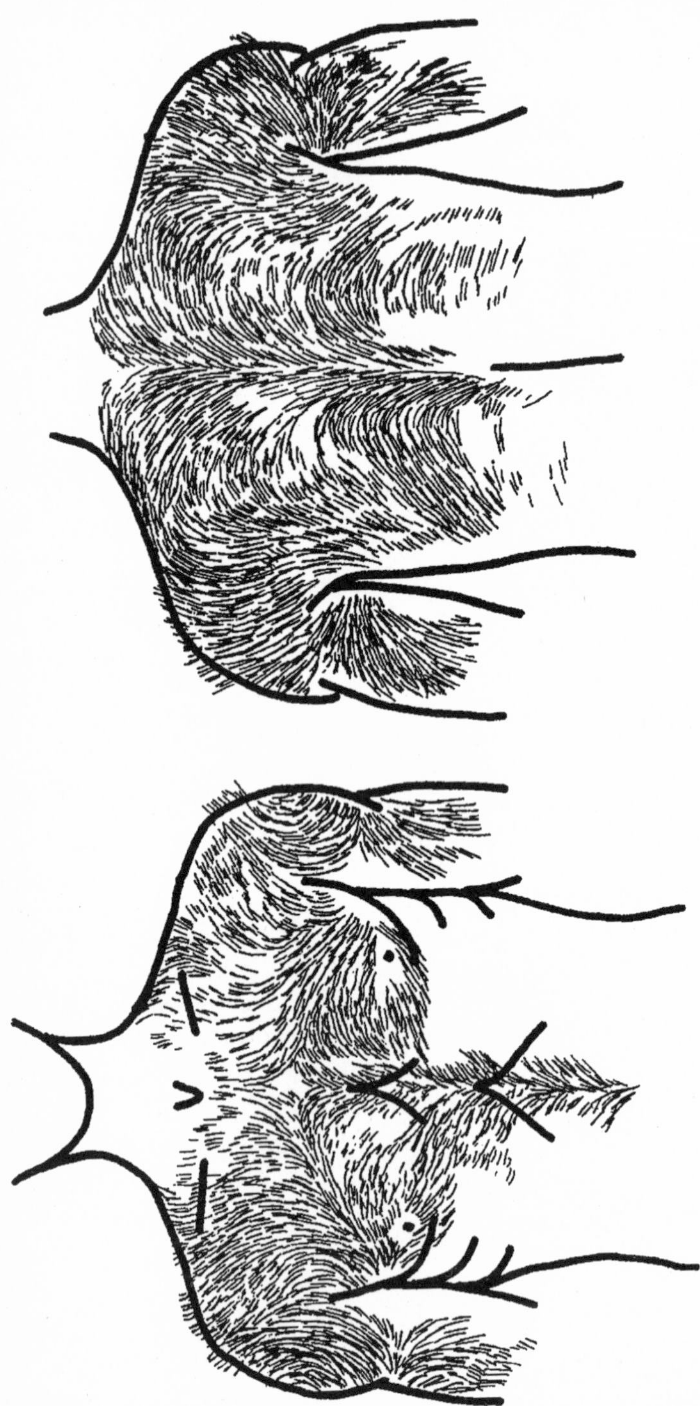

Figure 10.1 Flow of 'hairstreams' on the human body (n > 10,000).
The hair appears to rise from the armpit up to shoulders and neck, makes a U-turn and runs down the middle of the back. While there is considerable variation and asymmetry on the chest, there is none on the arms, shoulders and neck. This suggests a strong selection pressure that has prevented any noticeable degree of variation in those areas which determine the contour of the body.

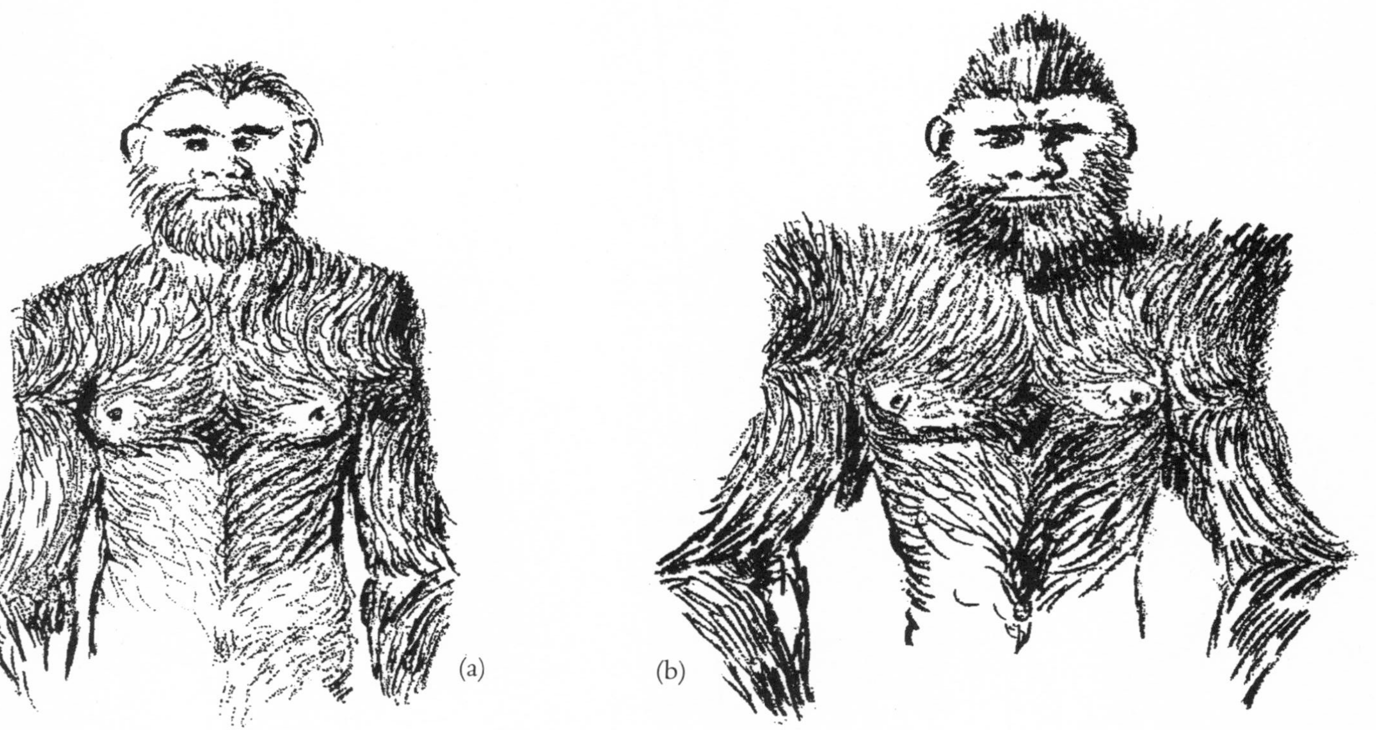

Figure 10.2 Hypothetical reconstruction of early hominid hair cover and the effect of pilo-erection.
(a) Individual in calm and friendly attitude; (b) same individual in a threatening, slightly aggressive posture.

an excited mood. It must be assumed that in this – Cro-Magnon type – man the pilo-erector muscles were still working perfectly well. The erected hair forms a sharp angle over the shoulder. To this day, humans possess an innate releasing mechanism which reacts to the contour that the human shoulder-line would assume if the hair were still present and the pilo-erector muscles still working. Long before man – probably as late as the end of the Palaeolithic – became practically hairless, the receding hair had been gradually replaced by adornments and clothing designed to mimic the contour that the erected shoulder hair would have presented (Leyhausen, 1969, 1983), thus satisfying the need for stimulation of the still extant releasing mechanism. A cursory look at modern fashion will prove that it still does so. There is no way in which the releasing mechanism could have survived several million years after the signal structure (the 'releaser') to which it is geared had become extinct. It could not have rested idle while the ape was already naked and the human not yet ready to meet the need of the releasing mechanism with substitutes formed out of adornments and clothing.

3 But let us now consider aquatic mammals. We can perceive roughly four groupings of mammals that spend at least a considerable proportion of their time in the water.

(i) There are two orders, the Cetacea and the Sirenia, whose members stay in the water all the time and are indeed unable to move on dry land. They are also hairless, and protect themselves against heat loss by a thick layer of subcutaneous blubber. To do this effectively they are almost all very large, and the smallest species live in warm tropical waters (fresh water dolphins). These animals meet, in an ideal manner, the criteria for aquatic mammals named by Morgan. Unfortunately, they represent a way of life which even the most ardent aquatic ape partisan does not claim for that ape. Their adaptations cannot provide us with arguments in favour of the Aquatic Ape hypothesis.

(ii) The pinnipeds, animals which spend most of their time in the water, have reduced their limbs to short rudders and to fin-like organs, are unable to move fast on dry ground, and come to shore only to rest and reproduce. Some species live on the high seas for most of the year, and come to dry land only for a relatively short period to give birth and mate and rear the young to some degree of independence. Some pinniped species are very bulky (walrus, elephant seal) and many have considerable layers of subcutaneous blubber. But not a single one has lost its pelt, and a number of them are famous for their fur and are severely hunted for it. It is therefore a well justified conclusion that an aquatic mammal that spends some proportion of its time ashore cannot do without a pelt, especially when it has to contend with climatic conditions where extreme heat may change rapidly to extreme cold, and the reverse.

(iii) Mammals adapted to swimming and diving which spend considerable time in the water for the purposes of foraging and self-protection constitute by far the most numerous group, containing members of six orders: monotremes, marsupials, rodents, insectivores, carnivores and ungulates. However, since all these animals also spend considerable time out of the water and are well able to run and jump, they should be described as semi-aquatic rather than aquatic. With one exception, all are well covered with hair. Many of them are famous fur-bearers, such as beaver, nutria, desman and the otter species. They have common adaptations for aquatic life, such as nostrils and ears which can be closed against the water, and short limbs with webbed feet.

The one exception mentioned above is the two hippopotamus species. Because of its habit of wallowing for hours in the warm waters of its habitat, the great Indian rhinoceros could also be described as semi-aquatic, although it rather belongs to group (iv) below. But the other rhinoceros species and the elephants are also hairless, and with the best of wills could not be described as even semi-aquatic, although they like bathing. The conclusion that all this suggests is that it is bulk and not their way of life which forces some mammals to do away with hair, because otherwise, under conditions of tropical temperatures, they would become overheated.

On the other hand, a minimum bulk is evidently required if an animal wants to replace by a layer of subcutaneous blubber the thermic insulation provided by a pelt. In a small body the ratio of surface to capacity is too unfavourable. A water-shrew or other small semi-aquatic mammal would therefore need a proportionally thicker coating of blubber than a whale to protect it from dangerous heat loss. But even a relatively thin pelt whose dense underwool is packed in tightly by terminal hair will effectively keep water from the skin. The air enclosed by the underwool is a most efficient heat insulator. In short, no aquatic or semi-aquatic mammal of small to medium body size could afford to shed its pelt, although many of them acquired subcutaneous fat as an additional means of keeping warm. The importance of the pelt to these animals is also evidenced by the fact that they all devote a great proportion of the time spent out of the water to grooming activities.

Everything which protrudes from the body, such as long ears, limbs and tails, presents a relatively excessive surface and is therefore detrimental to the maintenance of body temperature in a cooling medium. All aquatic mammals therefore have small external ears, or have lost them completely. They have short, thickset limbs, and those which do not use their tail as a rudder or propeller usually have a vestigial one or none at all.

(iv) A fourth group comprises mammals which do not really live in the water, but which take to it readily to escape either from the heat of the day or from all too persistent parasitic insects; examples are the water-buffalo and the Indian rhinoceros. Others flee to the water when threatened by their enemies, as do, for instance, the capybara and some antelopes (Sitatunga, Mrs Gray's antelope) and deer (Père David's deer, swamp deer). To all these animals the water means a refuge, but not really a way of life. They are often adapted to life in swamps and wetlands, and swim well, but avoid diving and too long sojourns in the water. It must be borne in mind that almost all mammals are able to swim well.

Let us now consider our hypothetical aquatic ape. Clearly, any comparisons with groups (i) and (ii) are out of the question. His aquatic adaptations could never have gone as far as those found in these two orders.

The way of life that Morgan and others depict as the aquatic ape's daily routine would classify him along with the group (iii) mammals. However, ape and human alike are lacking any of the structural adaptations common to these. Human ears are comparatively large and richly provided with blood vessels. The nostrils cannot be closed, and it is only the air pressure of well filled lungs which prevents the water from entering. Primates cannot dive with empty lungs. This is what many aquatic and semi-aquatic mammals do when they wish to sink deep quickly. No mammal which spends a considerable proportion of its daily routine moving around in the water has limb–body proportions even remotely approaching those found in apes and humans. This last fact alone would prove that the fictitious ape could at best have belonged to category (iv). That human babies are natural swimmers and divers and that older children and adults can be trained to do even better is no argument. There are several macaque and baboon species whose members are excellent swimmers and divers. That does not make them 'aquatic monkeys'.

The alleged physiological adaptations of humans to an aquatic life likewise do not stand up to scrutiny. That the heartbeat of divers slows down somewhat is not to be wondered at. It does so in any mammal when the chest is compressed so that pressure is brought to bear on its contents, notably the heart. Thus the heartbeat also slows down a little when you turn on to your left side in your sleep (unless you have situs inversus) instead of lying on your back or right side: the weight of the right lung and other internal organs inside the chest then rests, in part at least, on the heart, and that suffices to depress the heart rate just a little. The human skin is in no way adapted to being soaked in water for long periods, and has to be protected against osmotic pressure by covering it thickly with grease, as cross-Channel swimmers used to do, or by divers' suits. In any case, our survey lends no support whatever to the idea that human near-hairlessness could be due to an ancestral ape adapting to a semi-aquatic way of life. No even remotely comparable semi-aquatic mammal is hairless.

Last but not least: the Aquatic Ape hypothesis claims that at least one of the main factors driving our ancestral ape to the sea was pressure from leopards and other large predators. Leopards, the argument goes, are cats, and shun even shallow waters, and sharks do not enter them. The shallow coastal waters of East Africa, then, provided safety from all and sundry hazards. But as far as we know the shores of the Indian Ocean have always been infested by large crocodilians. Until fairly recent times, the range of the largest of extant crocodiles, the salt-water crocodile (*Crocodylus porosus*), extended westward to the African coast, and the indigenous Nile crocodile (*Crocodylus niloticus*) is by no means shy of salt water and was therefore able to colonise all the offshore islands, including Madagascar. Probably there were also other large crocodilians around, which are now extinct. They would all have gobbled up naked apes, particularly the babies, like geckos picking up insects that gather around a ceiling light. If I were a naked ape the size of a gibbon or slightly taller I should by far prefer to face the leopard.

In short, available evidence shows:

(1) Bipedal walk evolved in a brachiator, not in a wader in shallow water.
(2) Early hominids – even early *Homo sapiens* – were still fully covered by at least their terminal hair.
(3) No aquatic or semi-aquatic mammal of about the size of the hypothetical aquatic ape is naked.

Conclusion: there never was an aquatic ape.

REFERENCES

Hardy, A., 1960, Was man more aquatic in the past? *New Scientist*, **7**, 642–5.

Leyhausen, P., 1954, *Pan troglodytes* – Zweifüβergang [*Pan troglodytes* – Bipedal walking and running]. Film No. E7, Göttingen: Scientific Film Institute.

Leyhausen, P., 1969, Experimental analysis of a human releasing mechanism. (*XIth International Ethological Conference*, Rennes (France), 2–10 Sept, 1969.)

Leyhausen, P., 1983, Kleidung: Schutzhülle, Selbstdarstellung, Ausdrucksmittel [Clothing: protective covering, self-projection, means of expression]. In *Menschliches Verhalten*, ed. B. Sitter (Freiburg: Universitätsverlag), 137–52.

Morgan, E., 1972, *The Descent of Woman* (London: Souvenir Press).

Morgan, E., 1982, *The Aquatic Ape* (London: Souvenir Press).

For more detailed information on aquatic mammals see:

Grzimek, B. (ed). 1987 (vol. 4), 1988 (vols 1, 2, 3, 5), *Grzimeks Enzyklopädie: Säugetiere* (Munich: Kindler Verlag; English edition in preparation).

Walker, E.P., 1964, *Mammals of the World*, 3 vols (Baltimore: Johns Hopkins Press).

Weber, M., 1927, *Die Säugetiere* (The Mammals) (Jena: Gustav Fischer Verlag).

11 Human Regulation of Body Temperature and Water Balance

Marc Verhaegen

SUMMARY
There is no evidence that the physiological characteristics distinguishing man from other primates evolved as adaptations to life on the savannah. On the contrary, many of these features, especially those concerned with the regulation of temperature and water balance, would have been positively maladaptive in such an environment.

INTRODUCTION

In 1924 Raymond Dart discovered the first australopithecine skull in Taung, in a semi-arid region of South Africa. It was Dart who conceived the hypothesis that the ancestors of humans began to diverge from the apes because they migrated to a savannah-type environment. The theory appeared to represent the most straightforward method of connecting two pieces of 'evidence' – that is, Dart's supposedly savannah-dwelling hominid child and the belief that very much later human ancestors hunted big game on the African plains (Susman, 1987).

We now know that Dart's ideas were based, at least partly, on a misconception. He was convinced that the climate at Taung was as dry when the Taung baby lived there as it is today. It is now realised that the palaeo-environment of the Taung child was probably humid (Partridge, 1985; Brain, 1985). Moreover, the subsequent discoveries which have done so much to narrow the fossil gap have all been of hominids which lived and died near water (see Verhaegen, this volume, chapter 5). The savannah theory thus remains an artificial construction, a 'Just So Story' comparable with the hypothetical 'land bridges' in geology before the theory of plate tectonics.

Accounts of how our Plio-Pleistocene ancestors may have lived on the savannah include bouts of strenuous activity outside the gallery forest for hunting or digging (Hanna and Brown, 1983; but see Newman, 1970); dogged pursuit of swifter animals over one or two days (Carrier, 1984); and bipedal trekking after migrating herds of savannah ungulates (Sinclair, Leakey and Norton, 1986; but see Leutenegger, 1987; Verhaegen, 1987). Some of the more imaginative versions appear mutually contradictory. For example, the hypothesis of a foraging or hunting male accords ill with Wheeler's meridian theory that our ancestors became bipedal to minimise direct solar radiation at midday, and retained a hairy heat shield only on top of the head (Wheeler, 1984, 1988; in imitation of D. H. K. Lee, in Newman, 1970; and in Schmidt-Nielsen, 1979, p. 89). If we accept this reasoning, it must have been the women who ranged over the plains at noon, while the balding and bearded males rested in the shade.

ERECT POSTURE, NAKEDNESS AND SUBCUTANEOUS FAT

The suggestion has been made that erect posture and nakedness may have evolved to function in humans as a combined strategy of thermoregulation in an arid environment. In this connection it is noteworthy that (1) in no other species are hairlessness and erect posture found in combination, and (2) in no other species can either feature be shown to assist efficient temperature control on land.

Meerkats, prairie dogs and gerenuks frequently stand erect on extended hind limbs; kangaroos and several convergent rodents (for instance, *Pedetes*, *Dipodomys*, *Jaculus*) resort to bipedal locomotion when moving at speed, though their body posture with flexed hip and knee joints is very different from the human erect stance. But all these have retained a coat of fur which protects them from the sun (Montagna, 1965).

As for nakedness, it is found among real savannah or desert dwellers only in the underground tunnels of the naked mole-rat, a completely fossorial animal. In the African elephant and black and white rhino, which are functionally naked and live partly on the savannah, the hairlessness seems more of an affliction than an asset; these animals exploit every opportunity of wallowing to acquire a covering of mud as a protection against solar radiation. It is true that a few medium-sized savannah mammals, such as aardvarks, wart-hogs and hunting dogs, are comparatively sparsely haired. But this feature is unlikely to have evolved as a defence against the sun's heat, since these species spend the day in holes and are active at dusk or at night.

Humans lack the short reflective fur of diurnal savannah dwellers such as zebras and bovids, lions and camels (Wilson, 1979, pp. 752–3; Newman, 1970; Wheeler, 1984). Instead, they display a subcutaneous layer of white fat tissue, fairly evenly distributed over the surface of the central body parts and comprising on average around 20 per cent of body weight. This fat layer is (1) conspicuously absent in savannah mammals and conspicuously common in the larger aquatic ones, and (2) demonstrably maladaptive in a hot terrestrial environment.

There are no fat animals on the savannah, with the exception of small burrowing rodents or marsupials. In the case of these species, the fat is brown rather than white, internal or localised (for instance, in a fat tail) rather than subcutaneous and, unlike human fat, it is subject to seasonal fluctuation. Among larger animals, the dromedary has occasional need of a fat store against food shortage, but here again the fat is highly concentrated (in the hump), varies with the animal's feeding condition, and fluctuates between 0.5 and 8 per cent of its body weight. The only fat animal which exploits the grasslands around the rivers is the hippopotamus, but it does this at night and stays in the water during the day.

In the case of marine mammals, however, the fat tissue is universal among the larger species. It varies from 20 to 25 per cent of the body weight in fast swimmers to more than 40 per cent in the slower species (Slijper, 1958, 1979).

The adaptiveness of this feature in water has been further illustrated by studies of human athletes. For example, blacks – in whom subcutaneous fat comprises a somewhat lower percentage of overall body weight than in other races – tend to be the swiftest runners over both short and long distances, but they are relatively poor swimmers (Ghesquiere and Bunkens, this volume, chapter 16). Successful swimmers are on average fatter than the winners of track events, and many long-distance swimmers are even grossly fat (Pugh and Edholm, 1955). The fat layer has been shown to be an effective barrier against heat loss in water. A study of a fat Channel swimmer revealed that when lying still in bath water at 18°C for more than one hour, he complained of no discomfort other than boredom, whereas another subject with much less subcutaneous fat complained of intense discomfort and showed a drastic drop in rectal temperature after fifteen minutes (Pugh and Edholm).

Clearly, the possession of the fat layer facilitates spending more time in the water. The result of one recent experiment even suggested that the converse may also be true. It was found in a study of slightly obese women that, without dietary restriction, an hour's daily walking or cycling reduced body weight by 10 and 12 per cent respectively after six months, while a daily swim caused a weight gain of 3 per cent over the same period (Gwinup, 1987). On land, on the other hand, subcutaneous fat has the dual disadvantage of reducing speed and, in hot climates, of acting as a heat trap. An extra weight of fat tissue equivalent to only 10 per cent of body weight seriously reduces speed. Even in temperate climates, no terrestrial animal that has to run for its life – be it as predator or prey – has much fat. Hares, for instance, which escape predators by running, have much less body fat than rabbits, which take refuge in their burrows.

Excess fat can constitute a real risk to humans taking exercise, especially in hot and sunny environments (Austin and Lanking, 1986). In fact, it has been calculated that most land-based sports other than walking and table tennis are up to ten times more likely to lead to fatalities than swimming, despite the additional danger of drowning incurred by swimmers

(Dolmans, 1987). And the same fat layer that is advantageous in water, with its high thermal conductivity, is a handicap to effective temperature control on land. Stranded dolphins, even in cool environments, soon die of hyperthermia. And Pribilof fur seals are seriously distressed by any activity on land at air temperatures of only 10°C (McFarland *et al.*, 1979, p. 773). The alleged danger of overheating on the savannah – sometimes advanced as the reason for hairlessness – would have been compounded by the evolution of the fat layer.

BODY TEMPERATURE

In an endothermic species the normal temperature represents a compromise between the advantages and disadvantages of high body temperature in relation to its particular habitat and behaviour.

One of the advantages of high body temperature – especially the higher nervous tissue and muscle temperature – is the facilitation of faster reactions (McFarland *et al.*, p. 651). For every rise of 1°C, the velocity of the biochemical processes is more than doubled (compare the warming-up of athletes). Fast reactions are important in predators and their prey, in intra-species conflicts, and for birds in flight. For these purposes, generally speaking, the higher the nerve and muscle temperature, the better. The disadvantage lies in the high energy expenditure needed to sustain the temperature: the cost of keeping body tissues at about 38–42°C, as in most mammals and birds during the day, is enormous (Else and Hulbert, 1987). High temperatures may also incur other disadvantages – for example, problems of lipid and protein solubility and protein denaturation.

If the processes of thermoregulation in humans had evolved in response to a move from the trees to savannah, we would expect them to be characterised by a high normal temperature because of the need for speed, whether in flight or in pursuit, and a capacity to tolerate periods of higher temperature because of exposure to the tropical heat. Most hunted or hunting animals have a body temperature of at least 38°C. While the average rectal temperature in man is 37°C, in horses it is 38°C, in cattle and guinea pigs 38.5°C, in rabbits, sheep, dogs and cats 39°C, in goats 39.5°C (Slijper, 1958; Calloway, 1976). By contrast, animals which do not defend themselves by running away – such as hedgehogs, mole-rats, armadillos, monotremes, pottos and sloths – may have body temperatures lower than 35°C, and consequently incur much lower energy costs than other animals of the same size (Wilson, 1979, p. 747; McFarland *et al.*, 1979, p. 652; Calloway, 1976; Goffart, 1978).

If we exclude the group of slow-moving mammals listed above, a normal temperature as low as man's is found chiefly among the larger aquatic mammals. Hunting and hunted pinnipeds have a body temperature like ours or slightly higher – for instance, 37.5°C in fur seals and 36.5°C in sea-elephants. But aquatic mammals that can afford to move slowly often have lower temperatures, which saves energy and allows longer submersion. Hippopotamuses and many cetaceans have body temperatures of about 35.5°C, sea-cows probably even lower (Slijper, 1958, p. 359). In other words, humans have a normal temperature resembling that of sea mammals, lower than most terrestrial ones, and markedly lower than that of any active savannah species. As well as possessing such a high basic temperature, animals living in exposed habitats evolve the capacity to survive periods when the diurnal air temperature is very high. The oryx, for example, can sustain a rectal temperature of 45°C and Grant's gazelle of 46.5°C for many hours, whereas humans feel ill if their rectal temperature rises to 38°C. Different mechanisms have been developed in warm-blooded animals for selectively keeping their brain temperature lower than the body temperature (Taylor and Lyman, 1972). These mechanisms, well developed in savannah dwellers, are poorly developed in humans (Cabanac, 1986), so that in man a rectal temperature of 41°C may result in permanent brain damage (Cabanac, 1986; Krupp and Chatton, 1981, pp. 1, 939).

In a savannah-type environment there is an unusually wide difference between day and night temperatures. Consequently, one final characteristic of thermoregulation in animals living in this environment is that they have evolved a wide range of body temperatures. Many show a fluctuation of more than 6°C between day and night temperatures: the oryx, for example, ranges between 38°C and 45°C, and the gazelle's rectal temperature may increase by 5 or 6°C during a single run, which – through muscular warming-up – has the advantage of enhancing its speed (Taylor, 1970; Taylor and Rowntree, 1973). At the other extreme are the medium-sized and large aquatic mammals which display almost no body temperature fluctuations. For instance, the core temperature of the East Siberian dolphin shows fluctuations of less than 0.5°C (Slijper, 1958, p. 205). Human metabolism seems to be adapted to fluctuations of less than 1°C (Schmidt-Nielsen, 1979, figure 4), although naked Australian aborigines after a single night's sleep under the desert sky may have body temperatures as low as 35°C (Kanwisher, 1977, p. 500). Running a marathon may raise the body temperature by two degrees, but rises greater than that can be fatal.

This factor is stressed in textbooks of physiology: 'The range of body temperature in a group of healthy persons is quite small. Indeed, the coefficient of variation of body temperature in man is one of the smallest for which quantitative data are available' (Bell, Davidson and Scarborough, 1968). If we had been, as has been suggested, savannah-adapted over millions of years, it seems likely that we would have been able to accommodate with ease a temperature rise to more than 40°C in the afternoon. The peak figures of death by heat-stroke in Greece in the hot summers of 1987 and 1988 suggest that man is anything but a savannah animal.

WATER ECONOMICS

Drinking water

Among the commonest of mammalian adaptations to a hot, dry habitat is a minimal dependence on drinking water. Many small savannah and desert mammals (burrowing and nocturnal) do not drink at all. The same is true of some of the African ungulates such as the eland and the oryx (Taylor, 1970). Carnivores usually need to drink more because their diet consists of relatively large amounts of protein, which requires a lot of water for its excretion in the urine (Schmidt-Nielsen, 1979, p. 125). Yet in desert habitats even carnivores such as fennecs have the capacity to survive without drinking. Many arboreal primates such as langurs almost never drink because the moisture in their vegetarian diet is sufficient for their needs (Napier and Napier, 1985, p. 151). If the ancestors of human beings had left the forests and gone into more open environments, they would have evolved the capacity to become more conservative with water as a means of adapting to their habitat.

Precisely the opposite it true. Humans, even without exercise and in temperate climates, have to drink much more than any other terrestrial mammal. Otherwise they would become susceptible to cystitis and other infections, kidney stones, and especially dehydration. Without intervention, a dehydration of about 10 per cent may be fatal for humans, whereas most animals can rapidly recover from a dehydration of 20 per cent. For instance, dogs can survive a dehydration of 17 per cent, cats 20 per cent, camels and donkeys 25 per cent (Wilson, 1979, p. 753; Schmidt-Nielsen, 1979, pp. 15, 62, 89, 123–5).

Sweat production

Of all mammals, man has the highest sweat production (Newman, 1970). Montagna (1965) says: 'Sweating is an enigma that amounts to a major biological blunder; it depletes the body not only of water, but also of sodium and essential electrolytes'. But sweating is only one of the strategies mammals have evolved to prevent overheating. Many small mammals – such as rodents, marsupials and cats – use saliva instead of sweat for thermoregulation, spreading it over the more sparsely haired areas of the skin so that in evaporating it cools the body. Some larger mammals – such as dogs – reduce their body temperature by panting; others, like horses and cattle, sweat; sheep do both. But the maximum water loss per unit of skin surface in these species is always much smaller than in humans (Newman, 1970; Schmidt-Nielsen, pp. 54, 73, 83).

Although camels sweat, they have adapted to their arid environment by reducing water loss to a minimum; they do this by allowing their body temperature to rise during the day; the heat thus stored is given up at night without any expenditure of water. African hunting dogs (which, like dogs, do not sweat and do not salivate, and, unlike dogs, do not even pant) use the same strategy: they conserve water both by hiding in holes during the day and by allowing their body temperature to reach a level which in humans would be fatal, around 42°C (Kanwisher, 1977).

Of all the available strategies, human eccrine sweating combined with low body temperature is the least well adapted to savannah conditions and the least likely to have evolved in that type of habitat. As far as is known, fur seals are the only non-human mammals which sweat thermoactively through abundant eccrine glands (on their naked hind flippers) when they are overheated on land (G. A. Bartholomew, in McFarland *et al.*, 1979, p. 773).

Other water losses

Maximum urine concentration tends to vary according to the amount of water available in the environment and the diet (Table 11.1). Pigs and macaques, herbivores with a succulent diet, produce urine slightly more dilute than humans; that of freshwater beavers is much more dilute. On the other hand, the urine of dolphins is slightly more concentrated, and that of most land mammals like cats, dogs, sheep and rats is much more concentrated than in humans. In the savannah and desert dwellers, renal osmotic power is at the maximum. This seems to imply that human ancestors had ready access to a plentiful supply of fresh water or possibly brackish water, or at least to large quantities of fruits and fresh vegetables. Neither of these conditions is likely to have been fulfilled on the savannah. Even an evolution of only a few hundred thousand years in a mosaic gallery environment would have selected a higher urine concentration capacity.

The water content of human faeces tells a similar story. When camels drink daily, their faeces consist of 50–65 per cent water; when they have no access to drinking water, it is only 45 per cent (Schmidt-Nielsen, 1979, p. 61). Small desert rodents have a faecal water content in a similar range, between 45 and 50 per cent (Macmillen, 1972) as compared with about 70 per cent in the white rat. Human faeces normally consist of 75 per cent water (Diem and Lentler, 1978, p. 658).

The final channel of water loss is through exhaled air. Many animals in arid and semi-arid environments – such as kangaroos, giraffes and camels, as well as reindeer in the arctic desert – conserve most of the water breathed out from the lungs by utilising counter-current exchange of water during expiration. In humans, however, more saturated air is exhaled (Langman, 1985; Walker, Wells and Merrill, 1961).

Table 11.1 Maximum urine concentration in different mammals (Schmidt-Nielsen, 1979, pp. 181, 184; McFarland *et al.*, 1979, p. 674; Malvin and Rayner, 1968; Macmillen, 1972)

Species	*Maximum observed urine concentration in mOsm/l*
Beaver	520
Pig	1100
Man	1430
Rough-toothed dolphin	1700
Bottle-nose porpoise	1810
Quokka (wallaby)	2190
Hill kangaroo	2730
Camel	2800
White rat	2900
Sheep	3200
Cat	3250
Small savannah mammals	3900 or more
Australian hopping mouse	9370

Human water needs in hot, open environments

The total water expended by humans in sweat may easily reach 10 or 15 litres per day in hot and open environments (Newman, 1970; Schmidt-Nielsen, p. 12). Man needs to ingest water in large quantities to replace this loss. It might therefore be expected that he would have acquired the capacity to drink deep when water was available, and possibly to retain the water in his body.

As in the other instances quoted, the reverse is true. In the above-mentioned volume Schmidt-Nielsen makes this clear. Man's body is not adapted to store water: any excess taken in, for whatever reason, is rapidly excreted by the kidneys (p. 18). He has little, if any, ability to be trained to use less water (p. 22). When water is available, he is an unusually slow drinker. A very thirsty man can drink 3 per cent of his body weight in ten minutes, but a dehydrated camel, 30 per cent (p. 67). Moreover, when in danger of dehydration, man does not drink enough to replenish the water loss even if a plentiful supply of water is available (p. 9).

Table 11.2 Human characteristics compared with those of aquatic and savannah mammals

Humans	*Aquatic mammals*	*Savannah mammals*
Hind limbs in extension of trunk	All; resemblance with sea-lions	In gerenuk, suricata and prairie dog, for standing
Functionally naked skin	In all completely aquatic and many tropical semi-aquatic species, in Stellar sea-lion and elephant-seal	None; naked mole-rat is fossorial; elephant and rhinos need mud cover
Subcutaneous layer of white fat	In all medium-sized and larger species; usually thicker than in man	None
High drinking needs	In the freshwater semi-aquatic species (beaver)	None; except elephant (rhinos?)
Average rectal temperature less than 38°C	Probably all	None
Normal diurnal temperature fluctuation less than 1°C	Probably all	None; often 5°C and more
Eccrine sweat production for thermoregulation on land	Sea-lions (Pribilof fur seal); no sweat glands in completely aquatic species	None
Urine concerntration less than 1430 mOsm/l	Less than 1820 mOsm/l	More than 2400 mOsm/l

CONCLUSION

All the available evidence points to an extreme dependence on water in humans (Table 11.2). Even if our ancestors once lived in mosaic savannah environments, they would be expected to have evolved a more efficient system of water conservation than is in fact the case. 'Man suffers from a unique trio of conditions: hypotrichosis corpus, hyperhydrosis, and polydipsia' (nakedness, sweatiness and thirst) (Newman, 1970). Humans cannot withstand hyperthermia and cannot store heat. They have abundant sweat and tears, rather saturated expiration and dilute urine, watery faeces, a low drinking capacity, a naked skin, a rather thick subcutaneous fat layer over the central body parts, a rather low body temperature and a small circadian temperature fluctuation.

Each of these features suggests that man evolved in an environment where water was permanently and abundantly available. In combination, they point irresistibly to the conclusion that wherever man evolved these characteristics, it could not have been on the savannah.

ACKNOWLEDGEMENTS

I most sincerely thank Machteld Roede and especially Elaine Morgan for correcting and rewriting, and Morien Morgan for typing the manuscript.

REFERENCES

Austin, D.M. and Lanking, M.W., 1986, Body size and heat tolerance: a computer simulation. *Human Biology*, **58**, 153–69.

Bell, G.H., Davidson, J.M. and Scarborough, H., 1968, *Textbook of Physiology and Biochemistry* (London: Livingstone).

Brain, C.K., 1985, Interpreting early hominid death assemblages: the rise of taphonomy since 1925. In *Hominid Evolution*, ed. P.V. Tobias (New York: Liss), 41–6.

Cabanac, M., 1986, Keeping a cool head. *News in Physiological Sciences*, **1**, 41–4.

Calloway, N.O., 1976, Body temperature: thermodynamics of homeotherms. *Journal of Theoretical Biology*, **57**, 331–44.

Carrier, D.R., 1984, The energetic paradox of human running, and human evolution. *Current Anthropology*, **25**, 483–95.

Diem, K. and Lentler, C., 1978, *Tables Scientifiques* (Basel: Documenta Geigy).

Dolmans, A.J., 1987, Plotse dood bij sport. *Organorama België*, **24**, 21–5.

Else, P.L., and Hulbert, A.J., 1987, Evolution of mammalian endothermic metabolism: 'leaky' membranes as a source of heat. *American Journal of Physiology*, **253**, R1–7.

Ghesquiere, J., and Bunkens, H., 1991, The burden of locomotion in water: could the aquatic ape have overcome it? (This volume, chapter 16.)

Goffart, M., 1978, Physiological aspects of *Perodicticus potto*. In *Recent Advances in Primatology*, ed. D.J. Chivers and K.A. Joysey (New York: Academic Press), vol. 3: 179–80.

Gwinup, G., 1987, Weight loss without dietary restriction: efficacy of different forms of aerobic exercise. *American Journal of Sports Medicine*, **15**, 275–9.

Hanna, J.M. and Brown, D.E., 1983. Human heat tolerance: an anthropological perspective. *Annual Review of Anthropology*, **12**, 259–84.

Kanwisher, J., 1977, Temperature regulation. In *Introduction to Comparative Physiology*, ed. L. Goldstein (New York: Holt, Rinehart & Winston), 477–514.

Krupp, M.A. and Chatton, M.J., 1981, *Current Medical Diagnosis and Treatment* (Los Altos, California: Lange Medical Publications).

Langman, V.A., 1985, Nasal heat exchanges in a Northern ungulate, the reindeer (*Rangifer tarandus*). *Respiration Physiology*, **59**, 279–87.

Leutenegger, W., 1987, Origin of human bipedalism. *Nature*, **325**, 305.

Macmillen, R.E., 1972, Water economy of nocturnal desert rodents. *Symposia of the Royal Zoological Society of London*, **31**, 147–74.

Malvin, R.L. and Rayner, M., 1968, Renal function and blood chemistry in Cetacea. *American Journal of Physiology*, **214**, 187–91.

McFarland, W.N., Pough, F.H., Cade, T.J. and Heiser, J.B., 1979, *Vertebrate Life* (London: Collier Macmillan).

Montagna, W., 1965, The skin. *Scientific American*, **212**, 56–66.

Napier, J.R. and Napier, P.H., 1985, *The Natural History of the Primates* (London: British Museum (Natural History)).

Newman, R.W., 1970, Why man is such a sweaty and thirsty animal: a speculative review. *Human Biology*, **42**, 12-27.

Partridge, T.C., 1985, Spring flow and tufa accretion at Taung. In *Hominid Evolution*, ed. P.V. Tobias (New York: Liss), 171–87.

Pugh, L.G.C. and Edholm, O.G., 1955, The physiology of Channel swimmers. *Lancet*, **6893**, 761–8.

Schmidt-Nielsen, K., 1979, *Desert Animals* (New York: Dover Publications).

Sinclair, A.R.E., Leakey, M.D. and Norton, M., 1986, Migration and hominid bipedalism. *Nature*, **324**, 307–8.

Slijper, E.J., 1958, *Walvissen* (Amsterdam: Centen's).

Slijper, E.J., 1979, *Whales* (London: Hutchinson).

Susman, R.L., 1987, Pygmy chimpanzees and common chimpanzees: models for the behavioral ecology of the earliest hominids. In *The Evolution of Human Behavior: Primate Models*, ed. W.G. Kinzey (Albany: State University of New York Press), 72–86.

Taylor, R.C., 1970, Dehydration and heat: effects on temperature regulation of East African ungulates. *American Journal of Physiology*, **219**, 1136–9.

Taylor, R.C. and Lyman, C.P., 1972, Heat storage in sunning antelopes: independence of brain and body temperature. *American Journal of Physiology*, **222**, 114–17.

Taylor, R.C. and Rowntree, C.P., 1973, Temperature regulation and heat balance in running cheetahs: a strategy for sprinters? *American Journal of Physiology*, **22**4, 848–51.

Verhaegen, M., 1987, Origin of human bipedalism. *Nature*, **325**, 305–6.

Verhaegen, M., 1991, Aquatic features in fossil hominids? (This volume, chapter 5).

Walker, J.E.C., Wells, R.E. and Merrill, E.W., 1961, Heat and water exchange in the respiratory tract. *American Journal of Medicine*, **30**, 259–67.

Wheeler, P., 1984, The evolution of bipedality and loss of functional body hair in hominids. *Journal of Human Evolution*, **13**, 91–8.

Wheeler, P., 1988, Stand tall and keep cool. *New Scientist*, **1612**, 62–5.

Wilson, J.A., 1979, *Principles of Animal Physiology* (New York: Macmillan).

12 Adipose Tissue in Human Evolution

Caroline M. Pond

SUMMARY

The sparse data on the 'natural' distribution and abundance of adipose tissue in primates show that the basic anatomy of human adipose tissue is similar to that of terrestrial monkeys, and so was probably inherited directly from their primate ancestors. Superficial adipose tissue appears to extend over a greater area of the body in humans than in other terrestrial mammals, because of changes in the proportions of the limbs and in the shape of the girdles, the dorso-ventral flattening of the thorax and abdomen and the bipedal posture of the hip, knee and shoulder. The contrasts between humans and other primates have parallels in other mammals, and may be a direct consequence of the increased abundance of adipose tissue, which itself may be of very recent origin.

Experimental and comparative data on the physical properties and natural functions of adipose tissue in mammals are reviewed in this chapter. Superficial adipose tissue does not necessarily contribute significantly to thermal insulation except in specialised aquatic mammals. Anatomical, ecological and biochemical information provides no evidence that the distribution of adipose tissue in modern humans has evolved as an adaptation to thermal insulation, as required by the Aquatic Ape Theory, or as protection from mechanical damage. Other explanations for the exceptional features of human adipose tissue are briefly discussed. The greater fatness and modifications in the distribution of adipose tissue in young women are more likely to be conspicuous indicators of social and sexual status than an adaptation to energy storage for reproduction. The accumulation of mesenteric and omental adipose tissue in men and older women has no parallels in wild mammals and may not be physiologically adaptive.

INTRODUCTION

The anatomical arrangement of adipose tissue plays a central role in several theories of human evolution. For example, most of the secondary sexual structures implicated in Morris's (1967) explanation of some atypical features of human courtship and mating behaviour consist mainly of adipose tissue. The role of superficial adipose tissue as the principal natural insulation of an almost hairless body is an essential principle of the Aquatic Ape Theory or AAT (Hardy, 1960; Cunnane, 1980; Morgan, 1982; Verhaegen, 1985). A major tenet of both theories is that at some stage in the evolutionary history of *Homo* there were major shifts in the anatomical arrangements and the biological functions of adipose tissue. In spite of its importance to these theories, there is surprisingly little scientific information about the comparative anatomy of adipose tissue. Some theorists (Cunnane, 1980; Morgan, 1982; Verhaegen, 1985) have not recognised the relevance of experimental data on the physical properties of adipose tissue and fur in other aquatic mammals to interpretations of the natural function of these tissues in modern humans and their ancestors. Consequently, anthropologists lack objective criteria by which they can establish which features of human adipose tissue are truly unique, and which have precedents or parallels in other species.

There have been very few critical studies of the natural functions of adipose tissue in humans or other primates. The natural functions of biological structures are easy to suggest but difficult to prove rigorously, particularly for a tissue as variable in abundance as adipose tissue. A frequent source of misunderstanding is confusion of the role played by a tissue or organ in a particular situation, with *adaptation* of that structure to a natural function. For example, the fact that moderately obese young adults survive immersion in cold water for longer than lean individuals does not prove that insulation is *the* function of superficial adipose tissue; the fact that young women suffering from chronic anorexia or engaging in prolonged, strenuous exercise lose body fat and may become infertile does not prove that large quantities of adipose tissue are necessarily or naturally essential for reproduction. Some comparative or historical information is necessary to demonstrate that these properties of adipose tissue have evolved as adaptations to their postulated functions.

The purpose of this chapter is to describe the anatomy of human adipose tissue in relation to that of wild and domesticated mammals and to present a critical review, using comparative, physiological and palaeontological data, of some of the theories that have been proposed to explain the exceptional features of adipose tissue in humans. A fuller understanding of the factors that determine the distribution and abundance of adipose tissue in non-human mammals may help us to assess whether it is necessary or justifiable to postulate a major shift in the anatomical structure or in the natural function of adipose tissue in hominid evolution, as required by the Aquatic Ape Theory.

SOURCES OF INFORMATION ABOUT ADIPOSE TISSUE

Adipose tissue cannot be identified in fossils, so students of evolution must rely heavily upon comparisons between humans and other mammals, and between living races of humans, to identify evolutionary changes in the structure, properties or function of adipose tissue, and reconstruct the circumstances under which such changes might have taken place.

Skinfold thickness and X-ray photography have been used to measure the abundance of adipose tissue. But in certain depots, notably the buttocks (Harrison, 1985), the adipose tissue coheres so strongly to the underlying muscle that it is impossible to measure it accurately with calipers. Until recently, data about the total abundance of adipose tissue throughout the whole human body could be obtained only from cadavers, most of which were of elderly and ailing subjects (Clarys, Martin and Drinkwater, 1984). Physical techniques of image formation, particularly computed tomography (Keiffer and Heitzman, 1979), now permit accurate, direct measurement of the dimensions of adipose tissue in healthy people. The new technology produces much more data, but such information highlights rather than reduces the problems of interpreting the anatomy of adipose tissue in functional and evolutionary terms.

Disproportionate growth of certain adipose depots is a symptom (and possibly also a cause) of several progressive metabolic disorders (Krotkiewski *et al.*, 1983; Björntorp, 1987) from which modern humans, and probably also mammals in captivity, may suffer for many years before becoming obviously incapacitated. In modern Western populations, particularly those in which such disorders are common, 'average' body dimensions may not correspond to the 'optimal' or 'natural' values. As Tanner and Whitehouse (1975) put it after more than twenty years of measuring superficial adipose tissue in children: 'standards represent what is, not what ought to be'. Any hypothesis involving the social structure, behaviour or ecology of primeval humans is necessarily full of assumptions and inferences from other species, particularly other primates. All non-human descendants of immediate hominid ancestors are extinct, and the ranges of the living species of apes are greatly reduced. Apes readily become obese in captivity, and it is very difficult to study the anatomy of wild specimens. Consequently there is almost no detailed information about the distribution or average abundance of adipose tissue in any species more closely related to humans than cercopithecine monkeys. The habits of the few remaining groups of human hunter–gatherers have been strongly influenced by contact with other cultures, and may not be typical of the primitive condition.

In the case of *Homo sapiens* there is an additional source of information: artefacts and drawings of the human body, from many parts of the world and dating from the end of the Pleistocene Ice Age to modern times. Although 35,000 years is a very short time in evolutionary terms, such images tell us something about prehistoric human form, and, perhaps even more important, about how humans viewed themselves. Adipose tissue is conspicuous in only a small minority of the thousands of prehistoric representations of the human form that have been described, so there is no reason to suppose that the obesity on the scale represented in the North-West European Palaeolithic figure shown on Figure 12.1 was typical of the population as a whole. On the other hand, such images are unlikely to be purely imaginary: the artist had probably seen at least a few people with such a body shape. Furthermore, the conspicuous and sometimes exaggerated representations of the adipose masses suggest that such body conformations had social significance to the population in which they occurred, and may indicate that they were venerated or desired.

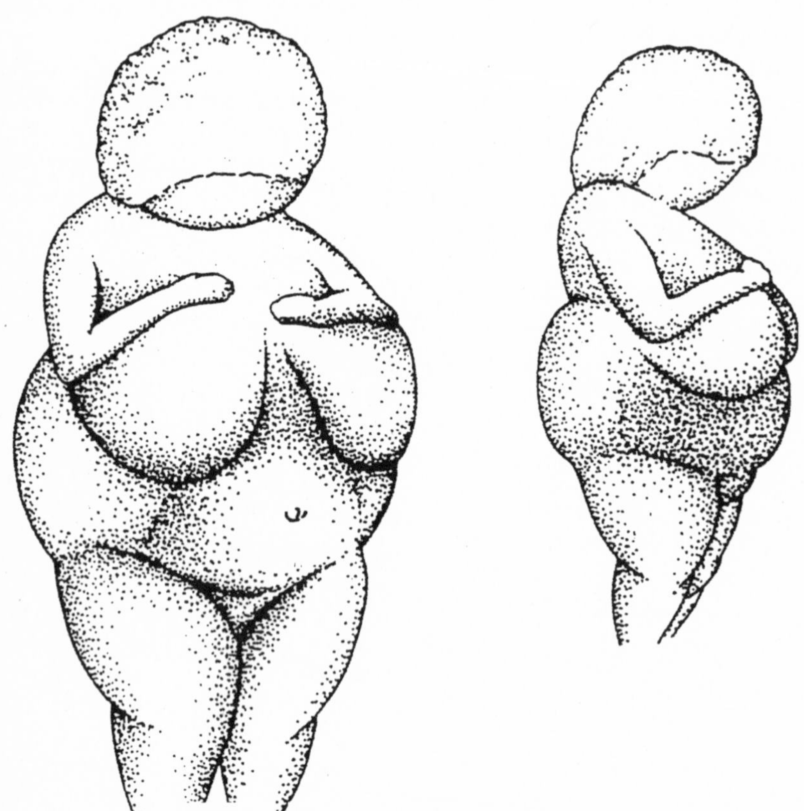

Figure 12.1 Small female figurine of Palaeolithic age from North-West Europe, seen from front and side.
(Reproduced by permission of Blackwell Scientific Publications.)

THE COMPARATIVE ANATOMY OF ADIPOSE TISSUE IN MAMMALS

University-based scientists rarely have the opportunity to examine a wide range of truly wild mammals. Most of their specimens, particularly of large species, come from zoos and other menageries, where exceptionally obese or emaciated animals are more likely to die, and hence to come to the attention of comparative anatomists, than those of normal body composition. Nonetheless, we have examined over two hundred specimens belonging to more than fifty species, and have identified some consistent features of the anatomy of mammalian adipose tissue (Pond and Mattacks, 1985a, 1985b, 1988, 1989; Pond, 1986, 1987c). Mammals and birds differ from the poikilothermic vertebrates in that adipose tissue occurs in a dozen or more discrete depots, associated with several different organs, including viscera and skeletal muscle. Contrary to the impression established by textbooks, in most species of mammals there is no continuous layer of 'subcutaneous' adipose tissue, except in the most obese specimens. The distinct depots can be characterised by site-specific differences in relative adipocyte volume (Pond and Mattacks, 1985a; Pond, 1986), as well as by their anatomical relations to other tissues.

Homologous depots can thus be identified in different species, regardless of the body composition of the specimens examined. The principal difference between species is the relative abundance of adipocytes in the various depots; ratios of volumes of adipocytes in identified depots remain remarkably constant over a wide range of species (Pond and Mattacks, 1989). Measurements of the activities of glycolytic enzymes and of lipid turnover *in vivo* confirm the existence of metabolic differences between depots that correlate with the anatomical origin of the adipose depot, not with adipocyte volume *per se* (Mattacks, Sadler and Pond, 1987; Pond and Mattacks, 1987a, 1987b; Pond *et al.*, 1991). Thus, although relative adipocyte volume provides a convenient means of identifying the depots, we do not yet understand its functional significance.

All the usual mammalian depots are present in *Macaca* monkeys, and their cellular dimensions and enzymatic properties are similar to those of other mammals (Pond and Mattacks, 1987b). The typical mammalian pattern of site-specific differences in adipocyte volume was described earlier in baboons, *Papio hamadryas,* by Lewis *et al.* (1983), but they did not recognise the generality of this pattern.

In many mammals, including *Macaca* monkeys, there are additional depots of adipose tissue, some of which may become massive compared to the typical depots and may overlie and obscure them. For example, small quantities of adipose tissue are found medially around the inner surface of the linea alba of the abdominal musculature of carnivores, primates and larger rodents, but not insectivores. In equids, camelids and some other large ungulates, this depot extends over much of the inner ventral wall of the abdomen and can be several centimetres thick in obese specimens. In some carnivores and primates there is also a medial adipose depot on the external surface of the abdominal wall (Figures 12.2 (c), (d)), which in lean *Macaca* monkeys forms a thin, narrow band along the mid-line, but in obese specimens it becomes massive, extending anteriorly to the sternum and laterally to the crest of the ilium.

Unfortunately, there is no detailed information about the anatomy of adipose tissue in any species more closely related to hominids.

The homologies of the adipose depots in wild mammals with those of humans are summarised in Figure 12.2. Both the thickness and the area covered by the adipose tissue vary with body composition; the extent of each depot shown is typical for well-nourished, but not obese, specimens of each species. There are species differences in the proportion of the segments of the limbs and in the shape of the girdles and trunk, as well as in the relative development of the depots. In typical quadrupedal mammals, the thorax and abdomen are flattened laterally, but in humans, the pelvis is exceptionally wide and the trunk is flattened dorso-ventrally. The pelvic girdle is foreshortened and, in the erect posture, the femur is fully extended. Compared to rodents, carnivores and ungulates, the humerus and femur of humans are relatively long, and the carpals, tarsals and digits of the hands and feet are relatively short. In typical mammals (for instance, ungulates and rodents), the normal planes of movement of the scapula and humerus are approximately parallel, but in humans the humerus rotates freely from the shoulder and the femur from the hip.

These changes in posture and skeletal proportions have affected morphology of the adipose tissue as well as that of the musculature. The ventral and side groin depots cover the sartorius, tensor fascia lata and the quadriceps muscles on the anterior surface of the thigh and the ventral and lateral areas of the posterior part of the abdominal wall (Figure 12.2 (d)). In typical mammals, the laterally flattened abdomen extends between relatively short thighs almost to the knee, so these groin depots form a broad band of adipose tissue on the flanks and on the outside of the abdomen. In obese specimens of short-legged species with crouching posture, such as guinea-pigs, the ventral groin depot may be so massive that it appears to extend to the ankles (Figure 12.2 (a)). In humans, the extended hip and relatively long femur result in these depots covering much of the anterior, lateral and medial surfaces of the hip and thigh, forming a 'subcutaneous' layer of adipose tissue from the ventral crest of the ilium to the knee. In middle-aged women these depots may become massive, and their abrupt termination just above the medial and anterior surface of the knee can be clearly seen in obese individuals (Figure 12.1). The outer abdominal wall is covered with the 'paunch', a non-paired adipose depot that originates from the mid-line (Figures 12.1, 12.2 (d)), and which may be thick and extensive in obese monkeys (Pond and Mattacks, 1987b) and in humans, particularly men (Lohman, 1981).

On the anterior, lateral thorax there is a bilaterally symmetrical depot situated medial to the panniculus muscle and lateral to the latissimus dorsi and pectoralis major, and extending along the posterior margin of the triceps brachii to the back of the elbow. It is slight in species such as deer (Figure 12.2 (b)), but extensive in rodents (Figure 12.2 (a)) and

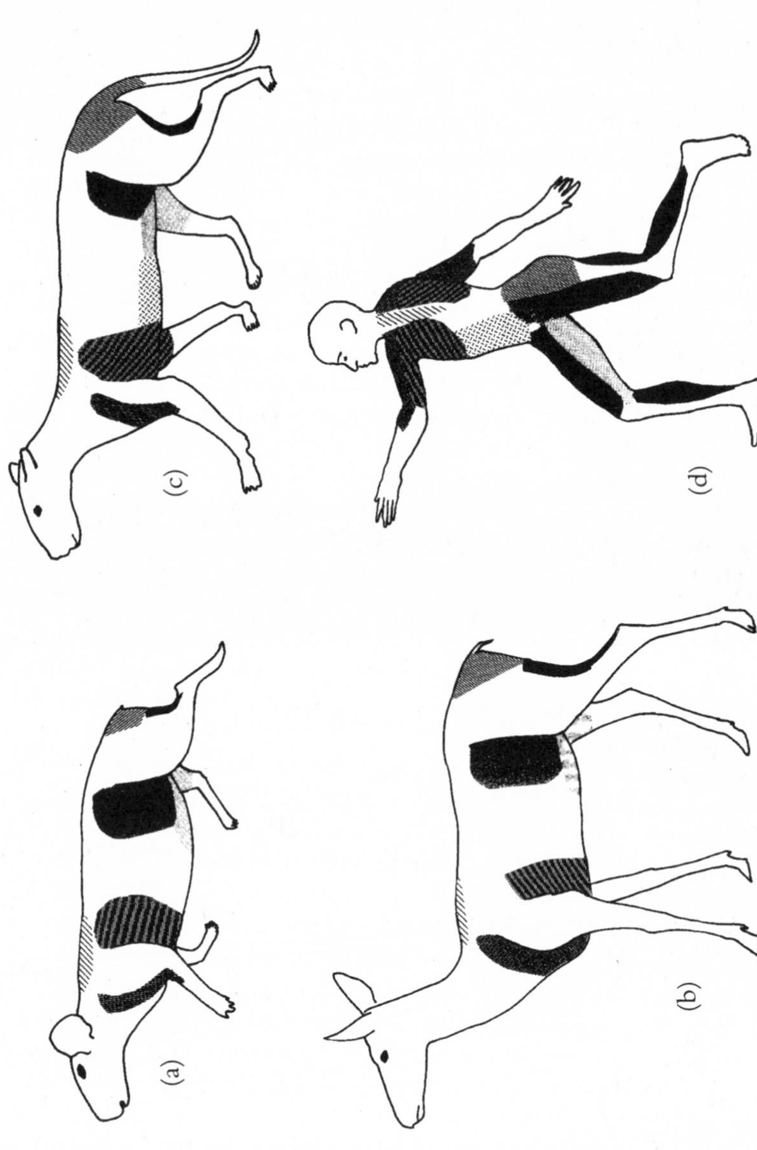

Figure 12.2 The principal superficial adipose in (a) guinea-pig, (b) deer, (c) tiger, (d) male human.
The specimens are drawn in postures that show as much as possible. Homologous depots have the same style of shading. Shading indicates the relative area, not the relative volume, of the depots.

carnivores (Figure 12.2 (c)). This depot has the same anatomical relations in primates, including humans, but, because of the reduction of the panniculus muscle, the relatively long humerus, the extension and rotation of the shoulder and the dorso-ventral flattening of the thorax, it extends over the ventral, lateral and dorsal surfaces of the chest and over the posterior and medial sides of the upper arm, where it overlies the triceps muscle (Figure 12.2 (d)). On the dorsal side of the thorax it forms the 'subscapular' sites, and on the ventral side it is associated with the mammary glands. Thus a depot that in quadrupedal mammals forms a condensed mass on the lateral thorax, appears to form an extensive 'subcutaneous' layer of adipose tissue over the chest and upper arm in humans. In men, both parts of this depot are approximately similar in thickness, but in women the pectoral portion is enlarged and forms the adipose tissue components of the breasts.

The adipose tissue over the human triceps muscle and that over the 'subscapular' site are among the easiest to examine with skinfold calipers. They are often recorded as though they were independent measures of fatness (e.g., Garn, Sullivan and Hawthorne, 1987). However, it is clear from the comparative anatomy that they are in fact parts of the same depot; no wonder measurements of their thickness correlate so much more highly with each other than with other depots (Garn *et al.*; Bouchard, 1987). The pair of depots that form the buttocks in humans is homologous with the (normally small) depots around the crest of the ischia and the proximal part of the tail in other mammals. Even in obese women, in whom the buttock depots may be massive, adipose tissue is almost absent on the mid-line over the sacrum and tapers sharply just below the dorsal crest of the ilium.

In most cursorial mammals, the knee is flexed and the three flexor muscles insert along the tibia, thereby covering the gastrocnemius muscle along most of its length. The popliteal depot is bounded laterally by the biceps femoris, medially by the semitendinosus and semimembranosus and ventrally by the gastrocnemius muscles, and envelopes the sciatic nerve, the femoral artery, the saphenous vein and popliteal lymph node. Therefore, in guinea-pigs and deer (Figures 12.2 (a), (b)) almost the whole of the popliteal depot is enclosed within the groove so formed, and only a small area of its posterior edge near the saphenous vein is in contact with the skin. The flexor muscles of the knee are inserted more proximally in climbing mammals such as felids, thereby exposing more of the gastrocnemius muscle and the popliteal adipose depot (Figure 12.2 (c)). But in humans, the flexor muscles are inserted just below the knee, which, in the fully erect posture, is extended completely. Consequently, most of the gastrocnemius muscle is not covered by the biceps femoris and semitendinosus muscles. The anatomical relations of the popliteal depot are the same as in other mammals, but the change in the site of insertion of the knee flexor muscles on to the tibia means that it extends from the back of the thigh to the ankle. The proximal part fills the groove at the back of the knee, where it can be clearly seen as a distinct mass even when overlain by other adipose tissue extending from depots on the medial and lateral sides of the thigh (Keiffer and Heitzman, 1979). In quadrupedal mammals, very little of the gastrocnemius muscle is in contact with the skin, but in humans the whole muscle is covered with skin, making the distal part of the popliteal depot appear to be 'subcutaneous'. In view of its origin as an intermuscular depot, it is not surprising that the dimensions of this adipose mass correlate very weakly with those of other superficial depots, and may shrink while adipose tissue elsewhere on the same person is expanding (Borkan and Norris, 1977).

In all mammals studied, including juvenile baboons (Lewis *et al.*, 1983), the central and posterior regions consist of relatively large adipocytes which have several atypical properties, including an exceptionally high capacity for glucose uptake (Mattacks, Sadler and Pond, 1987; Pond and Mattacks, 1987a) and a higher rate of fatty acid/triacylglycerol cycling than any of the eight other intra-abdominal and superficial depots studied (Mattacks and Pond, 1988). Both these properties increase with exercise and may be interpreted as enabling the popliteal depot to act as a local source of lipid for the adjacent locomotory muscles. In spite of the change in its anatomical relations, the adipose tissue on the calf retains the structural and biochemical features of a typical intermuscular depot (Evans, Mattacks and Pond, unpublished data, 1991).

Thus, although the basic features of the anatomy of human adipose tissue can be identified in other primates, changes in the proportions and posture of the limbs and trunk combine to create the *illusion* that there is 'subcutaneous' adipose tissue over a greater proportion of the body of humans than is the case in most other mammals. In moderately obese people (who form the great majority of those studied in modern Western populations), adjacent depots may overlap each other, making them difficult to identify at dissection and almost impossible to distinguish by palpation or medical imaging technology in living subjects. For example, components of the 'subcutaneous' adipose tissue that originate from the 'paunch' on the outer wall of the abdomen are clearly medial in origin, while those on the anterior thorax, back and hip are clearly bilaterally symmetrical. In lean persons, superficial adipose tissue is minimal on the dorsal mid-line over the spine, and on the ventral mid-line over the sternum and between the breasts. However, in moderately obese people the depots overlie each other, forming an almost continuous layer of 'subcutaneous' adipose tissue. Pearl and Johnson (1983) studied the fascias separating the layers of superficial adipose tissue that may have originated from adjoining depots. They reported that the fascia is maximal on the thorax and abdomen (where the bilateral depots overlap the medial paunch) and least developed on the medial thigh (covered by groin depot only) and on the lower leg (covered by popliteal depot only), as expected from the foregoing interpretation of the anatomy of human adipose tissue.

THE EFFECTS OF ADIPOSE TISSUE ABUNDANCE ON ITS DISTRIBUTION

The impression of massive subcutaneous adipose tissue in humans is further promoted by the fact that most humans, particularly women, are much fatter than most wild mammals. The proportion of the total adipose tissue in superficial and intra-abdominal depots varies considerably between individuals of similar body composition, but 'subcutaneous' adipose tissue is particularly characteristic of children and young women (Enzi *et al.*, 1986). There is some evidence that in other naturally obese mammals the proportion of adipose tissue in superficial depots may be greater in females. In captivity, the dwarf hamster, *Phodopus sungorus*, spontaneously becomes up to 38 per cent adipose tissue (Pond, Sadler and Mattacks, 1987), without showing any significant disturbances of behaviour or fertility. This proportion of adipose tissue is similar to that of 'normal' humans. In *Phodopus* the superficial adipose depots may become so massive that they cover the limbs to which they are attached, but, although they may seem to form a continuous layer of tissue, the individual depots can easily be distinguished and separated by dissection. The proportion of adipose tissue in superficial depots is greater in females, and the difference increases with increasing fatness. One possible explanation for these effects is that massive intra-abdominal adipose depots are incompatible with the production of relatively large litters.

In some, but by no means all, other wild mammals that become obese naturally – for example, the European badger (Figure 12.3) – the proportion of adipose tissue in superficial depots also increases with increasing fatness. In other words, in such species an apparent shift in the *distribution* of adipose tissue arises as a direct consequence of an increase in its *abundance*. This effect may partially explain the relatively large quantities of adipose tissue in women and children, most of whom have proportionately more adipose tissue than men of similar age, diet and habits (Bailey and Katch, 1981). Obesity is comparatively rare in adolescent boys and young men, but such individuals resemble women (and contrast with obese older men) in having thick, extensive superficial adipose tissue on the thighs, hips, upper arms and abdomen. Comparison of skinfold thickness of traditional and recently urbanised Canadian Eskimos also gave Schaefer (1977) the impression that in young adults of both sexes 'normal' adipose tissue is mainly internal, but 'additional' fat is deposited in superficial depots.

However, some features of adipose tissue in women, notably its presence in the greatly enlarged and rounded breasts and buttocks, cannot be explained simply as the consequence of its greater abundance. These features are not prominent until puberty and there are no corresponding sex differences in other primates (Pond and Mattacks, 1987b). In typical mammals most of the adipocytes (in small, fast-growing rodents, possibly all) form during suckling, and enlarge when-

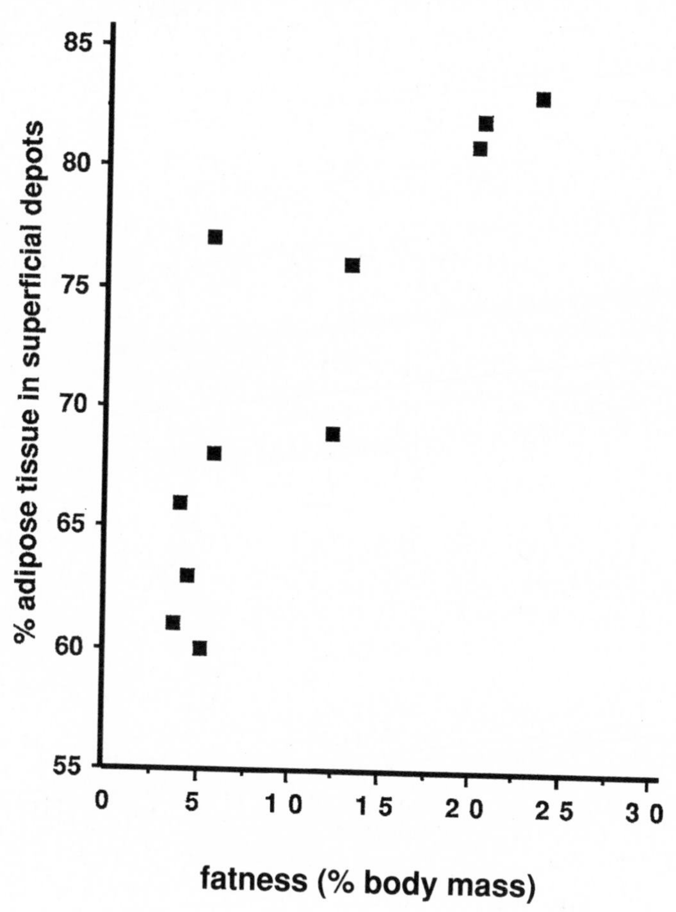

Figure 12.3 Mass of adipose tissue in superficial depots as a percentage of the total dissectible adipose tissue in 11 adult male badgers *Meles meles* (total body mass 8.8–13.6 kg), collected at random from southern England.

ever nutritional status promotes it (Kirtland and Gurr, 1979). Pregnancy may lead to adipose tissue expansion, but there are few detectable changes at sexual maturity. However, in humans puberty is accompanied by changes in the relative growth of adipose tissue in both sexes, which in girls are particularly extensive and conspicuous (Marshall and Tanner, 1986). Thus both in the timing of its expansion and in its distribution, the adipose tissue of women deviates further from other primates than does that of men (Pond and Mattacks, 1987b).

Only cetaceans, pinnipeds and a few species of carnivores and rodents normally have as much fat as 'typical' humans, although other wild species may become obese following long periods of confinement, and domesticated strains of mammals and birds are often obese (Pond, 1978; Pond and Mattacks, 1985b; Pond, 1987c). In such 'exceptionally' obese specimens, the normal superficial depots increase in both thickness and area to form an almost continuous layer of adipose tissue under the skin, including such unlikely sites as in the tail and ears. The effect is particularly prevalent among the Carnivora, possibly because the abdominal cavity is relatively small in these mammals, with the liver and the guts each amounting to only about 2 per cent of the body mass in large species such as lions (Pond and Ramsay, 1991). However, the fact that 'subcutaneous' adipose tissue is found in a few specimens under abnormal conditions does not mean that it is functional or natural in these wild mammals, or in humans.

This analysis shows that the basic elements of the anatomy of human adipose tissue can be identified in non-human primates and that the anatomical steps leading to the distribution of adipose tissue in modern humans can be elucidated from the comparison with other mammals. The exceptional features of the anatomy of human adipose tissue are a direct consequence of the changes in body proportions and in its total abundance. The modern condition can be explained without postulating a major evolutionary shift in the distribution of adipose tissue, as required by the Aquatic Ape Theory. Three major features peculiar to humans are:

(1) The average fatness of humans is much greater than that of monkeys.
(2) Superficial adipose tissue is much more conspicuous in humans, partly as a result of its greater abundance, but also because of hair reduction.
(3) There are substantial sex differences in both abundance and distribution of adipose tissue that appear in early childhood but increase markedly at puberty.

THE FUNCTIONS OF ADIPOSE TISSUE IN HUMANS AND OTHER MAMMALS

The principal, and best understood, function of metabolically active adipose tissue is as a long-term energy store.* In this role its mass varies greatly, sometimes over a short time. In a swimming, running or flying animal, a load with variable mass would cause minimum disruption to balance and posture if it were located at the centre of gravity. The lipid stores of many fishes, amphibians and reptiles are concentrated into a few localised depots, often situated inside the abdomen (Pond, 1978). But mammals and birds differ from the poikilothermic vertebrates in that adipose tissue occurs in a dozen or more discrete depots, associated with several different organs, including viscera, skeletal muscle and the skin. The most widely disseminated explanation for this situation is that adipose tissue acts as insulation and/or as support for other organs. In other words, adipose tissue is believed to have acquired additional functions that require it to be widely distributed over the body surface and around 'delicate' organs. Both of these roles are to some extent incompatible with its original role as an energy store. Insulative capacity is proportional to thickness, so to function effectively and continuously as an insulator the superficial adipose tissue should expand and shrink homogeneously, and be thickest over the most exposed or most vulnerable organs.

The notions that the superficial adipose tissue is adapted to insulate the body against heat loss and/or to protect underlying tissues from mechanical damage are two of the most firmly established of all theories in biology. The insulation theory is widely quoted in both the learned and the elementary biological literature, almost invariably without supporting anatomical or experimental evidence, and it is a major tenet of the Aquatic Ape Theory. Some recent examples include: 'Over most of the body it [the human hypodermis] forms a layer of adipose tissue which provides thermal insulation and mechanical protection' (Wood and Bladon, 1985); 'The primary function of fat deposits in other [non-human] animals is insulation from the cold' (Brown and Konner, 1987). Cunnane (1980) and Verhaegen (1985) also assumed that the principal function of superficial adipose tissue in all homeotherms is insulation. In spite of its widespread acceptance, very few data support the insulation theory, even in the case of some aquatic mammals.

Still air and stagnant water are effective thermal insulators, and the formation of a stagnant layer of air or water around the body is the principal mechanism of heat retention in many aquatic mammals and birds. However, the specific conductivity of adipose tissue is only a little

* Structural adipose tissue such as the paw pads of carnivores and the depots around and behind the eye is metabolically inert.

less than half that of stagnant water (Frisch, Øritsland and Krog, 1974), and numerous observations on mammals native to cold climates suggest that its contribution to insulation may be minimal. More than twenty-five years ago, Irving *et al.* (1962) measured the skin and core temperatures of Alaskan fur seals, *Callorhinus ursinus*, during experimental immersion in cold sea water. Even after prolonged immersion, the skin of the adult seals was only 5°C less than the deep body temperature. The thick, water-repellent fur trapped a layer of air that effectively insulated the surface of the skin from the ice-cold water. Polar bear fur is wettable, but the woolly underfur and stiffer guard hairs maintain a stagnant layer of water next to the skin that insulates the body like a diver's wetsuit and that provides effective insulation for several hours of immersion in cold water (Øritsland, 1970; Frisch, *et al.*, 1974). The availability of seals, the principal food of polar bears, is seasonal and irregular, and they accumulate large quantities of adipose tissue, much of it in superficial depots (Øritsland, 1970; Pond *et al.*, 1991). However, allometric comparison of the distribution of adipose tissue in polar bears with that of other Carnivora shows that the proportion of adipose tissue in superficial depots and its partitioning between the anterior and posterior areas of the body, are no different from that which would be expected in a temperate-zone carnivore of similar size and body composition (Pond and Ramsay, 1991). These data do not support the hypothesis that the large quantities of adipose tissue in superficial depots are *adapted* to function as thermal insulation. The biochemical properties of the subcutaneous adipose tissue also suggest that they contribute little to passive insulation in the arctic species (Pond *et al.*, 1991).

Although in hairless cetaceans such as fin whales, 96 per cent of the total adipose tissue is superficial (Pond and Mattacks, 1988a), the blubber over the most exposed areas of the back and shoulders is similar in thickness to that on the outer abdominal wall, and all the superficial depots are depleted at about the same rate (Lockyer, McConnell and Waters, 1985). In semi-aquatic mammals such as coypu (*Myocastor coypu*) and otters (*Lutra lutra*), the distribution of adipose tissue is not significantly different from that of their terrestrial relatives, nor is that of thick-furred or tropical species obviously different from that of temperate and thin-furred forms (Pond and Mattacks, 1985b; Pond, 1987a, 1987b; Pond and Ramsay, 1991). Even the hairless hippopotamus is very lean (Hillaby, 1962), although other non-ruminant artiodactyls, the terrestrial pigs and peccaries, have substantial quantities of subcutaneous fat. Pinnipeds are the only aquatic mammals for which there is evidence of an adaptive change in the partitioning of adipose tissue between internal depots (where it contributes nothing to insulation) and superficial sites (where it could combine the functions of energy store and insulator); almost all of the substantial quantities of adipose tissue in seals is superficial (Irving *et al.*, 1962; Pond and Mattacks, 1985b).

Many small hibernating mammals accumulate large quantities of adipose tissue before hibernation, much of which is in superficial depots, but its anatomical location may not indicate that its major function is insulation (Webb and Schnabel, 1983) and there are other equally plausible explanations for its distribution. Thus thick layers of 'subcutaneous' adipose tissue form on the back and thorax of hedgehogs (*Erinaceus europaeus*) but there is none on the abdominal wall, suggesting that the arrangement may have more to do with facilitating the defence posture of 'rolling into a ball' than with insulation. The edible dormouse *Glis glis* develops dissectible adipose tissue amounting to more than 30 per cent by weight before hibernation, but less than 70 per cent of it is in superficial depots, and the 'subcutaneous' fat is not uniform in thickness (Pond, unpublished observations). As in badgers (Figure 12.3), selective accumulation of adipose tissue in the superficial depots may be the simplest way of accommodating a large but transient increase in body mass with the minimum disruption to movement.

The biochemical data are also inconsistent with the notion that adipose tissue in superficial depots is adapted to act as an insulator in terrestrial or semi-aquatic mammals. The dwarf hamster, *Phodopus sungorus* (see page 202) is small (adult body mass 25–60g) and remains active throughout the year in the severe climate of Mongolia and Siberia. We measured the rates of lipid synthesis *in vivo* in the major adipose depots of this species at rest and after an hour of moderate exercise (Mattacks and Pond, 1988). The rates of lipid turnover in the various 'superficial' adipose depots are far from constant, and it would not bring about adaptive changes in the thickness of insulation in response to long-term or short-term changes in exercise regime. Intra-abdominal and groin depots show minimal structural and metabolic (Mattacks and Pond, 1988) response to exercise, but lipid from adipose tissue in interscapular and shoulder depots is readily mobilised during exercise. These depots on the back, neck and shoulder are situated between major organs and areas of skin most exposed to the elements, and hence would be much more important as insulators than the groin depots that spread over and hence 'insulate' the principal locomotory muscles of the hind limb. In fact, it is the intra-abdominal depots that have the metabolic properties that would be expected of adipose tissue of which the principal function is insulation. If the homologous depots in humans have similar properties then the insulating function of adipose tissue is clearly not as well integrated as it could be with its role as an energy source during prolonged exercise or starvation.

As already explained, there are few major differences in the distribution of adipose tissue between humans and furred primates. The relative thicknesses of the superficial depots are not consistent with the role of insulation in air or in water: the back, head and neck are much more exposed to the elements during both walking upright and swimming than the ventral trunk or the inner surface of the thigh, but superficial adipose tissue is thickest over the ventral abdominal wall (paunch) and, in women, on the thorax (breast adipose tissue) and on the proximal segments of the limbs (Figure 12.2 (d)). As in most terrestrial mammals, adipose tissue along the dorsal mid-line anterior to the pelvis is minimal, amounting to a thin, fibrous layer in all but the most obese people (Clarys, Martin and Drinkwater, 1984). There is no evidence that the 'subcutaneous' adipose tissue is selectively spared in starvation: Ashwell *et al.* (1986) found that in obese women on a severely restricted diet the superficial and intra-abdominal depots are depleted at about the same rate. Johnston, Cohen and Beller (1985) concluded that the greatest differences between the arctic and temperate-zone races were in the proportions of the skeleton and musculature, not in the distribution or abundance of adipose tissue. In a carefully planned study, Schaefer (1977) demonstrated that Eskimos pursuing a traditional lifestyle and diet have less subcutaneous adipose tissue than Canadians of European descent. Laboratory studies of young men also showed that heat loss in cold water depends more upon body proportions and muscle development than upon skinfold thickness (Toner, Sanka, Foley and Pandolf, 1986). Humans are fatter at birth than almost all other mammalian neonates (Adolph and Heggeness, 1971) and, because infants are much more sedentary than adults, adipose tissue might be expected to be more important as an insulator. Even so, the ability of neonates to maintain a constant body temperature correlates more closely with their lean body mass than with the thickness of their superficial tissue (Johnston, *et al.*, 1985).

Most of the paintings and figurines from the end of the last glaciation, when the climate was colder than it is now, show humans as 'stick men'. In the minority of artefacts in which body contour is represented, the medial abdominal 'paunch', the breasts, buttocks and the lateral and medial thigh depots are shown as distinct bulges, but the shoulders, arms and lower leg are shown as lean (Figure 12.1). There is no indication of a smooth, continuous layer suitable for insulation or streamlining.

Another explanation for the distribution of adipose tissue is its role in the protection of vital organs (Pond, 1978; Wood and Bladon, 1985). In many harem-forming mammals such as red deer and elephant seals, the males become fatter before the breeding season, and eat little and lose weight during the rut. In certain species some of the additional adipose tissue accumulates on conspicuous sites, making the animal appear more massive. In a few such species, notably elephant seals, such prominent superficial adipose depots also sustain many of the injuries inflicted by rival males (Halliday, 1980). However, such ideas cannot explain known sex- and age-related differences in the distribution of human adipose tissue. Although anthropologists argue about the role of hunting and intra-specific conflict, it is generally accepted that only adult males were involved in most forms of physical combat (Daly and Wilson, 1983). But in almost all living races, superficial 'protective' adipose tissue is thicker and more extensive in women than in men, and in children and the elderly than in young adults. Adipose tissue is not distributed in a way that would protect delicate and vulnerable parts of the body: it is minimal over exposed vital organs such as the head and neck. Those who have bruised the coccyx or sacrum would probably confirm that some protective padding over these areas of the spine would prevent prolonged discomfort, but, as in typical caudate mammals, adipose tissue over the 'tail' is minimal even when it is massive on the adjacent buttocks and thighs. Neither site-specific differences in the collagen content of adipose tissue nor the allometric scaling of collagen content to body mass is consistent with the idea that adipose tissue is adapted to the protection of vital organs (Pond and Mattacks, 1989).

SEX DIFFERENCES IN THE ANATOMY OF HUMAN ADIPOSE TISSUE

Sex differences in the distribution of adipose tissue are among the most familiar and distinctive features of our species, and one of the most difficult to reconcile with the Aquatic Ape Theory. Verhaegen (1985) postulated that male aquatic apes fished while the females gathered plant food. However, such a scenario predicts that males would be more exposed to cold and should therefore have more superficial adipose tissue than females, but the opposite is the case in all living human races.

Many of the supposed contrasts between humans and other mammals in the *distribution* of adipose tissue, and many, but not all, of the sex differences, are a simple and direct consequence of sex or species differences in its *abundance*. Therefore, we have to answer the questions: Why are humans so fat, and when in their evolutionary history did they become so fat? Why are women and children so much fatter than men? Are these properties adaptive? If so, what causal or historical relationship does increased fatness have to other specifically human features, such as reduction of hair, bipedalism, low fecundity, delayed maturity and elaborate social behaviour? What is the significance of sex and individual differences in the shape of certain superficial depots?

Sex differences in the abundance of adipose tissue

In many animals, nutrient stores increase prior to reproduction and are depleted while the energy demands of courtship, pregnancy and incubation or feeding of the young are high. In many mammals there are endocrine mechanisms that prevent conception, or promote spontaneous abortion, if maternal energy stores are insufficient. Some authors, notably Frisch and McArthur (1974) and Frisch (1988), have been impressed by the observation that among American women raised on rich, Western diets, menstruation and ovulation are inhibited when the mass of adipose tissue falls below 15 per cent of the body mass, and have insisted that the phenomenon is adaptive. The hypothesis that a high proportion of adipose tissue is essential to fertility seems attractive enough when only information from modern, Westernised humans is considered, but when viewed in the context of comparative data on fecundity and energetics of reproduction in wild mammals, some serious difficulties emerge.

Adipose tissue of some wild mammals, including that of most non-human primates, is normally present in such small quantities that its contribution to the total energetic cost of reproduction must be small. Furthermore, the extra nutritional requirements for pregnancy and lactation of primates, particularly the large species, are very low compared to other mammals, mainly because primates grow exceptionally slowly both *in utero* and after birth. The energetic cost of human reproduction is very low; among women in The Gambia, West Africa, who are engaged in farming and similar traditional occupations, the energetic cost of reproduction is so low that it is difficult to measure (Prentice and Prentice, 1988), and the correlation between milk production and skinfold thickness is surprisingly weak, even among lean women eating a barely adequate diet (Prentice, Prentice and Whitehead, 1981). As in most other mammals, appetite, intestinal area and digestive efficiency increase in women during late pregnancy and in lactation (Pond, 1977), suggesting that much of the additional requirements of breast-feeding are normally met by increased intake and utilisation of dietary nutrients. There is no evidence that humans, or indeed any other primate, are adapted to suckle their offspring for long periods without feeding, as do polar bears (Ramsay and Stirling, 1988). The lipid content of the milk of most higher primates, including humans, is much lower than that of most other mammals (Ben Shaul, 1962). So, although adipose tissue is present in many women in quantities sufficient to support a baby through the whole of pregnancy and much of the lactation period, there is little direct evidence that it normally does so, even in subsistence economies. Such large quantities of adipose tissue may be critical to successful reproduction only in severe famine.

Frisch's ideas are not consistent with other basic aspects of human ecology: the tropical or warm temperate terrestrial habitat of early hominids, exploitation of many different food sources, social cooperation in hunting and gathering, migration over long distances, food storage and the lack of seasonal breeding. All these features suggest that, far from being vulnerable to the failure of a single food source, humans and their hominid ancestors had omnivorous, cooperative habits which buffered them against severe, prolonged starvation. Many other large mammals reproduce successfully, and often more prolifically, with much less adipose tissue; it is difficult to see why an omnivorous, non-hibernating species should require so much adipose tissue to produce such relatively small quantities of low-fat milk for so few, slow-growing offspring. When the physiology and ecology of humans are compared to those of other large mammals, the conclusion that the high adipose tissue content of women is an adaptation to the energetic cost of maternity is untenable.

Sex differences in the distribution of adipose tissue

When correlated for differences in body composition, stature and skeletal proportions, sex differences in the distribution of human adipose tissue are relatively minor and are most marked in small depots, particularly those on the calf, breast, thigh and buttock (Bailey and Katch, 1981), and in younger, lean individuals (Schaefer, 1977). In contrast to most mammals, sex differences in the distribution of adipose tissue in humans are influenced by sex hormones throughout adult life (Krotkiewski *et al.*, 1983). Such features have few parallels in other mammals (Pond, 1987b, 1987c) and have been exhaustively studied and discussed during the last thirty years.

Few issues have been the focus for a wider range of speculation based on so few facts than the evolutionary origin and physiological function of the mammary adipose tissue. Morris (1967) suggested that pectoral swellings promoted frontal intercourse. Morgan (1982) believed that the enlargement of the breast occurred during the aquatic phase of human ancestry as an adaptation to the transport of infants in deep water. Gallup (1982), much influenced by the writings of Frisch and McArthur (1974), concluded that prominent breasts were an indicator of sexual status that became necessary following the elimination of an overt oestrus phase. Cant (1981) was also persuaded by the critical energy store hypothesis, and suggested that both the breast and the buttock adipose depots were indications of the woman's nutritional status and hence of her fecundity and competence as a mother.

The facts of the matter are as follows. In most mammals, the mammary glands are associated with the adipose tissue in the groin and/or the posterior abdominal wall, and the mother nurses while standing or lying down. In all higher primates the single pair of nipples is pectoral, and nursing takes place while the mother is sitting or carrying the infant under her belly. Mammary adipose tissue forms from the posterior and medial part of the bilaterally symmetrical depot on the thorax, that is present, albeit in much smaller quantities, in other mammals (see Figure 12.2). In spite of the importance attributed to them, the breasts are normally a relatively small depot, typically about 0.5 l (Campaigne *et al.*,

1979), which is about 4 per cent of the total adipose tissue in young women. Rebuffé-Scrive (1987) expressed surprise that, in lactating women, lipids seem to be more readily mobilised from the 'femoral' (groin) depots than from the adipose tissue in the breast itself. However, this situation is to be expected from the comparative anatomy.

The reduction of body hair makes the enlargement of the breast before and during lactation much more conspicuous than in furred mammals. In most mammals, the mammary glands do not mature until towards the end of pregnancy. But in girls, growth of the mammary adipose tissue is among the earliest major anatomical changes in puberty, preceding the menarche by about two years. The breasts may be almost full-size before fertility and adult sexual and maternal behaviour have developed. From early childhood, girls are fatter than boys on a similar diet, and adolescence begins earlier and is completed sooner in fatter, taller girls (Marshall and Tanner, 1986). Regression of mammary adipose tissue occurs sometime after fertility has declined, and is not necessarily accompanied by a change in total body composition (Lanska *et al.*, 1985). Breast adipose tissue has no special physiological relations with the mammary gland (Rebuffé-Scrive, 1987), and it does not necessarily enlarge disproportionately with parity (Lanska *et al.*, 1985). These facts suggest that mammary adipose tissue in women and girls is not solely, or even primarily, related to its role in the energetics of lactation. It simulates and exaggerates the form of the lactating breast, generating the appearance of fertility in girls long before they are actually capable of successful reproduction.

Expansion of muscle and adipose tissue on the hip and thigh begins early in adolescence, but maximum growth of the pelvic skeleton occurs after that of the long bones, and the birth canal does not reach adult dimensions until up to five years after the menarche (Moerman, 1982). Thus, in spite of its importance to successful reproduction, the maturation of the pelvic skeleton is not complete until long after the development of the conspicuous secondary sexual characters. In women, femoral and buttock adipose tissue has properties that may enable it to be mobilised selectively in lactation (Rebuffé-Scrive, 1987), but the process has never been demonstrated in other mammals. Far from being an accurate indicator of total body composition, the thickness of buttock adipose tissue correlates very weakly with that of other depots (Harrison, 1985).

EXPLANATIONS: SEXUAL SELECTION AND LIFE HISTORY STRATEGY

Many observers, starting with Darwin (1871), have tried to explain differences in human behaviour and appearance as having arisen under sexual selection. Sexual selection normally involves competition between males for females, and/or active choice of one sex, normally the male, by the other. In species in which the first process predominates, reproductive males are normally much larger than the females, are physically stronger, grow more rapidly and have shorter life spans. They may also have characters that enhance their apparent size, and possess horns or other adaptations to fighting. When the latter mechanism operates, the choosing sex is drab and undertakes most of the parental care; the 'selected' sex contributes much less to raising the offspring, and has conspicuous secondary sexual characters and elaborate courtship behaviour, both of which appear at the time of sexual maturity. Secondary sexual characters usually originate as indicators of physiological state, particularly in species in which the rate of reproduction is low and parental investment is high, but they may be augmented and elaborated by sexual selection to the extent that mortality from both predation and physiological malfunction is increased (Halliday, 1987). Sexual selection, particularly male/male competition for females, occurs in several different families of primates, and may account for sexual dimorphism in body size and some features of the skin and hair of the adult males. Some of the best studied examples are plains-living species such as hamadryas baboons, in which females remain in their natal troop throughout life, while males leave before sexual maturity and later compete to 'take over' harems of females (Dunbar, 1984).

Compared to other species, humans show few features of typical sexual selection: the sexes are only slightly (about 8 per cent) dimorphic for stature and body mass. Sexual dimorphism is less pronounced in *Homo sapiens* than in pre-Pleistocene hominids (Krantz, 1982), and the modern characters seem to have arisen from the females evolving towards smaller body size rather than the males becoming larger (Willner and Martin, 1985). Some of the male secondary sexual characters, including facial and body hair, deep voice and maximum physical strength, are not fully developed until long after boys achieve adult levels of fertility (Marshall and Tanner, 1986), and such characters vary considerably between individuals and their form changes with age.

In its typical form, sexual selection acts mainly on males, and so produces greater divergence from the ancestral condition in males than in females. However, the limited information available shows that it is the anatomy of adipose tissue in men and elderly women that most closely resembles that of other primates, and the distribution of adipose tissue in young women that seems to have changed most from the ancestral condition (Pond and Mattacks, 1987b). What features of human reproductive strategy could have promoted the evolution of such specialisations in young females only?

Adipose tissue in women

Low fecundity, prolonged infant dependency and extensive parental care would promote selection for maximal physiological and social fitness for reproduction. In rhesus monkeys (Vessey and Meikle, 1987), gelada baboons (Dunbar, 1984) and probably other social primates including hominids, a female's social rank and reproductive success are closely correlated; the offspring of low-ranking rhesus females have higher mortality and occupy lower status as young adults than those born to high-ranking mothers. Rank is determined by the female's relationship to the dominant male and by her interactions with other females. In an *ad-lib*-fed, captive troop of rhesus monkeys, rank was found to be correlated with fatness (Small, 1981). Social systems like that of the gelada baboon are typical of many higher primates, but some arboreal monkeys (Moore, 1984), humans, gorillas and chimpanzees (Daly and Wilson, 1983) are atypical in that young adult females migrate between groups more than males of the same age. In such circumstances, the females must establish their eligibility to join another group, as well as maintain or advance their position in the dominance hierarchies.

Bipedalism was among the earliest and most significant developments in hominid evolution, preceding and probably promoting important changes in diet and habits that led to the intellectual capabilities and the social organisation of modern humans (Lovejoy, 1981). Once started, the rate of enlargement of the cranial capacity of hominids was exceptionally rapid. Although most of the fossil data come from adult and sub-adult remains, it is likely that dimensions of the neonatal head also increased rapidly in evolutionary time. These evolutionary changes would promote selection for females in which the shape of the pelvis permitted successful parturition, which, together with the upright posture, have promoted much more extensive sexual dimorphism of the pelvis and femur than in other primates (Schultz, 1949). Until about 3 million years ago, sexual dimorphism in hominids was most striking in the dentition, but between 1.5 and 0.1 million years ago, pelvic dimensions and stature became the most divergent features (Krantz, 1982). Sex differences in the development of the buttock and femoral adipose depots exaggerate the contrasts in the shape of the adult pelvis and femur, and hair reduction makes the body contours much more conspicuous. These depots, together with the breast adipose tissue and the minimisation of intra-abdominal and superficial 'paunch' depots (Pond and Mattacks, 1987b), generate the 'hour-glass figure' by which young women are easily recognised at a distance (by all other members of the species). Such a body conformation correlates with *skeletal* features that facilitate reproduction, not with energy storage or other *metabolic* adaptations to fecundity. Steatopygia, greatly enlarged legs and sex differences involving adipose tissue are characteristic of negroes, among whom sexual dimorphism in stature and in features of the skin and hair are minimal (Shattock, 1909; Daly and Wilson, 1983).

Halliday (1980) also stressed the lack of correlation between the appearance of female secondary sexual characters and fertility, and concluded that the unusual mating habits of humans had evolved as an adaptation to minimising male rivalry and the maintenance of long-term pair bonds. These concepts can be extended to suggest that the enlarged breasts and prominent buttocks assert the female's adult status, her capacity to give birth successfully to infants with enlarged cranial capacity and hence her eligibility to enter another troop regardless of her fertility. The appearance of sexual maturity may enable a girl to join another group at a younger age, and perhaps also further her opportunities to migrate between groups several times during their reproductive life. Such migration may increase her reproductive fitness by increasing her social and sexual experience, by enabling her to achieve higher dominance rank before giving birth, and by increasing the diversity of the paternity of her offspring. Such a theory also accounts for the observations of Frisch and McArthur (1974) on the relationship between body composition, menarche and the maintenance of normal menstruation in adolescent girls. They found that disturbances or relapses in the development of sexual and maternal behaviour are associated with delayed development or regression of breasts, buttocks and other indicators of adult status as well as with menstruation and fertility. Males normally mate only with adult females, so mature breasts and buttocks may play a role in sexual behaviour, possibly according to the scenario proposed by Morris (1967), but at least the adipose tissue components of these structures should not be equated with the indicators of sexual receptivity in other primates – for instance, skin colour and texture in mandrills and gelada baboons (Dunbar, 1984).

Like other secondary sexual characters that evolve under sexual selection, body conformations that maximise the *social* components of the bearer's reproductive fitness may be irrelevant or even detrimental to his or her physiological well-being. The high degree of fatness of young women may be thus a consequence of selection for a particular body conformation, and may not itself be *physiologically* adaptive. In fact, the converse may be the case: humans, particularly women, may be evolving the ability to maintain metabolic fitness in the presence of so much adipose tissue. Indeed, obesity has fewer detectable deleterious efforts on the health of women of normal body conformation than on that of men (Krotkiewski *et al.*, 1983).

Adipose tissue in men

Obesity is rarer in boys and young men than in girls and women, but is more strongly associated with genetic and endocrinological abnormalities in males (Krotkiewski *et al.*, 1983). As in women of similar body composition, much of the adipose tissue of young males is superficial, but it becomes abundant enough to be conspicuous in only a small minority of exceptionally obese boys. During adolescence, the rate of growth of adipose tissue lags behind that of the skeleton and musculature, so that boys typically become leaner for a period in their teens and accumulate adipose tissue relatively slowly during early manhood (Marshall and Tanner, 1986). In middle-aged and elderly men and in many post-menopausal women, adipose tissue often accumulates in the intra-abdominal depots, particularly the omentum and mesentery, and in the 'paunch' on the outer wall of the abdomen, producing the characteristic 'pot-belly' and spindly limbs (Borkan and Norris, 1977). Thus sex differences in adipose tissue distribution arise in part from differences in the timing of its relative growth and in average body composition.

Large quantities of mesenteric and omental adipose tissue are very rare in wild animals, even when obese (Pond and Ramsay, 1991), and adipose tissue may be almost absent from the mesentery in some species, such as seals, dolphins, hedgehogs and moles (Pond, 1986, 1987c; Pond and Mattacks, 1985a, 1988). In badgers, the mesentery and omentum account for about half of all intra-abdominal adipose tissue, or less than 5 per cent of the total in the fattest specimens (see Figure 12.3). Thus, although the 'pot-belly' figure is very widespread among older people of both sexes, comparable body conformations are not found in wild populations. However, these depots enlarge disproportionately in some macaque monkeys (Pond and Mattacks, 1987b) and older guinea-pigs (Pond *et al.*, 1986) that have been confined in small cages and fed on an *ad-lib* diet all their lives. Characters that appear only in the elderly are not subject to natural selection in the same way as those that develop before or during reproduction and parenthood. Disproportionate accumulation of adipose tissue in the mesentery and omentum is probably not adaptive, and indeed may be a symptom or a cause of physiological malfunction (Björntorp, 1987; Bray, 1988).

REFERENCES

Adolph, E.F. and Heggeness, F.W., 1971, Age changes in body weight and fat in fetal and infant mammals. *Growth*, **35**, 55–63.

Ashwell, M., McCall, S.A., Cole, T.J. and Dixon, A.K., 1986, Fat distribution and its metabolic complications: interpretations. In *Human Body Composition and Fat Distribution*, ed. N.G. Norgan (The Hague: Euronut), 227–42.

Bailey, S.M. and Katch, V.L., 1981, The effect of body size on sexual dimorphism in fatness, volume and muscularity. *Human Biology*, **53**, 337–49.

Ben Shaul, D.M., 1962, The composition of the milk of wild animals. *International Zoo Yearbook*, **4**, 333–42.

Björntorp, P., 1987, Adipose tissue distribution and morbidity. *Recent Advances in Obesity Research*, **5**, 60–5.

Borkan, G.A. and Norris, A.H., 1977, Fat redistribution and the changing body dimensions of the adult male. *Human Biology*, **49**, 495–514.

Bouchard, C., 1987, Genetics of body fat, energy expenditure and adipose tissue metabolism. *Recent Advances in Obesity Research*, **5**, 16–25.

Bray, G.A., 1988, Role of fat distribution during growth and its relationship to health. *American Journal of Clinical Nutrition*, **47**, 551–2.

Brown, P.J. and Konner, M., 1987, An anthropological perspective on obesity. *Annals of the New York Academy of Sciences*, **499**, 29–46.

Campaigne, B.N., Katch, V.L., Freedson, P. and Sady, S., 1979, Measurement of breast volume in females: description of a reliable method. *Annals of Human Biology*, **6**, 363–7.

Cant, J.G.H., 1981, Hypothesis for the evolution of human breasts and buttocks. *American Naturalist*, **117**, 199-204.

Clarys, J.P., Martin, A.D. and Drinkwater, D.T., 1984, Gross tissue masses in adult humans: data from 25 dissections. *Human Biology*, **56**, 459–73.

Cunnane, S.C., 1980, The aquatic ape theory reconsidered. *Medical Hypotheses*, **6**, 49-58.

Daly, M. and Wilson, M., 1983, *Sex, Evolution and Behavior* (Boston: Willard Grant Press).

Darwin, C.R., 1871, *The Descent of Man and Selection in Relation to Sex* (London: Murray).

Dunbar, R.I.M., 1984, *Reproductive Decisions: An Economic Analysis of Gelada Baboon Social Strategies* (Princeton, N.J.: Princeton University Press).

Enzi, G., Gasparo, M., Biondetti, P.R., Fiore, D., Semisa, M. and Zurlo, F., 1986, Subcutaneous and visceral fat distribution according to sex, age and overweight, evaluated by computed tomography. *Journal of Clinical Nutrition*, **44**, 739–46.

Frisch, J., Øritsland, N.A. and Krog, J., 1974, Insulation of furs in water. *Comparative Biochemistry and Physiology*, **47A**, 403–10.

Frisch, R.E., 1988, Fatness and fertility. *Scientific American*, **258**, 70–7.

Frisch, R.E. and McArthur, J.W., 1974, Menstrual cycles: fatness as a determinant of minimum weight for height necessary for their maintenance or onset. *Science*, **185**, 949–51.

Gallup, G.G., 1982, Permanent breast enlargement: a sociological analysis. *Journal of Human Evolution*, **11**, 597–601.

Garn, S.M., Sullivan, T.V. and Hawthorne, V.M., 1987, Differential rates of fat change relative to weight change at different body sites. *International Journal of Obesity*, **11**, 519-25.

Halliday, T.R., 1980, *Sexual Strategy* (Oxford: Oxford University Press).

Halliday, T.R., 1987, Physiological constraints on sexual selection. In *Sexual Selection: Testing the Alternatives*, ed. J.W. Bradbury and M.B. Anderson (Chichester, U.K., and New York: J. Wiley & Sons), 247–64.

Hardy, A.C., 1960, Was man more aquatic in the past? *New Scientist*, **7**, 642–5.

Harrison, G.A., 1985, Anthropometric differences and their clinical correlates. *Recent Advances in Obesity Research*, **4**, 144–9.

Hillaby, J., 1962, Harvesting the hippo. *New Scientist*, **291**, 588–90.

Irving, L., Peyton, L.J., Bahn, C.H. and Peterson, R.S., 1962, Regulation of temperature in fur seals. *Physiological Zoology*, **35**, 275–84.

Johnston, F.E., Cohen, S. and Beller, A., 1985, Body composition and temperature regulation in newborns. *Journal of Human Evolution*, **14**, 341–5.

Johnston, F.E., Laughlin, W.S., Harper, A.B. and Ensroth, A.E., 1982, Physical growth of St. Lawrence Island Eskimos: body size, proportion and composition. *American Journal of Physical Anthropology*, **58**, 397–402.

Keiffer, S.A. and Heitzman, E.R., 1979, *An Atlas of Cross-sectional Anatomy: Computed Tomography, Ultrasound Radiography, Gross Anatomy* (New York: Harper & Row).

Kirtland, J. and Gurr, M.I., 1979, Adipose tissue cellularity: a review. 2: The relationship between cellularity and obesity. *International Journal of Obesity*, **3**, 15–55.

Krantz, G.S., 1982, The fossil record of sex. In *Sexual Dimorphism in Homo sapiens*, ed. R.L. Hall (New York: Praeger Scientific Press), 85-105.

Krotkiewski, M., Björntorp, P. Sjöström, L. and Smith, U., 1983, Impact of obesity on metabolism in men and women: importance of regional adipose tissue distribution. *Journal of Clinical Investigation*, **72**, 1150–62.

Lanska, D.J., Lanska, M.J., Hartz, A.J. and Rimm, A.A., 1985, Factors influencing the anatomic location of fat tissue in 52935 women. *International Journal of Obesity*, **9**, 29-38.

Lewis, D.S., Bertrand, H.A., Masoro, E.J., McGill, H.C., Carey, K.D., and McMahon, C.A., 1983, Preweaning nutrition and fat development in baboons. *Journal of Nutrition*, **113**, 2253–9.

Lockyer, C.H., McConnell, L.C. and Waters, T.D., 1985, Body composition in terms of anatomical and biochemical assessment of body fat in north Atlantic fin and sei whales. *Canadian Journal of Zoology*, **63**, 2328–38.

Lohman, T.G., 1981, Skinfold thickness and body density and the relationship to body fatness: a review. *Human Biology*, **53**, 181–225.

Lovejoy, C.O., 1981, The origin of man. *Science*, **211**, 341–50.

Marshall, W.A. and Tanner, J.M., 1986, Puberty. In *Human Growth: a Comprehensive Treatise*, vol. 2, ed. F. Falkner and J.M. Tanner (London and New York: Plenum Press).

Mattacks, C.A. and Pond C.M., 1988, Site-specific and sex differences in the rates of fatty acid/triacylglycerol substrate cycling in adipose tissue and muscle of sedentary and exercised dwarf hamsters (*Phodopus sungorus*). *International Journal of Obesity*, **12**, 493–505.

Mattacks, C.A., Sadler, D. and Pond, C.M., 1987, The effects of exercise on the activities of hexokinase and phosphofructokinase in superficial, intra-abdominal and intermuscular adipose tissue of guinea-pigs. *Comparative Biochemistry and Physiology*, **87B**, 533–42.

Moerman, M.L., 1982, Growth of the birth canal in adolescent girls. *American Journal of Obstetrics and Gynecology*, **143**, 528–32.

Moore, J., 1984, Female transfer in primates. *International Journal of Primatology*, **5**, 537–87.

Morgan, E., 1982, *The Aquatic Ape* (London : Souvenir Press).

Morris, D., 1967, *The Naked Ape* (London: Cape).

Øritsland, N.A., 1970, Temperature regulation of the polar bear (*Thalarctos maritimus*). *Comparative Biochemistry and Physiology*, **37**, 225–33.

Pearl, R.M. and Johnson, D., 1983, The vascular supply to the skin; an anatomical and physiological reappraisal–Part 1. *Annals of Plastic Surgery*, **11**, 99–105.

Pond, C.M., 1977, The significance of lactation in the evolution of mammals. *Evolution*, **31**, 177–99.

Pond, C.M.,1978, Morphological aspects and the ecological and mechanical consequences of fat deposition in wild vertebrates. *Annual Review of Ecology and Systematics*, **9**, 519–70.

Pond, C.M., 1986, The natural history of adipocytes. *Science Progress Oxford*, **70**, 45–71.

Pond, C.M., 1987a, Fat and figures. *New Scientist*, **114**, (4 June), 62–6.

Pond, C.M., 1987b, The great ape debate. *New Scientist*, **116** (12 November), 39–42.

Pond, C.M., 1987c, Some conceptual and comparative aspects of body composition measurements. In *Techniques in the Behavioral and Neural Sciences: vol. 1 Feeding and Drinking*, ed. F.M. Toates and N.E. Rowland (Amsterdam: Elsevier Science), 499–529.

Pond, C.M. and Mattacks, C.A., 1985a, Anatomical organization of mammalian adipose tissue. In *Functional Morphology in Vertebrates*, ed. H.R. Duncker and G. Fleischer (Stuttgart: Springer-Verlag), 485–9.

Pond, C.M. and Mattacks, C.A., 1985b, Body mass and natural diet as determinants of the number and volume of adipocytes in eutherian mammals. *Journal of Morphology*,

185, 183–93.

Pond, C.M. and Mattacks, C.A., 1987a, Comparative aspects of hexokinase and phosphofructokinase activity in intermuscular adipose tissue. *Comparative Biochemistry and Physiology*, **87B**., 543–51.

Pond, C.M. and Mattacks, C.A., 1987b, The anatomy of adipose tissue in captive *Macaca* monkeys and its implications for human biology. *Folia Primatologica*, **48**, 164–85.

Pond, C.M. and Mattacks, C.A., 1988, The distribution, cellular structure and metabolism of adipose tissue in the fin whale *Balaenoptera physalus*. *Canadian Journal of Zoology*, **66**, 534–7.

Pond, C.M. and Mattacks, C.A., 1989, Biochemical correlates of the structural allometry and site–specific properties of mammalian adipose tissue. *Comparative Biochemistry and Physiology*, **92A**, 455–63.

Pond, C.M. and Ramsay, M.A., 1991, Allometry of the distribution of adipose tissue in Carnivora. *Canadian Journal of Zoology* (in press).

Pond, C.M., Sadler, D. and Mattacks, C.A., 1987, Sex differences in the distribution of adipose tissue in the Djungarian hamster, *Phodopus sungorus*. *Nutrition Research*, **7**, 1325–8.

Pond, C.M., Mattacks, C.A., Thompson, M.C. and Sadler, D., 1986, The effect of age, dietary restriction, exercise and maternity on the abundance and volume of adipocytes in twelve adipose depots of adult guinea-pigs. *British Journal of Nutrition*, **56**, 29–48.

Pond, C.M., Mattacks, C.A., Colby, R.H. and Ramsay, M.A., 1991, The anatomy, chemical composition and metabolism of adipose tissue in wild polar bears (*Ursus maritimus*). *Canadian Journal of Zoology* (in press).

Prentice, A.M. and Prentice, A., 1988, Reproduction against the odds. *New Scientist*,**118** (14 April), 42–6.

Prentice, A., Prentice, A.M. and Whitehead, R.G., 1981, Breast-milk concentration of rural African women. 2: Long-term variations within a community. *British Journal of Nutrition*, **45**, 495–503.

Ramsay, M.A. and Stirling, I., 1988, Reproductive biology and ecology of female polar bears (*Ursus maritimus*). *Journal of Zoology, London*, **214**, 601–34.

Rebuffé-Scrive, M., 1987, Regional adipose tissue metabolism in women during and after reproductive life and in men. *Recent Advances in Obesity Research*, **5**, 82–91.

Schaefer, O., 1977, Are Eskimos more or less obese than other Canadians? A comparison of skinfold thickness and ponderal index in Canadian Eskimos. *American Journal of Clinical Nutrition*, **30**, 1623–8.

Schultz, A.H., 1949, Sex differences in the pelves of primates. *American Journal of Physical Anthropology*, **7**, 401–23.

Shattock, S.G., 1909, On normal tumour-like formations of fat in Man and the lower animals. *Proceedings of the Royal Society of Medicine and Pathology*, **2**, 207–70.

Small, M.F., 1981, Body fat, rank and nutritional status in a captive group of rhesus monkeys. *International Journal of Primatology*, **2**, 91-5.

Tanner, J.M. and Whitehouse, R.H., 1975, Revised standards for triceps and subscapular skinfolds in British children. *Archives of Diseases of Childhood*, **50**, 142-5.

Toner, M.M., Sanka, M.N., Foley, M.E. and Pandolf, K.B., 1986, Effects of body mass and morphology on thermal response in water. *Journal of Applied Physiology*, **60**, 521–5.

Verhaegen, M.J.B., 1985, The aquatic ape theory: evidence and a possible scenario. *Medical Hypotheses*, **16**, 17–32.

Vessey, S.H. and Meikle, D.B., 1987, Factors affecting social behaviour and reproductive success of the male rhesus monkey. *International Journal of Primatology*, **8**, 281–92.

Webb, D.R. and Schnabel, R.R., 1983, Functions of fat in hibernators: thermal aspects. *Journal of Thermal Biology*, **8**, 369–74.

Willner, L.A. and Martin, R.D., 1985, Some basic principles of mammalian sexual

dimorphism. In *Human Sexual Dimorphism*, ed. J. Ghesquiere, R.D. Martin and I. Newcombe. *Symposium of the Society for the Study of Human Biology*, **24**, 1–42.
Wood, E.J. and Bladon, P.T., 1985, *The Human Skin* (London: Edward Arnold).

13 Body Hair Reduction and Tract Orientation in Man: Hydrodynamics or Thermoregulatory Aerodynamics?

Peter E. Wheeler

SUMMARY

The alleged hydrodynamic advantages of both the sparsity and the alignment of human body hair are frequently cited in favour of the theory that some early hominids lived in water. This hypothesis can be challenged on thermoregulatory grounds alone. It is extremely unlikely that naked-skinned hominids would be energetically viable as aquatic mammals, because of the large surface area to volume ratio resulting from their relatively small size and elongate body form. Alternatively, both the sparsity and the orientation of human body hair can be satisfactorily explained as thermoregulatory adaptations evolved by a large-brained savannah primate to facilitate essential evaporative cooling. In this context, by opposing the direction of natural convection currents rising up the body of a bipedal hominid, the hair tracts may have maximised airflow over the wetter skin surface during the evolutionary period when body hair was being progressively reduced.

INTRODUCTION

There are two ways in which the covering of body hair on modern man differs from that of all other living primates. The first, and most obvious, of these is that, although follicles are still present, the hair emanating from them is so sparse that over most of the body the underlying skin is exposed directly to the environment. The second difference is in the alignment of these hair tracts. This is most easily seen in the covering of body hair, or lanugo, developed by the human foetus during the sixth month and normally shed before birth. On the lower human trunk the hair tracts do not run in parallel down the body, but are inclined diagonally inwards towards the mid-line on both the back and the abdomen (Figure 13.1). However, the extent of this subtle, although significant, realignment should not be overstated.

Both these features were among the key pieces of evidence cited by Hardy (1960) in proposing his aquatic hypothesis of human evolution. In its present form this hypothesis, which has been expanded and elaborated by various authors (Morgan, 1972, 1982, 1987; LaLumiere, 1981; Morris, 1977; Verhaegen, 1985), suggests that between about 4 and 8 million years ago ancestral hominids became adapted to life in the water, before returning to a terrestrial existence. Although most modern adherents of these ideas appear to believe that this period of our

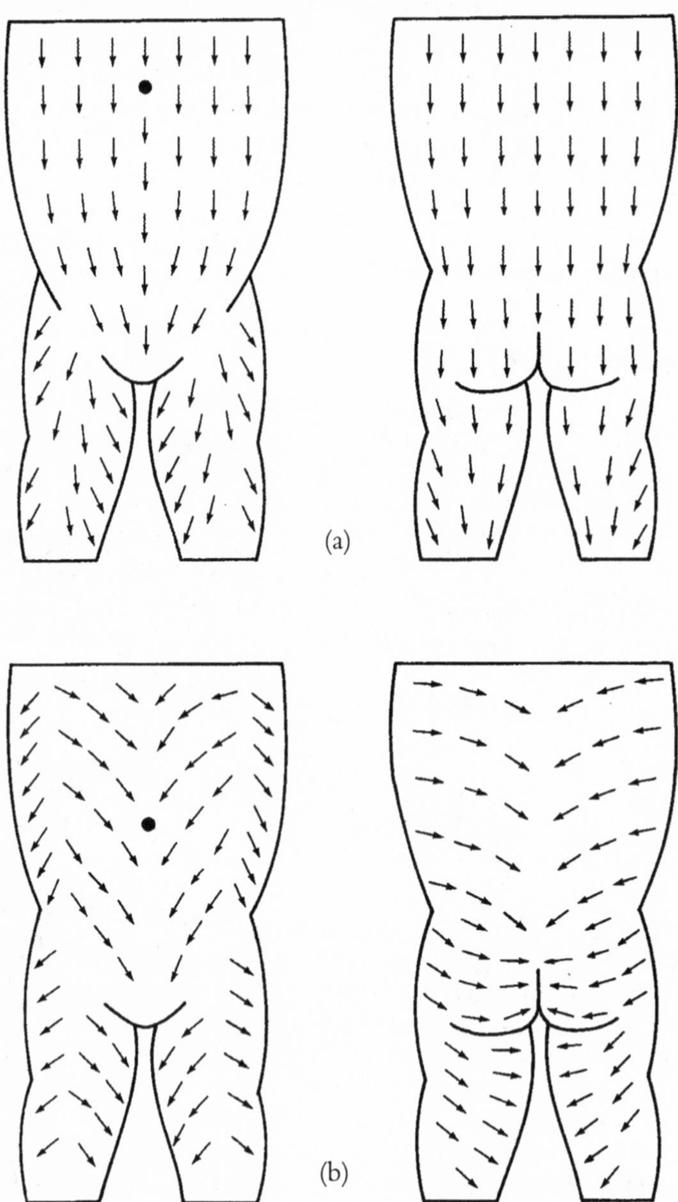

Figure 13.1 Schematic diagrams of the alignment of the major hair tracts on the trunk and limbs of (a) the African apes (*Gorilla gorilla* shown here) and (b) modern man.
The main difference is that on man these tracts converge diagonally towards the mid-line of the body on both its dorsal and ventral surfaces. (See also Hardy, 1960.)

evolutionary history was spent in marine, rather than freshwater, environments, there appears no general agreement on other aspects of the ecology envisaged for these aquatic apes. For example, if they were swimming and diving in open water they would have been subject to selection pressures very different from those which would have prevailed if they simply foraged by wading in relatively shallow water.

Within the context of this aquatic hypothesis, both the reduction and the realignment of body hair are interpreted as hydrodynamic adaptations to reduce the drag of the hominid when moving through the water. The loss of functional body hair would have prevented a static boundary layer of fluid from being trapped next to the skin, thereby allowing a freer movement of water over the body surface. The proposal is that, during the transitional period when this reduction was taking place, streamlining was improved by aligning the remaining tracts to follow the path that this flow of water is claimed to have taken over the body (Hardy, 1960). Such a change would only have been selectively advantageous if relatively fast swimming, with the body in a horizontal position, was important to survival. It would have been of no benefit if the hominids spent their time in shallow water with the trunk held upright. However, despite these potential hydrodynamic advantages, there would have been other physical factors in operation which make it extremely unlikely that the human naked skin could have evolved in water.

THERMOREGULATORY PROBLEMS OF AQUATIC MAMMALS

If an aquatic mammal is to evolve a naked skin, the hydrodynamic benefits must outweigh the costs that may be incurred. For a higher vertebrate the most significant of these is the higher rate of heat transfer from its body to the surrounding fluid, because of the higher thermal conductivity of water. This presents two major thermoregulatory problems to any aquatic mammal. First, its zone of thermal neutrality – that is, the range of environmental temperatures across which it can regulate core temperature just by modulating its conductance – is much narrower in water. This is due to an increase in the lower critical temperature, the temperature below which homeothermy can only be maintained by additional metabolic heat production. Consequently, at all environmental temperatures below this lower critical temperature the energetic costs of life in water will exceed those experienced on land. This difference, which translates directly to a higher food requirement, will continue to increase as environmental temperature falls. Second, since endogenous heat production cannot continue to increase indefinitely, a temperature will be reached below which exposure will result in death from hypothermia. This lethal limit at which summit metabolism is attained will be considerably lower on land than in the water.

Therefore, a mammal immersed in water must either be able to produce more heat than its terrestrial counterpart, and sustain the additional energetic costs that this involves, or reduce its rate of heat loss. Consequently, a dense coat, together with the insulating boundary layer of fluid that it traps next to the skin, is retained by the majority of aquatic and amphibious mammals. Despite claims to the contrary (Hardy, 1960), these are not just low-temperature species requiring this insulation for the periods they spend out of water. In fact, the only aquatic mammals to have lost most of their body hair are the cetaceans, sirenians, hippopotamuses and a few of the larger pinnipeds (Wheeler, 1985). The reason why the balance of selection pressures is different in these forms, and favours the evolution of a naked skin, is their body mass. Larger animals possess lower thermal conductances (Herreid and Kessel, 1967; Bradley and Deavers, 1980), primarily as a direct consequence of their lower surface area to volume ratios. They are also better able to carry a thick insulating layer of fat or blubber. Although man is better endowed with fat than other primates, its development is extremely limited in comparison with pinnipeds and cetaceans, in which it can comprise up to 50 per cent of total body mass (Kanwisher and Sudnes, 1968; see also Pond, this volume, chapter 12).

Because surface area to volume ratio has such a major influence on the rate of heat loss, all these naked-skinned aquatic mammals display marked specialisations of body shape. Most are extremely fusiform, with a rotund shape and reduced, or even completely lost, external limbs. This adaptation, which minimises the area of skin in contact with the water, has the double advantage of both reducing heat loss and improving the hydrodynamic profile of the animal. However, an associated penalty is that its potential for terrestrial locomotion is usually lost or severely compromised.

Despite this reduction in size, the appendages of aquatic mammals are still a potential major site of heat loss because of their comparatively high surface area. However, excessive heat loss is usually prevented by regional heterothermy (Scholander and Schevill, 1953; Irving, 1973), a thermoregulatory strategy also employed by many terrestrial higher vertebrates in cold climates (Irving, 1966). This entails bringing the warm arterial blood supply entering a limb into close contact with the cool venous blood draining from it within a vascular network, or rete, located at its base. The resulting counter-current exchange greatly reduces the flow of body heat from the well insulated core into the appendage. This allows the temperature of the extremity to be held well below that of the rest of the body, thereby reducing the temperature gradient, and consequently the rate of heat flow, between it and the surrounding water. In the case of species inhabiting cold waters, this may entail the limbs operating below 5°C. To enable them to remain functional at these reduced temperatures, alterations of tissue biochemistry are necessary (Irving, Schmidt-Nielsen and Abrahamson, 1957).

Of particular importance are changes in the membrane composition of the excitable cells of the neuromuscular system, which would otherwise experience cold-block and be unable to conduct action potentials (Chatfield, Lyman and Irving, 1953; Miller and Irving, 1963; Miller and Dehlinger, 1969). Despite these modifications their functioning cannot be considered as completely normalised, since the speeds of impulse transmission and muscle contraction will still be somewhat lower than at more normal temperatures. This is not usually too much of a problem, as the appendages of marine mammals are generally rather simple structures used for propulsion and for maintaining directional stability. The considerably more complex human limbs lack vascular retes at their bases, although some limited counter-current heat exchange can take place between the large blood vessels within the arm (Bazett, 1968). Together with a general vasoconstriction of the extremities, this allows the distal portion of the limb to fall to 20–25°C during exposure to low environmental temperatures. Although this has the advantage of conserving energy (Keatinge, 1969), it results in a progressive impairment of the normal manipulative ability and sensitivity of the fingers as their temperature drops below that of the core. Some cold-adapted racial groups are able to retain considerable dexterity of the hand during cold-exposure (Eagan, 1966; Steegman, 1975), a response which can be enhanced by previous thermal acclimation (LeBlanc, 1975). However, this is achieved by restoring the hand's warm arterial blood supply to keep its temperature above that of the surrounding water. Therefore, during immersion the circulation can either reduce heat loss from the hand or maintain its manipulative abilities, but not both. This argues strongly against the suggestion (Hardy, 1960) that the dextrous and sensitive human hand evolved as an aquatic adaptation for foraging on the seabed.

Even when regional heterothermy is utilised in conjunction with such morphological adaptations as large size, fusiform body shape and thick subcutaneous insulation, it appears that marine mammals still require additional physiological specialisations to cope with the energetic demands of life in the water. The few available data show that pinnipeds and cetaceans possess resting metabolic levels at least twice those characteristic of other eutherian mammals (Kanwisher and Sudnes, 1968; Mount, 1979). In contrast, the more sluggish sirenians have a relatively low metabolic rate associated with a labile core temperature, which is allowed to fall as water temperature drops below about 22°C (Macdonald, 1984). There is no evidence that the early hominids pursued either strategy, as both the metabolism and core temperature of man are typical of other terrestrial eutherians. However, some cold-adapted racial groups do allow their body temperatures to fall slightly, by about 2°C, during periods of cold stress (Hong, 1963; Hammel, 1964).

THE ENERGETICS OF HOMINIDS IN WATER

In view of this conspicuous lack of the specialised thermoregulatory adaptations possessed by aquatic mammals, it is not surprising that death from hypothermia is an all too frequent consequence of prolonged immersion in water (Keatinge, 1969). The energetic reasons for this unfortunate outcome can be clearly seen in Figure 13.2 (a). This shows representative values for the effect of environmental temperature on resting metabolic rate for an adult weighing approximately 70 kg (although there is considerable individual variation). It should be noted that the depicted relationship has been somewhat simplified, as there is no abrupt transition from conductance-modulated to heat-production-modulated thermoregulation in man (Hardy, Stolwijk and Gagge, 1971), making it difficult to define the lower critical temperature (TLC) with precision. In air, heat production starts to increase at air temperatures lower than about 25°C (Mount, 1979). Since sustainable thermoregulatory metabolism in man is approximately three times basal metabolic rate (BMR) (Swift, 1932), prolonged exposure to temperatures down to about 2°C can be tolerated (Burton and Edholm, 1969). Immersion in water results in an approximate threefold increase in thermal conductance, which raises the TLC to around 33°C (Burton and Bazett, 1936). Assuming that thermogenic capacity in the water is the same as on land, this means that summit metabolism will be attained in water as warm as 25°C. Below this temperature, heat loss will exceed production and there will be a decline in core temperature, resulting in death from cardiac arrest when it reaches about 25°C (Burton and Edholm, 1969). It is generally accepted that most unclothed individuals cannot tolerate long-term exposure to water below about 20°C, although the heat produced by strenuous muscular activity will allow survival for limited periods at even lower temperatures (Keatinge, 1969). When considering human potential as an aquatic mammal, it must be remembered that survival at these water temperatures should not be equated with ecological viability. The situations discussed above all assume that sufficient energy reserves are continually available to fuel the necessary high levels of thermogenesis, and therefore that food supply is never a limiting factor. This is extremely unlikely to be the case, and although it may be theoretically possible to survive in water at 20–25°C,

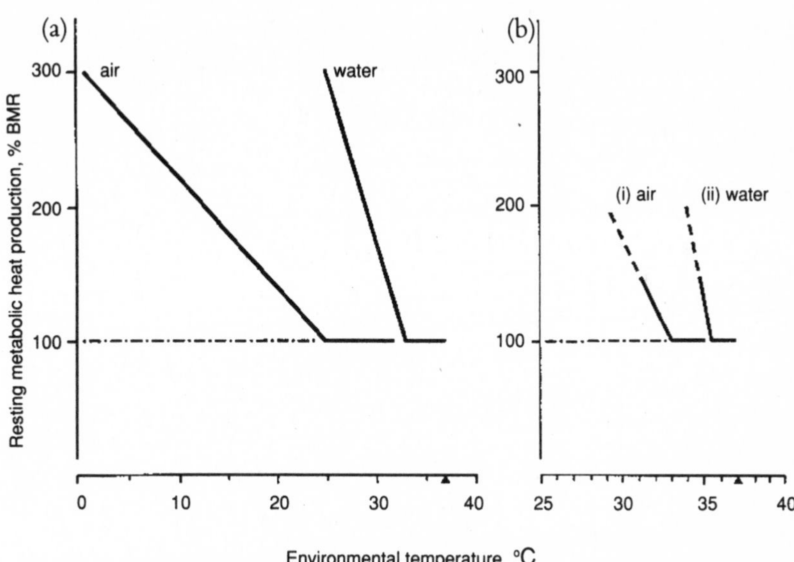

Figure 13.2 The relationship between the resting metabolic heat production (expressed as a percentage of BMR) required to maintain homeothermy and environmental temperature in air and water.

(a) In a nude adult human subject weighing approximately 70 kg. The depicted lower critical temperatures (T_{LC}) of 25 and 33°C, in air and water respectively, are typical literature values (Burton and Bazett, 1936; Mount, 1979), although the actual temperatures reported do vary, between both studies and individual subjects. If environmental temperature falls below that at which maximum metabolic heat production, approximately three times BMR in adult humans, is attained, then core temperature will fall, eventually resulting in death from hypothermia.
(b) (i) In babies weighing approximately 3 kg in air (Hey and O'Connell, 1970). At this age maximum resting heat production (solid line) is only about 1.5 times BMR, although during activity this can increase to almost twice BMR (broken line).
(ii) The predicted relationship for an infant of similar size immersed in water. This was calculated by assuming that the relation between the thermal conductances of the body surounded by air and water, which will be largely determined by the physical characteristics of these fluids, is the same as that observed in adults (Figure 13.2 (a)).

the hominid's energy budget will find it increasingly difficult to cope with the additional demands placed upon it as temperature falls below 33°C.

As previously stated, there are significant individual differences in the rate of heat loss during immersion, and in general those endowed with thicker deposits of subcutaneous fat display the greatest tolerances (Pugh and Edholm, 1955; Keatinge, 1960; Irving, 1973). It could be argued that any hypothetical aquatic ancestor may have possessed more insulating fat than modern humans. However, set against any advantage gained in this way will have been the problem of his higher surface area to volume ratio, resulting from a smaller body size. The earliest known hominids appear to have been not much larger than the chimpanzee *Pan troglodytes* (Johanson and White, 1979), probably weighing about 35 kg. The recent discovery of a partial postcranial skeleton of *Homo habilis* (Johanson *et al.*, 1987) indicates that human body mass has increased significantly, to its present adult mean of about 60 kg, only during the last 1.8 million years. It is also extremely unlikely that any appreciable reduction in thermal conductance was achieved by the evolution of a more rotund body shape. The fossil record clearly indicates that the Australopithecines, and even the earliest recognised member of the genus *Homo* (Johanson *et al.*), retained long-limbed proportions similar to the anthropoid apes. Although the hind limbs of these forms are somewhat shorter than modern man's, this potential advantage is offset by their relatively longer arms. Consequently, the relative distance between the hand and core was even greater than in *Homo sapiens*, which would have made the maintenance of normal manipulative functioning of the fingers in water even more difficult.

So far only the effect of immersion on adult hominids has been considered. The problem of survival in water will be even greater for the smaller juveniles, and in particular for new-born babies. The adherents of the Aquatic Ape Theory clearly believe that some of this early period of life was also spent in the water, suggesting that a new-born baby's extensive subcutaneous fat deposits evolved as an aid to buoyancy (Morgan, 1982, 1987). Even with this fat, the lower critical temperature of a ten-day-old baby, weighing approximately 2.5 kg, is as high as 33°C in air (Hey and O'Connell, 1970), and in water this would increase still further to around 35.5°C (Figure 13.2 (b)). Like most new-born mammals, the thermogenic capacity of human babies is significantly less than that of adults (Hey, 1974; Hill and Rahimtulla, 1965). The summit metabolism of a resting ten-day-old is approximately 1.5 times BMR, and even during periods of muscular activity this only increases to about twice BMR (Hey, 1974). Consequently, such infants would be unable to maintain homeothermy in water as warm as 34°C, only 3°C below their core temperature. Therefore, it is difficult to envisage how babies could have survived in the sea, as even in the tropics there are very few coastal areas where surface temperatures exceed 24°C throughout the year. In contrast, an additional advantage of life on land is that some extra heat can be provided when necessary by the parent holding the infant against the body. It is difficult to see how this could be accomplished in water, without drowning the offspring.

In the extremely unlikely event that the early hominids did evolve the adaptations necessary to prevent excessive heat loss in water, further thermoregulatory problems would still have had to be surmounted. The proponents of the Aquatic Ape Theory generally accept that the later stages of human evolution, which are reasonably well documented in the fossil record, probably took place on the African savannah. In fact they go as far as to suggest that some of the features acquired during the proposed aquatic interlude would have been preadaptive for this next evolutionary step. However, the extremely efficient insulation that the early hominids must have developed would have made this transition very difficult. The low thermal conductances of marine mammals such as pinnipeds and cetaceans make metabolic heat dissipation out of the water difficult, and they readily develop hyperthermia at relatively low air temperatures (Whittow, 1976). Even a relatively small amphibious mammal like the beaver will experience hyperthermia above temperatures as low as 20°C (Steen and Steen, 1965). Because of the fundamental incompatibility between the thermoregulatory adaptations required for life in the water and hot terrestrial environments, it is difficult to imagine a more potentially hostile environment for a hypothetical short-limbed hominid, well endowed with thick subcutaneous fat, to colonise than the savannahs of equatorial Africa. The hippopotamus (*Hippopotamus amphibius*), which does exploit the grasslands in the vicinity of river and lakes throughout much of this region, usually leaves the water only at night, when the lower ambient temperatures and the absence of direct solar radiation greatly reduce the risk of overheating. The sensory specialisations of primates, with their high reliance on vision, would seem to militate heavily against a similar nocturnal foraging strategy.

THE THERMOREGULATORY HYPOTHESIS

Although fluid flow may have caused the selection pressure which shaped the direction of the hair tracts on the human body, this could have happened for reasons other than that of streamlining an aquatic ape. Probably the most widely accepted of the numerous hypotheses which have been proposed to account for the functional naked skin of humans (Morris, 1967) is that it evolved to facilitate the dissipation of excess body heat in an animal inhabiting a warm terrestrial environment. The loss of body hair and of the boundary layer of air trapped by it both reduces the overall thermal conductance and allows large amounts of additional heat to be lost by sweating. In fact, the naked skin together with its associated sweat glands provides humans with the most effective mammalian whole-body cooling system known. This requirement does not necessarily imply that the early hominids had a particularly energetic mode of life, since, as previously discussed (Wheeler, 1984), they would have lacked the ability of other savannah mammals to selectively cool the heat-sensitive brain, and would have been therefore unusually sensitive to hyperthermia in this very thermally stressing environment.

Proponents of the Aquatic Ape Theory have challenged the idea that the human naked skin can be satisfactorily explained as a thermo-regulatory adaptation. Most of their arguments rely on drawing superficial analogies with other savannah mammals, all of which have retained a covering of body hair. However, these criticisms usually fail to appreciate the full complexity, and interspecific differences, of mammalian thermoregula-tory strategies.

For example, it has been claimed that since a wide variety of mammals sweat, the idea that a naked skin is a prerequisite for this form of cooling is a 'misconception' (Morgan, 1987). However, the possession of active cutaneous sweat glands, which vary markedly in density between species (Robertshaw, 1968; Robertshaw and Taylor, 1969; Mount, 1979), should not necessarily be equated with effective heat dissipation. There are two principal reasons why the presence of dense body hair reduces the efficiency of evaporative cooling. First, it traps a relatively static layer of air next to the body hair, which restricts airflow over the wetted skin surface. Therefore, as sweat evaporates the relative humidity of this boundary layer increases, limiting further fluid loss. Second, some of the secreted fluid evaporates from the fibres of the coat, and consequently it takes most of its latent heat of vaporisation from the surrounding air rather than from the body of the animal. These two factors severely limit the rate at which even copiously sweating mammals can lose heat if they retain dense body hair. For example, ungulates are among the species with the greatest reliance on cutaneous, as opposed to respiratory, evaporative cooling (Mount). These possess an average of 800–1500 sweat glands per cm^2 (Macfarlane, 1968), which compares favourably with human densities of between approximately 2000 per cm^2 on the palms and soles of the feet and 100–200 per cm^2 over most of the rest of the body (Mount). However, at high environmental temperatures the maximum rate of evaporative heat loss from the skin of the cow is only 25 per cent of that from a similar area of human skin under comparable conditions (Bianca, 1965).

Another finding cited as evidence against the thermoregulatory hypothesis (Morgan, 1982, 1987) is that artificial removal of the pelage from a sheep can result in a rise in its temperature when exposed to high levels of direct solar radiation (Parer, 1963; Macfarlane, 1976). This entirely predictable outcome occurs because the layer of air normally trapped by the coat acts as a barrier not only to the loss of metabolic heat but also to the uptake of energy from the environment. However, this observation has little direct relevance to the evolution of the human naked skin, for two main reasons. First, the pattern of evaporative cooling in man is very different from that of sheep. The latter possess relatively fewer and less active cutaneous sweat glands, relying instead mainly on evaporation from the respiratory tract – by panting – to dissipate excess heat at high environmental temperatures (Macfarlane, 1968; Johnson, 1976). Consequently, the shorn animal has to endure a considerably elevated external heat load, while only slightly increasing its potential for evaporative cooling. It is a critical assumption of the thermoregulatory hypothesis that the loss of body hair by hominids occurred only in association with the development of an elaborate sweat-gland system. Second, the sheep, like all savannah mammals other than man, is a quadruped. As previously discussed (Wheeler, 1984), bipedalism was probably the essential preadaptation required to allow the evolution of a naked skin by mammals the size of hominids in environments where they are exposed to high radiant heat loads. The reason is that a quadruped exposes more than twice the surface area to the sun at high elevations, when the intensity of its incident radiation is greatest, than does a similarly proportioned biped. This confers on the biped the double benefit of reducing both its total heat load and the area of its skin presented perpendicularly to the most intense fluxes, where it is at greatest risk of thermal and ultraviolet-B damage. It is even possible that these thermoregulatory advantages were important selection pressures favouring the original adoption by hominids of bipedalism as a mode of terrestrial locomotion. Morgan (1987) has suggested that shade-seeking during the most thermally stressing period of each day would remove the need for such a postural adaptation. Although hominids probably could have survived by adopting such a strategy, those individuals which did would have been at a competitive disadvantage to any not needing to restrict their diurnal activity in this way. As these animals were probably exploiting scattered or clumped food resources (Lovejoy, 1981) this difference would have been particularly significant because, in such species, foraging success is principally determined by the available search time.

In summary, this thermoregulatory hypothesis asserts that the full benefit of cutaneous evaporative cooling can only be realised by a naked-skinned mammal, and that such hair loss will probably be a net advantage only to a species possessing both well developed sweat glands and a bipedal posture. Since no other savannah mammal possessed this unique combination of features, it is only to be expected that they have all retained a shielding covering of body hair.

This thermoregulatory hypothesis not only satisfactorily accounts for the evolution of man's functionally naked skin, but it can also provide a plausible, although somewhat speculative explanation for the pattern of the residual hair tracts. Throughout the transitional period when the coat was being progressively reduced, it will have been advantageous if the remaining hair was orientated to minimise the amount of direct solar radiation reaching the skin, while maximising the air flow over it. Fortunately, there is no conflict between the solutions to these problems. To optimise the interception of incident energy with the minimum amount of hair, this should lie tangentially to the incoming rays. Therefore, the alignment of the hair tracts on humans is ideal to shield the skin from the sun at high elevations, when its fluxes are strongest. However, it should be noted that in this respect the human hair tract pattern offers little, if any, advantage over that of the living anthropoid apes. Although hair tract direction can have little influence on forced convective airflow over the skin because of the continually changing orientation of the body to the prevailing wind, the situation with regard to the air currents produced by natural convection, which predominates at windspeeds below 0.2m per second (Kerslake, 1972), is very different.

This process, in which air warmed by contact with the skin expands and rises, has been studied in modern humans. The flow of this convective boundary layer is laminar as it rises up alongside the lower limbs, but becomes turbulent as its velocity increases over the upper body (Lewis *et al.*, 1969; Clarke and Toy, 1975). Natural convection will be particularly strong in open equatorial environments, since both the body and ground surfaces are being heated by direct solar radiation. These currents can be utilised to promote the evaporation of sweat if the remaining body hair is orientated to encourage them to flow down to the skin surface, rather than deflect them across the surface of the coat. To achieve this it will be advantageous if the hair lies in direct opposition to the path taken by the natural convection currents rising up the body. Model experiments (Figure 13.3 (a)) indicate that the observed pattern of hair tracts on the human body is close to the optimum arrangement. Convergence of the currents flowing up the insides of the legs creates a region of higher pressure in the region of the crutch. As this column of air divides and passes over the lower abdomen and back, it spreads sideways from the mid-line of the body, displacing the relatively lower-pressure air which has risen directly up the outer surfaces of the legs, and runs counter to the hair tracts on the trunk. The orientation of the hair tracts on the shoulders and upper chest and back will have had little thermoregulatory significance, since over these surfaces the rising air currents are more turbulent and become detached from the body.

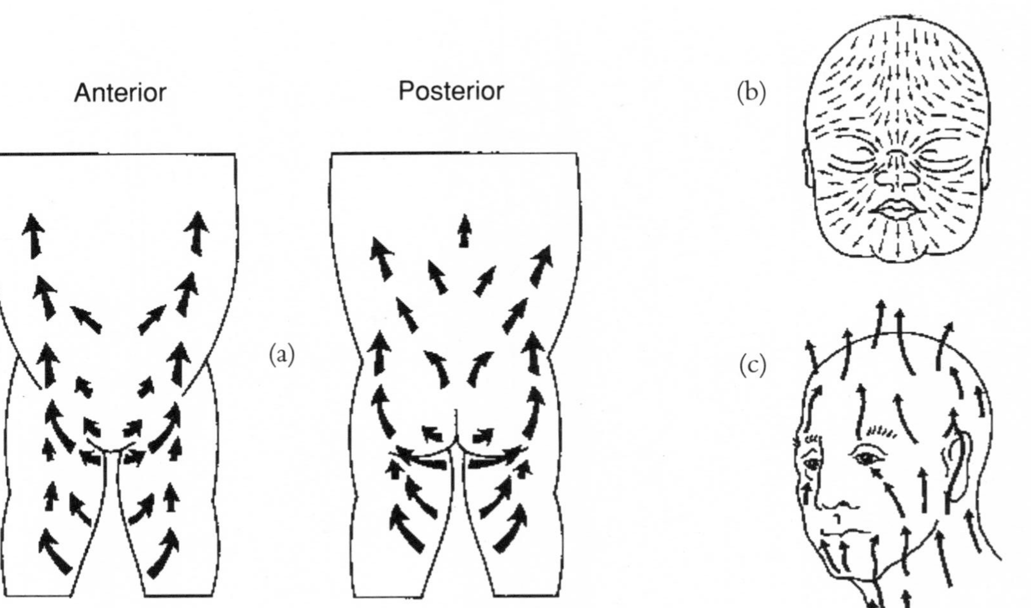

Figure 13.3 Natural convective airflow.

(a) The 1:5 scale model represents a hypothetical bipedal hominid, weighing 35 kg and standing 1.25 m high, proportioned approximately intermediate between reconstructions of *Australopithecus afarensis* and the chimpanzee *Pan troglodytes*. Both the model and the supporting horizontal surface were painted black and radiantly heated from above, using visual and infra-red wavelengths. Small holes in the baseboard allowed the introduction of smoke from below to visualise, and photographically record, the resulting airflow. Although there was a slight amount of wandering, the arrows show the routes usually taken by the rising convection currents.

(b) Hair tracts on the head of a human foetus (after Hardy, 1960). The alignments of those on an adult are similar.

(c) Natural convective airflow over the human head, as visualised by Schlieren photography (after Lewis *et al.*, 1969).

However, there appears to be an extremely good correspondence between the pattern of hair tracts and the natural convection currents, as visualised by Schlieren photography of living subjects (Lewis *et al.*, 1969), over the head (Figure 13.3 (c)).

CONCLUSION

Therefore, an aquatic period in our past is not needed to explain either the sparsity or the arrangement of hair on the human body. In fact, the energetic costs of a naked skin for a mammal of the shape and size of hominids argue strongly against such an aquatic mode of life. If the changes in the orientation of the hair tracts on the lower human body do have any functional significance, then one plausible explanation for them would be in terms of a thermoregulatory adaptation, enhancing cutaneous evaporation in the period before functional hair was completely lost, without the need to invoke any water currents running in the opposite direction. If correct, this interpretation is particularly interesting, because the pattern is clearly that of air currents over a biped rather than a quadruped. This means that body hair must still have been sufficiently dense to exert an effect on the airflow over the skin after the evolution of bipedality, which is consistent with the proposal (Wheeler, 1984, 1985) that an upright posture was an essential preadaptation for the acquisition of a naked skin.

REFERENCES

Bazett, H.C., 1968, The regulation of body temperatures. In *Physiology of Heat Regulation and the Science of Clothing*, ed. L.H. Newburgh (New York: Hafner).

Bianca, W., 1965, Cattle in a hot environment. *Journal of Dairy Research*, **32**, 291–345.

Bradley, S.R. and Deavers, D.R., 1980, A re-examination of the relationship between thermal conductance and body weight in mammals. *Comparative Biochemistry and Physiology*, **65A**, 465–76.

Burton, A.C. and Bazett, H.C., 1936, A study of the average temperature of the tissues, the exchanges of heat and vasomotor response in man by means of a bath calorimeter. *American Journal of Physiology*, **117**, 36.

Burton, A.C. and Edholm, O.G., 1969, *Man in a Cold Environment* (New York and London: Hafner).

Chatfield, P.O., Lyman, C.P. and Irving, L., 1953, Temperature adaptations of nerves in leg of gull. *American Journal of Physiology*, **172**, 639–44.

Clark, R.P. and Toy, N., 1975, Natural convection around the human head. *Journal of Physiology, London*, **244**, 283–93.

Eagan, C.J., 1966, Effects of cold on circulation in fingers of Eskimos and whites. *International Journal of Biometeorology*, **10**, 293–304.

Hammell, H.T., 1964, Terrestrial animals in cold: recent studies of primitive man. In *Adaptation to the Environment*, ed. D.B. Dill (American Physiological Society), 413–34.

Hardy, A., 1960, Was man more aquatic in the past? *New Scientist*, **7**, 642–54.

Hardy, J.D., Stolwijk, J.A.J. and Gagge, A.P., 1971, Man. In *Comparative Physiology of Thermoregulation, vol. II: Mammals*, ed. G.C. Whittow (New York: Academic Press),

328–80.

Herreid, C.F. and Kessel, B., 1967, Thermal conductance in birds and mammals. *Comparative Biochemistry and Physiology*, **21**, 405–14.

Hey, E.N., 1974, Physiological control over body temperature. In *Heat Loss from Animals and Man: Assessment and Control*, ed. J.L. Monteith and L.E. Mount (London: Butterworth), 77–95.

Hey, E.N. and O'Connell, B., 1970, Oxygen consumption and heat balance in the cot-nursed baby. *Archives of Disease in Childhood*, **45**, 335–43.

Hill, J.R. and Rahimtulla, K.A., 1965, Heat balance and the metabolic rate of new-born babies in relation to environmental temperature. *Journal of Physiology, London*, **180**, 239–45.

Hong, S.K., 1963, Comparisons of diving and non-diving women of Korea. *Federation Proceedings*, **22**, 831–3.

Irving, L., 1966, Adaptations to cold. *Scientific American*, **214**, 94–101.

Irving, L., 1973, Aquatic mammals. In *Comparative Physiology of Thermoregulation, vol. III: Special aspects of thermoregulation*, ed. G.C. Whittow (New York: Academic Press), 47–96.

Irving, L., Schmidt-Nielsen, K. and Abrahamson, N.S., 1957, Melting points of animal fat in cold climates. *Physiological Zoology*, **30**, 93–105.

Johanson, D.C. and White, T.D., 1979, A systematic assessment of early African hominids. *Science*, **203**, 321–30.

Johanson, D.C., Masao, F.T., Eck, G.G., White, T.D., Walter, R.C., Kimbel, W.H., Asfaw, B., Manega, P., Ndessokia, P. and Suwa, G., 1987, New partial skeleton of *Homo habilis* from Olduvai Gorge, Tanzania. *Nature*, **327**, 205–9.

Johnson, K.G., 1976, Evaporative temperature regulation in sheep. In *Progress in Animal Biometeorology*, vol. I, part I, ed. H.D. Johnson (Amsterdam: Swets & Zeitlinger), 140–7.

Kanwisher, J. and Sudnes, G., 1968, Physiology of a small cetacean. *Hvalradets Skrifter*, **48**, 45.

Keatinge, W.R., 1960, The effects of subcutaneaous fat and of previous exposure to cold on the body temperature, peripheral blood flow and metabolic rate of men in cold water. *Journal of Physiology, London*, **153**, 166-78.

Keatinge, W.R., 1969, *Survival in Cold Water* (Oxford: Blackwell).

Kerslake, D., 1972, *The Stress of Hot Environments* (Cambridge: Cambridge University Press).

LaLumiere, L.P., 1981, The evolution of human bipedalism. *Philosophical Transactions of the Royal Society of London, Series B*, **292**, 103–7.

LeBlanc, J., 1975, *Man in the Cold* (Springfield, Illinois: Charles C. Thomas).

Lewis, H.E., Foster, A.R., Mullan, B.J., Cox, R.N. and Clark, R.P., 1969, Aerodynamics of the human microenvironment. *Lancet*, **i**, 1273–7.

Lovejoy, C.O., 1981, The origin of man. *Science*, **211**, 341–50.

Macdonald, D. (ed.), 1984, *The Encyclopaedia of Mammals: I* (London: Allen & Unwin).

Macfarlane, W.V., 1968, Adaptation of ruminants to tropics and deserts. In *Adaptation of Domestic Animals*, ed. E.S.E. Hafez (Philadelphia: Lea & Febinger), 164–82.

Macfarlane, W.V., 1976, Adaptation to climatic zones and the ecophysiology of ruminants. In *Progress in Animal Biometeorology*, vol. I, part I, ed. H.D. Johnson (Amsterdam: Swets & Zeitlinger), 425–33.

Miller, L.K. and Dehlinger, P.J., 1969, Neuromuscular function in cold. *Comparative Biochemistry and Physiology*, **28**, 915–21.

Miller, L.K. and Irving, L., 1963, Sensitivity of rat nerve to cold. *American Journal of Physiology*, **204**, 359–62.

Morgan, E., 1972, *The Descent of Woman* (London: Souvenir Press).

Morgan, E., 1982, *The Aquatic Ape* (London: Souvenir Press).

Morgan, E., 1984, The aquatic hypothesis. *New Scientist*, **1405**, 11–13.

Morgan, E., 1987, Lucy's child. *New Scientist*, **1540**, 13–15.

Morris, D., 1967, *The Naked Ape* (London: Cape).

Morris, D., 1977, *Manwatching* (London: Cape).

Mount, L.N., 1979, *Adaptation to Thermal Environment* (London: Edward Arnold).

Parer, J.T., 1963, Wool length and radiant heating effects in sheep. *Journal of Agricultural Science, Cambridge*, **60**, 141–4.

Pugh, L.G.C. and Edholm, O.G., 1955, The physiology of Channel swimmers. *Lancet, ii*, 761–8.

Robertshaw, D., 1968, The pattern and control of sweating in the sheep and the goat. *Journal of Physiology, London*, **198**, 531–9.

Robertshaw, D. and Taylor, C.R., 1969, A comparison of sweat gland activity in eight species of East African bovids. *Journal of Physiology, London*, **203**, 135–43.

Scholander, P.F. and Schevill, W.E., 1953, Counter-current vascular heat exchange in the fins of whales. *Journal of Applied Physiology*, **8**, 279–82.

Steegman, A.T., 1975, Human adaptation to cold. In *Physiological Anthropology*, ed. A. Damon (London: Oxford University Press), 130–66.

Steen, I. and Steen, J.B., 1965, Thermoregulatory importance of the beaver's tail. *Comparative Biochemistry and Physiology*, **15**, 267–70.

Swift, R.W., 1932, The effects of low environmental temperatures upon metabolism. 2: The influence of shivering, subcutaneous fat and skin temperature on heat production. *Journal of Nutrition*, **5**, 227–49.

Verhaegen, M., 1985, The aquatic ape theory: evidence and a possible scenario. *Medical Hypotheses*, **16**, 17–32.

Wheeler, P.E., 1984, The evolution of bipedality and loss of functional body hair in hominids. *Journal of Human Evolution*,**13**, 91–8.

Wheeler, P.E., 1985, The loss of functional body hair in man: the influence of thermal environment, body form and bipedality. *Journal of Human Evolution*, **14**, 23–8.

Whittow, G.C., 1976, Temperature regulation in marine mammals. In *Progress in Animal Biometerorology*, vol. I, part I, ed. H.D. Johnson (Amsterdam: Swets & Zeitlinger), 88–94.

14 Human Respiratory Adaptations for Swimming and Diving

John M. Patrick

SUMMARY

This chapter reviews those features of the human respiratory system that might represent adaptations beneficial for hominids spending appreciable periods of their lives in shallow water. Large static lung volumes provide buoyancy, but the ability to increase mean lung volume by voluntary breathing control (together with the relatively high body fat content) seems much more valuable in this regard. Several reflexes help to keep water out of the airway by causing broncho-constriction or by reducing ventilatory drive, but these are rather weak in *Homo sapiens*. The pattern of breathing utilised for human speech is also the pattern that provides the greatest mean buoyancy and the least chance of inhaling water. The ability to switch to this pattern has required the development of voluntary breathing-control. No conclusive evidence is available to link the respiratory characteristics of modern *Homo* with those that might have provided selective advantages to earlier hominids living in an aquatic habitat. However, the ability to control breathing from the cerebral cortex rather than from the brain stem could be regarded as a respiratory adaptation suiting hominids to life in shallow water.

INTRODUCTION

In the three published reviews of the Aquatic Ape Theory (Hardy, 1960; Morgan, 1982; Verhaegen, 1985), it has been suggested that there are several adaptations in the respiratory system that contribute to the ability of humans to survive in water. These are:

(a) the respiratory and metabolic components of the so-called 'diving reflex' (cf. Scholander, 1966);
(b) the anatomical and physiological features of the nose and nasopharynx (Morgan, 1982; Verhaegen, 1985); and above all:
(c) the ability to switch the control of breathing from an automatic to a voluntary mechanism (cf. Phillipson *et al.*, 1978). Morgan has also drawn a striking evolutionary parallel between this voluntary type of breathing control, which is required for living in water, and the breathing control required for the production of speech.

Although these respiratory adaptations have not been emphasised, they would have been of vital importance for an aquatic ape, because periods of submergence inevitably occur during wading, paddling, floating, swimming or diving; and even the shortest submersion entails a disturbance of normal respiratory function. So these and other possible respiratory adaptations demand specific discussion when the merits of this controversial evolutionary hypothesis are being considered.

We shall not need to concern ourselves here with diving physiology proper, nor consider the acute effects on the human body of the hydrostatic pressure of great depths. At 100 m the total pressure is 11 atmospheres, and the chest is squeezed to 10 per cent of its volume on the surface. Nevertheless, unassisted 'free' or 'skin' dives to this depth have been recorded: the breath can be held for about 5 minutes on submergence during a deep dive; and commercial diving to a depth of 25 m is common in the Yellow Sea off Korea and Japan. However, the evolutionary selection pressures that we need to consider are those promoting the ability to work and play in relatively shallow water, and certainly not far below the surface. So the term 'dive' in this chapter is simply synonymous with 'going under water'.

We can confine our discussion, therefore, to those features of the human respiratory system that (1) provide buoyancy, (2) keep water out of the airway, and (3) allow short periods of submergence. The first two are straightforward: any small variation that tends to keep the airway opening up out of the water or tends to prevent water from entering the airway would seem to offer a selective advantage in an aquatic environment. However, the evolution of the ability to 'dive' demands a compromise between conflicting requirements. On the one hand, safety requires not only a clear physiological signalling to the diver of the developing asphyxia but also a quick recovery on resurfacing. On the other hand, productivity while hunting for food or treasure below the surface depends upon the ability to prolong the dive. The former criterion is met by brisk responses to hypoxia and hypercapnia, and the latter by blunted ones. Arguments for or against adaptation to an aquatic environment that are based on breath-holding ability may therefore be two-edged.

LUNG SIZE AND BUOYANCY

During the evolution of aerial respiration in aquatic vertebrates, the buoyancy provided by the air in the lungs would have been just as important as the facility for gas exchange, because it would have helped to keep the animal on the surface (Wind, 1976). Much more recently, the readaptation of primates to an aqueous environment would again have been facilitated by having a buoyant body mass. Buoyancy would have been advantageous for life in shallow water long before any adaptations that permit 'diving' would have had a chance to prove beneficial. To stay on the surface, the density of the body has to be less than that of the water we float in, and the difference has to be great enough to keep not just the top of the head but the airway opening itself above the surface. The colder and saltier the water is, the more dense it is, and therefore the easier it is for a given object to float. So if ancestral hominids went through an aquatic phase in tropical fresh waters, they would have required considerable buoyancy aids; less so if they were living in tropical seas, but still more than we need now when we bathe in the North Atlantic.

There are no systematic studies of the factors contributing to primate buoyancy (see Wind, 1976), but my impression is that lung volume is a less important contributory factor than body fat. For example, in a warm freshwater swimming-pool, I float head-up with my mouth and nose well above the surface when I hold my breath with my lungs fully inflated. But when my sons do the same, they sink to the bottom. They are as tall and as large-lunged as I am, but they are not so fat; and I only have to exhale about half my vital capacity before my body density rises to unity and my mouth and nose sink irretrievably below the surface. Tenney and Remmers (1963) compared lung sizes among species across a wide range of sizes, and showed that some but not all marine species have a slightly greater lung volume than terrestrial species with the same body mass (Kooyman, 1973). Nevertheless, men have larger lung volumes than women (after allowing for body size), and it is possible that this sex difference may have evolved during an aquatic phase as an adaptive compensation for men's relative deficiency of fat deposits. In addition, the study by Lane and Mitchem (1963) suggested an ethnic factor in buoyancy: 10 per cent of their white subjects, but 70 per cent of their black subjects, sank when they assumed a curled posture in water after a full inspiration. Ghesquiere and Bunkens (this volume, chapter 16), show theoretically that black subjects might be less buoyant than whites. This needs direct confirmation, because there are ethnic differences in lung size at a given stature, with blacks having the smaller lungs (Patrick, 1988).

Dobeln and Holmer (1974) showed that the measured sinking force was proportional to the body weight in water, and was positive even for the lightest of their fifteen white subjects; that is, they all tended to sink and therefore submerge the airway opening. So they had to expend energy in treading water, in order to keep the airway clear of the surface. However, the body's weight in water was reduced by 8.2 N for every extra litre of air inspired, and this made a substantial contribution to the energy saving. The greater the average lung volume (or respiratory mean level) over a period encompassing several breaths, the greater was the saving of energy. So the best strategy for fat and thin persons alike, black and white, male and female, irrespective of the initial lung volume, is to breathe high up in the chest and to have fast then prolonged inspirations (Kooyman, 1973). This can be achieved by voluntary control of breathing, and we shall return to this important topic later.

KEEPING WATER OUT OF THE AIRWAY

Besides buoyancy, a second requirement for survival in an aquatic environment would be the ability to prevent water from splashing or pouring into the airway. For example, the nostrils of seals and other diving mammals are normally closed off, and require muscular action to open them again on emergence from water. The human nasal musculature cannot close the nostrils, and its evolutionary origins could equally well have been the result of selection favouring a range of facial expressions. The oral breathing-route, which can be closed off, is a secondary one which comes into use during and after infancy. To be sure, the soft palate can be lifted to occlude the naso-pharynx and thus prevent the influx of water, but this mechanism is primarily utilised during swallowing, to allow food and liquid from the mouth to cross the airway into the oesophagus, and it has apparently evolved independently of any aquatic phase.

It has been argued by Morgan (1982) that the downward-pointing shape of the human nose might have evolved for the same reason that children hold their noses when jumping head-first into water: to prevent the penetration of water into the sinuses during diving. Certainly it is easier to submerge with the nose pinched off, but an equally plausible terrestrial explanation is that this shape is to direct the circulation of inspired air to the olfactory mucosa, which lies superiorly, to promote the sense of smell; and also to prevent cold, unhumidified and unfiltered air from reaching the openings into the sinuses (Proetz, 1953).

It has also been suggested (Verhaegen, 1985) that an equivalent in humans to the nose-closing of seals is the cyclical or externally triggered nasal obstruction effected by swelling of the nasal mucosa. Verhaegen stated that the nasal resistance oscillates with a period of about 90 seconds, pointing out that this corresponds with the interval between dives in the Ama of Korea and Japan. There are at least two problems with this hypothesis: (1) the period is 2–3 hours rather than 90 seconds, and the total nasal resistance is barely changed by the oscillation, which alternates between the two sides (Principato and Ozenburger, 1970); and (2) the resistance is not raised but lowered by two important consequences of diving: (a) the exercise and (b) the raised carbon dioxide pressures (Dallimore and Eccles, 1977).

Nevertheless, mammals have many reflexes which help to protect the airway as a whole against penetration by droplets, particles or irritant vapours. These reflexes differ widely between species, and have been extensively reviewed by Widdicombe (1986). Broadly speaking, there are receptors on the face, in the nose and the upper airway, on the larynx and in the larger bronchioles, and these are triggered by a variety of stimuli. There is also a variety of responses, but the ones that are relevant here are those tending to close the airway (at the level of the soft palate, the larynx or the bronchioles), and also those tending to reduce or inhibit breathing movements. There have been rather few studies of these reflexes in human subjects, so much of the evidence comes from animal experiments indicating many species differences, some of which are between 'diving' and 'terrestrial' mammals.

These protective reflexes can be triggered in human subjects as well as in many other mammals by the application of water to the area of the face around the mouth and nose, and they are accompanied by a reduction in heart rate and by other cardiovascular and metabolic changes. These together protect the heart and brain from hypoxia, by reducing the rate of oxygen consumption and redistributing the blood-flow away from less vital organs. This combination of responses is termed the 'diving reflex', and has recently been thoroughly reviewed by Elsner and Gooden (1983) and by Daly (1984). These diving responses can be studied relatively simply in the laboratory, without the need for submergence: only the face need be wetted.

We have studied the bronchomotor response to face immersion in ten normal male subjects (Mukhtar and Patrick, 1984), and measured the maximum airflow during a forced expiration at two different lung volumes: this gives an index of the diameter of the small airways. The subjects immersed their faces in cold fresh water at 10°C for 15 seconds, and half of them showed a significant bronchial narrowing. The extent of the broncho-constriction, however, was only about 14 per cent. Similar findings have been reported by Josenhans, Melville and Ulmer (1969), and a slightly greater effect was seen by Keatinge and Nadel (1965) when their subjects took ice-cold showers but kept their faces dry. This sort of reflex would be advantageous to an aquatic hominid; but, again, it would be more so if it were greater in magnitude and if it were triggered by warmer water too. It appears to offer little protection to the respiratory tract now.

If the airway does not close to prevent the entry of water, perhaps respiratory movements might be stopped instead. The reflex apnoea seen in diving mammals when they submerge is remarkable. Daly, Elsner and Angell-James (1977) have studied the harbour seal, anaesthetised but able to breathe through a tracheostomy tube. When a face-mask filled with water at 20°C was applied to the snout, the seal stopped breathing at once and exhibited a profound bradycardia too. Surprisingly, this diving response is not confined to diving mammals, but is also seen in rabbits and in sheep and lambs (Tchobroutsky, Merlet and Rey, 1969). When water touches the larynx of new-born dogs, breathing stops for a while, but as the puppies get older the reflex gradually disappears (Boggs and Bartlett, 1973). Curiously, salt water does not have the same effect. This type of reflex probably occurs in human neonates, who apparently can safely be born under water. It would be advantageous for adult aquatic apes only if it persisted into adulthood, and if sea water were equally effective in triggering it.

We have repeated Daly's harbour seal experiment in conscious young men breathing through a respiratory valve mounted in the bottom of a bowl of water (Mukhtar and Patrick, 1986). When cold water is flooded onto the face of human subjects breathing air or carbon dioxide, either at rest or in exercise, there is at most a small fall in ventilation which comes on slowly with a time course that appears to parallel the change in face temperature. We showed that the response was not due to anxiety, to airway cooling or to brain cooling: it appears to be due to the cooling of the face. Folgering and Olivier (1985) found a somewhat greater effect in resting subjects with cold ice-packs. So here is another possible adaptive response that would be of advantage to an aquatic hominid, but again it is slow in onset, small in extent, and not triggered by immersion in warmer water.

So far the evidence for human respiratory adaptations that would facilitate living in an aquatic habitat appears rather meagre. First, lung volumes do not seem adapted to provide much extra buoyancy. Second, the nose and nasopharynx do not close the airway off to any useful extent, and their shapes are not uniquely designed for protection against water entry. And third, the respiratory diving reflex that is triggered by water on the adult face causes no more than a 15 per cent reduction in airway diameter and a 15 per cent reduction in the respiratory centre's drive to breathe. Furthermore, it is slow in onset and ineffective in warm water. Nevertheless, there remains another mechanism in humans that can both contribute to buoyancy and effectively seal off the airway. This extremely powerful mechanism is the cortical control of breathing.

CORTICAL CONTROL OF BREATHING

For most of the time our breathing is under automatic control from 'low' (that is, brain-stem) centres: this provides a ventilation volume appropriate to the requirements for normal metabolic gas exchange. But there are times when we need to use the chest and lungs to generate truncal pressures for straining and for lifting loads, and for blowing and phonation. For these, the mechanism is switched to a cortical controller, and a variety of motor programmes is available. Patterns of breathing very different from the automatic one are seen, and the switch between the two is extremely rapid (Phillipson *et al.*, 1978). During speech, the inspirations are short and steep and the expirations long and slow in order to provide low airflow rates for phonation. Quite apart from its importance for communication (Morgan, 1982), the ability to produce this 'phonatory breathing pattern' would have two advantages for the aquatic ape: it would permit efficient swimming and it would promote buoyancy.

It is technically difficult to study breathing patterns during natural swimming, because the use of any snorkel-like equipment alters the spontaneous pattern. But the anecdotal evidence is that the pattern which does occur resembles that during phonation on land. Holmer (1972) reports that 'respiration in swimming is influenced by stroke rhythm and water pressure. Rapid inspiration is followed by slower expiration under water'. The respiratory movements have to be entrained or synchronised with the limb movements, because the head and trunk move up and down through the surface with each stroke. Respiratory patterns are not entrained with limb movements during laboratory cycle-ergometer or treadmill exercise in naïve subjects (Kay, Petersen and Vjeby-Christensen, 1975); so the evolution of this mechanism of voluntary control which enables speech to occur is particularly suitable for swimming. Non-automatic respiratory control while swimming can provide buoyancy too. Dobeln and Holmer (1974) showed that by voluntarily adopting a breathing pattern similar to that of phonation on land, the mean lung volume during the respiratory cycle is increased and the average sinking force can be reduced by 10 per cent, thus reducing the metabolic cost of paddling to keep afloat by about 150 ml O_2 per minute. The reflex inspiratory gasp (Keatinge and Nadel, 1965) that occurs when the body is immersed head-out in cold water also contributes to buoyancy.

The second example of cortical respiratory control relevant to swimming and diving is voluntary breath-holding. We all know from our own experience that we can hold our breath for about a minute, and that this period can be extended by holding with a full chest and also by over-ventilating to blow off some carbon dioxide beforehand. Japanese macaques have also been observed holding their breath when preparing to dive. The consequences of the cessation of effective gas exchange ultimately compel the automatic medullary mechanisms to take control again and restart respiratory movements at the breaking-point. For safe diving, it is clearly important that timely warning of the impending breaking-point is sensed, so that the diver can return to the surface and avoid inhaling water. The carbon dioxide drive contributes to this warning, and if carbon dioxide is blown off too vigorously in a pre-dive hyperventilation, the hypoxia that is induced by the underwater exercise during breath-holding may lead to unconsciousness and drowning (Craig and Babcock, 1962).

For prolonged productive diving we might expect to see adaptations that delay the onset of the breaking-point. One possible mechanism would be for the control system to become less sensitive to the asphyxial stimuli, and this is what happens in the seal (Daly, Elsner and Angell-

James, 1977). An aquatic ape might be expected to have possessed a similar respiratory diving reflex. The evidence from human subjects is somewhat conflicting, but it provides no suggestion that respiratory drive during submersion is profoundly reduced like the seal's. We have already seen that the fall in ventilation on human face immersion is small. Mukhtar and Patrick (1986) also measured maximum breath-holding times when the subjects' faces were in air (56 seconds), in cold water (66 seconds), and in warm water (56 seconds): that is, cold face immersion only modestly enhances breath-holding abilities. Hayward *et al.* (1984) have done the experiment differently, pitching their subjects bodily into a pool at different temperatures. By contrast, they found that the maximum submersion times fell from 45 seconds at 35°C to 15 seconds at 0°C. Sudden immersion of the whole body in cold water thus reduces breath-hold times, perhaps because of the reflex inspiratory drive described by Keatinge and Nadel (1965). Overall, the reflex effect of face immersion on ventilatory control is small.

CONCLUSION

My conclusion, therefore, is that the only respiratory adaptation that might be of any importance in promoting human survival in an aquatic environment is our capacity for cortical control of breathing. This enables us to time the respiratory cycle appropriately in relation to our paddling or swimming movements, so that we can keep the face out of water long enough to take an inspiration safely. If we submerge, voluntarily or not, we can hold our breath for a minute or so, and longer if we have first taken a full inspiration. Nevertheless, it is not possible to argue convincingly that this mechanism evolved as an adaptation to an aquatic environment; also, it provides obvious selective advantages in terrestrial environments. It enables us to use the chest to control abdominal and pelvic pressures for straining and lifting, and to control thoracic pressures for the production of speech – and for blowing one's own trumpet.

REFERENCES

Boggs, D.E. and Bartlett, D., 1973, Chemical specificity of a laryngeal apnoeic reflex in puppies. *Journal of Applied Physiology*, **53**, 455–62.

Craig, A.B. and Babcock, S.A., 1962, Alveolar PC02 during breath-holding and exercise. *Journal of Applied Physiology*, **17**, 874–8.

Dallimore, N.S. and Eccles, R., 1977, Changes in human nasal resistance associated with exercise, hyperventilation and rebreathing. *Acta Otolaryngologica*, **84**, 416–21.

Daly, M. de B., 1984, Breath-hold diving: mechanisms of cardiovascular adjustments in the mammal. In *Recent Advances in Physiology*, no. 10, (London: Arnold), 201–45.

Daly, M. de B., Elsner, R. and Angell-James, J. E., 1977, Cardiorespiratory control by carotid chemoreceptors during experimental dives in the seal. *American Journal of*

Physiology, **232**, H508–16.

Dobeln, W. von and Holmer, I., 1974, Body composition, sinking force, and oxygen uptake of man treading water. *Journal of Applied Physiology*, **37**, 55–9.

Elsner, R., Angell-James, J.E. and Daly, M. de B., 1977, Carotid body chemoreceptor reflexes and their interactions in the seal. *American Journal of Physiology*, **232**, H517–25.

Elsner, R. and Gooden, B.A., 1983, *Diving and Asphyxia*. Monographs of the Physiological Society, Cambridge, no. 40.

Folgering, H. and Olivier, O., 1985, The diving response depresses ventilation in man. *Bulletin européen de Physiopathologie Respiratoire*, **21**, 143–7.

Ghesquiere, J. and Bunkens, H., 1991, The burden of locomotion in water: could the aquatic ape have overcome it? (This volume, chapter 16.)

Hardy, A., 1960, Was man more aquatic in the past? *New Scientist*, **7**, 642–5.

Hayward, J.S., Hay, C., Matthews, B.R., Overweel, C.H. and Radford, D.D., 1984, Temperature effect on the human dive response in relation to cold-water near-drowning. *Journal of Applied Physiology*, **56**, 202–6.

Holmer, I., 1972, Oxygen uptake during swimming in man. *Journal of Applied Physiology*, **33**, 502–9.

Josenhans, W.T., Melville, G.N., Ulmer, W.T., 1969, The effect of cold facial stimulation on airway conductance in healthy man. *Canadian Journal of Physiology and Pharmacology*, **47**, 453–7.

Kay, J.D.S., Petersen, E.S. and Vjeby-Christensen, H., 1975, Mean and breath-by-breath pattern of breathing in man during steady-state exercise. *Journal of Physiology*, **251**, 657–69.

Keatinge, W.R. and Nadel, J.A., 1965, Immediate respiratory response to sudden cooling of the skin. *Journal of Applied Physiology*, **20**, 65–9.

Kooyman, G.L., 1973, Respiratory adaptations in marine mammals. *American Zoologist*, **13**, 457–68.

Lane, E.C. and Mitchem, J.C., 1963, Buoyancy as predicted by certain anthropometric measurements. *Research Quarterly*, **35**, 21–8.

Morgan, E., 1982, *The Aquatic Ape* (London: Souvenir Press).

Mukhtar, M.R. and Patrick, J.M., 1984, Bronchoconstriction: a component of the 'diving response' in man. *European Journal of Applied Physiology*, **53**, 155–8.

Mukhtar, M.R. and Patrick, J.M., 1986, Ventilatory drive during face immersion in man. *Journal of Physiology*, **370**, 13–24.

Patrick, J.M., 1988, Ventilatory capacity in tropical populations: constitutional and environmental influences. *Proceedings of the IUBS/SSHB Symposium on Working Capacity in Tropical Populations, 1984*. (Cambridge: Cambridge University Press), 31–50.

Phillipson, E.A., McClean, P.A., Sullivan, C.E. and Zamel, M., 1978, Interaction of metabolic and behavioural respiratory control during hypercapnia and speech. *American Review of Respiratory Disease*, **117**, 903–9.

Principato, J.J., and Ozenburger, J.M., 1970, Cyclical changes in nasal resistance. *Archives of Otolaryngology*, **91**, 71–7.

Proetz, A.W., 1953, *Applied Physiology of the Nose*, 2nd edn. (St Louis: Mosby).

Scholander, P.F., 1966, The master switch of life. *Scientific American*, **209** (6), 92–9.

Tchobroutsky, C., Merlet, C. and Rey, P., 1969, The diving reflex in rabbit, sheep and newborn lamb and its afferent pathway. *Respiration Physiology*, **8**, 108–17.

Tenney, S.M. and Remmers, J.E., 1963, Comparative quantitative morphology of the mammalian lung: diffusing area. *Nature*, **197**, 54–6.

Verhaegen, M.J.B., 1985, The aquatic ape theory: evidence and a possible scenario. *Medical Hypotheses*, **16**, 17–32.

Widdicombe, J., 1986, Reflexes from the upper respiratory tract. In *Handbook of*

Physiology. 3: The Respiratory System. vol II: Control of breathing (The American Physiological Society), 363–94.

Wind, J., 1976, Human drowning: phylogenetic origin. *Journal of Human Evolution*, **5**, 349–63.

15 The Significance of the Human Diving Reflex

Erika Schagatay

SUMMARY

Hardy (1977) and Morgan (1982) have both argued that the existence of a human 'diving reflex' provides strong evidence in favour of the Aquatic Ape Theory, but the reflex has received relatively little attention in the subsequent debate. This chapter describes the cardio-vascular component of this reflex, and discusses its importance in the AAT discussion.

THE DIVING REFLEX IN ANIMALS AND MAN

Diving mammals and birds have developed a series of mechanisms for oxygen conservation which permit prolonged diving. Among the most pronounced adjustments are a redistribution of the circulating blood (by selective vasoconstriction) and a lowering of the pulse rate (bradycardia). This 'diving reflex' leads to oxygen-saving by diverting blood-flow away from organs that can function anaerobically, while maintaining the flow to organs like the heart and brain which are more sensitive to asphyxia (Andersen, 1966), as well as to working muscle groups (Butler and Woakes, 1987). The consequent reduction in the work of the heart results in a further saving of oxygen (Lin, 1982). The response is initiated when the head of a diving mammal is submerged, and when the animal returns to the surface the changes are reversed and the lactic acid – produced by any anaerobic metabolism – is removed. These 'debit and credit' measures enable certain marine mammals, such as the Weddell seal, to withstand submersion for more than one hour (Kooyman *et al.*, 1980).

Humans react in a similar way during breath-hold diving (Gooden, 1972). The reflex is strongest when the whole body is exposed to cold water (Lin, 1984), but it is still clearly operative when only the face is immersed and the breath is held (Furedy *et al.*, 1983). Apnoea alone reduces the heart rate by about half as much as apnoea plus facial cooling (Hurwitz and Furedy, 1986). Cold stimulation of the face without wetting produces a similar bradycardia, indicating that facial cold receptors are involved in triggering the response (Kawakami, Natelson and Dubois, 1967). Probably these cold receptors are most densely distributed on the forehead (Schuitema and Holm, 1988). This would explain the efficacy of the traditional way of treating fever or stress with an ice-bag on the forehead (Bergmark, 1985).

FACTORS INFLUENCING DIVING BRADYCARDIA IN HUMANS

A method often used in laboratory studies of the diving reflex in humans is breath-holding combined with face immersion. The resulting bradycardia is the measure used most often for quantifying the reflex. Many factors influence the magnitude of the bradycardia. Both water and ambient air temperatures are important (Moore *et al.*, 1972). The bradycardia is inversely proportional to water temperature within a range that is determined by the ambient air temperature (Schagatay and Holm, to be published).

Humans, like sea otters, dive after inspiration, but a maximal inspiration counteracts the development of diving bradycardia (Gooden, 1982; Ferrigno *et al.*, 1986). If the intrathoracic pressure gets too high it inhibits the return of venous blood to the heart, and the pulse rate increases to compensate for a smaller stroke volume. Skilled divers like the Ama of Korea and Japan and Indonesian skin-divers are known to dive after less than maximal inspiration (Hong and Rahn, 1967; Schatagay, unpublished observations). An important factor determining the magnitude of bradycardia is the duration of breath-holding, because the reflex has a gradual onset and during the initial 30–40 seconds the bradycardia is proportional to breath-holding time. After about 40 seconds the bradycardia is fully manifested at a level which is usually maintained throughout the dive (Figure 15.1). In many investigations only the first 30 seconds of submersion have been studied. Stress can attenuate or abolish the diving bradycardia (Gooden, 1982). Much of this effect can be avoided if inexperienced subjects perform one or two test dives before the experimental dive. If three to five breath-holds are performed at short intervals, the duration of breath-holding increases because of the so-called short-term training effect (Sterba and Lundgren, 1988). This effect is different from the effect of long-term training, and can be avoided by spacing dives apart with adequate periods of rest.

The individual ability to hold the breath can be improved by training (Hentsch and Ulmer, 1984). The increase in breath-holding time involves learning to make the appropriate preparations for diving – physiologically by slight hyperventilation, and psychologically by resisting the drive to breathe. These factors probably account for some of the differences between a group of trained Indonesian divers and an untrained control group of Swedish students (Figures 15.1 and 15.2). Factors such as the use of adequate lung inflation, stress avoidance and relaxation in the professional divers may also contribute to the differences

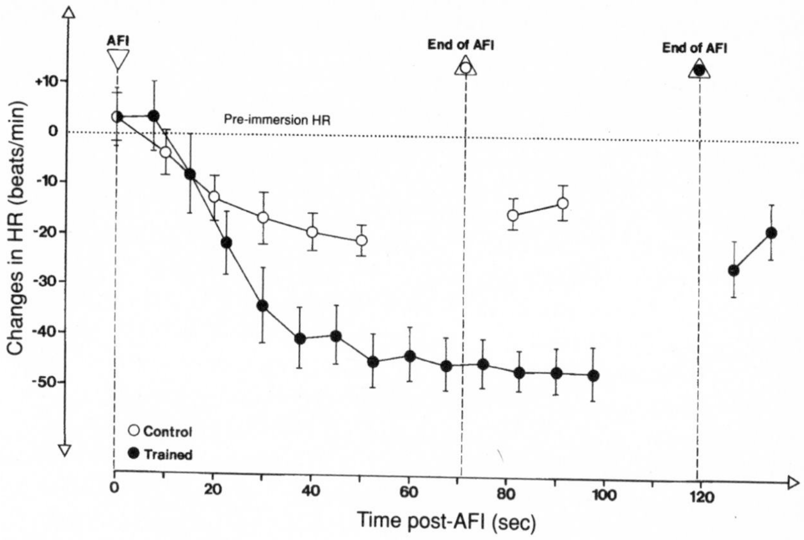

Figure 15.1 Changes in heart rate (HR) from pre-immersion values during apnoeic face immersion (AFI) in untrained Swedish control and trained Indonesian subjects.

The values are means ± SE for n=10 in each group. The arrows indicate onset of and mean end of AFI for the two groups. The tests were performed supine, at rest and in an ambient temperature of 31° ± 1C. Each subject breath-held at spontaneously chosen lung volume for as long as possible while immersing the face in water of 20° ± 1C.

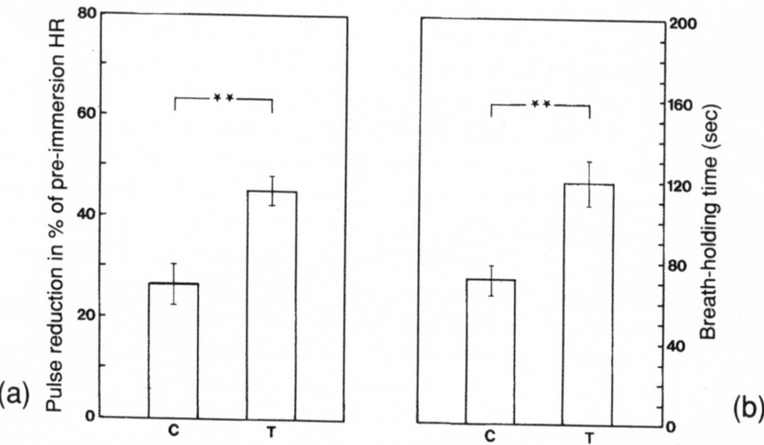

Figure 15.2 Comparison of mean (±SE) pulse reduction (a) and mean (±SE) breath-holding time (b) between untrained Swedish control (C) and trained Indonesian (T) subjects.

The pulse reduction values are obtained from the last 30 seconds of each AFI, and expressed as a percentage of the individual pre-immersion pulses.

both in diving time and bradycardia between the two groups. Other effects of lifelong training may also contribute to the pronounced bradycardia in the Indonesian divers. Ethnic differences between the two groups cannot be ruled out.

COMPARATIVE ASPECTS OF DIVING BRADYCARDIA

When terrestrial, semi-aquatic and aquatic species are compared, bradycardia on immersion correlates with their involvement in diving. The extent of the response in trained humans is intermediate between the response in terrestrial mammals and that found in diving mammals (Strauss, 1970). In deep-diving animals like the Weddell seal the heart rate may fall by up to 90 per cent (Strauss), while in semi-aquatic species like the beaver and musk-rat the bradycardia is 40–60 per cent of the pre-submersion value (Gilbert and Gofton, 1982).

In many early studies of aquatic animals bradycardia was induced by forced submersion, which has later been shown to display extreme responses which may seldom occur in the animals' normal range of activities (Butler and Jones, 1982; Kooyman, 1989). In the harbour seal the reduction in heart rate on forced submersion was 94 per cent of the pre-submersion rate, while on trained face immersion it was about 80 per cent. Studies of free-diving Weddell seals reveal that these animals depress the heart rate between 40 and 80 per cent, depending on the duration and type of diving (Kooyman).

The human diving reflex has been described as similar to the reflex found in marine mammals, but attenuated or modified (Gooden, 1982; Ferrigno *et al.*, 1986). However, the data used in such comparisons have generally been derived from subjects with little or no training in breath-hold diving. The heart rate reduction on face immersion in untrained human subjects generally varies between 10 and 40 per cent (Mathew, 1981), but some untrained subjects may reduce their pulse rate by 70–80 per cent or more (Arnold, 1985). The 45 per cent mean pulse rate reduction in the trained Indonesians (Figure 15.2 (a)) is in accordance with observations in Ama divers (Hong and Rahn, 1967), and is in the range of the responses found in semi-aquatic mammals.

A bradycardia also occurs in species that do not naturally dive (Lin, 1982). Dogs trained to immerse their snouts voluntarily in water exhibited a heart rate reduction of 43 per cent of the pre-immersion value (Lin *et al.*, 1983). These dogs had been selected for their ability to learn breath-holding. Other studies of terrestrial animals have often included either forced submersion or anaesthesia, and this makes comparisons with natural divers difficult. There appear to have been no studies of voluntary breath-holding, face immersion or diving in monkeys or apes. This is possibly because such behaviours are not easily taught, due to the animals' fear of water or because of problems with voluntary control of breathing. A study of anaesthetised infant macacas reveals weak bradycardia when apnoea is induced by electrical nerve stimulation (Sutton, Taylor and Lindeman, 1978). Without data from fully aware, unrestrained primates it is difficult to assess the evolutionary origin of the human diving reflex.

In marine mammals the effect of the diving reflex in making prolonged diving possible seems clear, but in humans there is some doubt as to whether the reflex is efficient enough to cause a reduction in the rate of oxygen consumption (Butler and Woakes, 1987). When bradycardia and breath-holding time are compared between apnoea in air and apnoea with face immersion in untrained and trained divers, we find that in the trained group the increase in bradycardia between dry and wet apnoea corresponds to an increase in breath-holding time (Table 15.1). This suggests that the diving reflex may have an oxygen conservation function in trained divers, while other factors are more important in determining breath-hold duration in untrained subjects. Considering the engagement of the trained divers in working dives with long durations, the benefit of a measure for oxygen conservation is obvious, and dives exceeding two minutes produced with lungs filled to only 70–80 per cent may be difficult to explain without including an effective diving reflex.

Table 15.1 Comparison of bradycardia and breath-holding time between apnoea in air (A) and apnoeic face immersion (AFI) in untrained control and trained divers

time (sec)

	Control		*Trained*	
	A	AFI	A	AFI
Pulse reduction (% of pre-immersion)	10.5 ± 4	26.3 ± 4	25.0 ± 5	45.0 ± 3
Breath-holding	79.0 ± 15	71.0 ± 8	76.0 ± 5	119.3 ± 11

The values are means ± SE for n=10 in each group.

ALTERNATIVE EXPLANATIONS FOR THE PROMINENCE OF THE HUMAN DIVING REFLEX

One suggestion is that the reflex helps the baby to survive the unusually long delivery, but this does not explain the differences between divers and non-divers, the persistence of the reflex into adulthood, or its temperature-dependence. A more favoured explanation is that the reflex has arisen as a protection against accidental drowning. The chances of reviving a drowned person increase if the accident has occurred in cold water. Notwithstanding the temperature-dependence of the diving reflex, this observation can be at least partially explained by the reduction in metabolism that occurs when the body is cooled. This explains why children survive near-drowning better than adults: they are cooled down faster because of their smaller body/surface ratio (Hayward *et al.*, 1984). Even the brain can recover from 30 minutes' oxygen starvation, provided it is cooled down quickly enough.

THE TEMPERATURE-DEPENDENCE OF THE DIVING REFLEX

The temperature-dependence of the diving reflex may at first seem difficult to relate to a tropical diver, especially since the reflex has often been shown to have its maximal effect at about 10°C. The warm surface water of a tropical sea normally has a chilling effect sufficient to cause a moderate diving bradycardia. This is because the stimulation of the cold-receptors is not only dependent on the water temperature, but also on the state of acclimatisation before the immersion to the ambient air temperature. The dependency on ambient air temperature also implies that a maximal diving bradycardia is more easily reached at warmer water temperature in a tropical environment than where the environmental temperature is low. Thus a water temperature of about 20°C may elicit maximal diving bradycardia in a tropical diver.

A temperature-dependent diving reflex may have been of adaptive value during an aquatic phase of hominid evolution. If engaged in shallow diving the diver does not spend much time descending and ascending, and a series of short dives with short surface intervals is productive. When diving deeper, the diver encounters colder water, and the deeper the dive, the more important it is for the reflex to function fully for maximisation of bottom time.

THE 'SEA PEOPLE'

The existence of ethnic groups leading a self-sufficient life dependent on marine food sources obtained largely by diving suggests that modern *Homo* possesses adaptations to diving, swimming and being in water for long periods. Adults in one such group in Indonesia spend a daily average of 6 hours in water, and the children 4–5 hours. The children swim before they can walk, and contribute to the family economy by diving from the age of six. Individuals spend up to 10 hours daily in the water (with a surface temperature higher than 29°C), and with short intervals for bringing the catch home to primitive houseboats or huts on poles close to small islands.

Going into the water during the hottest part of the day serves as a good means of thermoregulation, and may have been one reason for early *Homo* to enter the water.

The diving skills of the Indonesian divers include breath-holding times of up to 4 minutes and diving depths of 30 m or more, although a typical dive seldom exceeds 2 minutes or 15 m (Schagatay, unpublished observations). Whatever the origin of these skills, these groups – who call themselves the 'sea-people' – demonstrate that a semi-aquatic way of life is within the range of present-day human physiological adaptation.

REFERENCES

Andersen, H.T., 1966, Physiological adaptations in diving vertebrates. *Physiological Reviews*, **46**, 212–43.

Arnold, R.W., 1985, Extremes in human breath-hold, facial immersion bradycardia. *Undersea Biomedical Research*, **12**, 183–90.

Bergmark, M., 1985, *Bad och Bot* [Bath and Cure], (Stockholm: Prisma).

Butler, P.J. and Jones, D.R., 1982, The comparative physiology of diving in vertebrates. *Advances in Comparative Physiology and Biochemistry*, **3**, 179–364.

Butler, P.J. and Woakes, A.J., 1987, Heart rate in humans during underwater swimming with and without breath-hold. *Respiration Physiology*, **69**, 387–99.

Ferrigno, M., Hickey, D.D., Liner, M.H. and Lundgren, C.E.G., 1986, Cardiac performance in humans during breath-holding. *Journal of Applied Physiology*, **60**, 1871–7.

Furedy, J.J., Morrison, J.W., Helsgrave, R.J. and Arabian, J.M., 1983, Effects of water temperature on some noninvasively measured components of the human dive reflex: an experimental response-topography analysis. *Psychophysiology*, **20**, 569–78.

Gilbert, F.F. and Gofton, N., 1982, Heart rate values for beaver, mink and muskrat. *Comparative Biochemistry and Physiology*, **73A**, 249–51.

Gooden, B.A., 1972, Drowning and the diving reflex in man. *Medical Journal of Australia*, **2**, 583.

Gooden, B.A., 1982, The diving response in clinical medicine. *Aviation, Space and Environmental Medicine*, **53**, 273–6.

Hardy, A., 1977, Was there a *Homo aquaticus*? *Zenith*, **15**(1), 4–6.

Hayward, J.S., Hay, C., Matthews, B.R., Overweel, C.H. and Radford D.D., 1984, Temperature effect on the human dive response in relation to cold-water near-drowning. *Journal of Applied Physiology*, **56**, 202–6.

Hentsch, U. and Ulmer, H.V., 1984, Trainability of underwater breath-holding time. *International Journal of Sports Medicine*, **5**, 343–7.

Hong, S.K. and Rahn, H., 1967, The diving women of Korea and Japan. *Scientific American*, **216** (5), 34–43.

Hurwitz, B.E. and Furedy, J.J., 1986, The human dive reflex: an experimental, topographical and physiological analysis. *Physiology and Behaviour*, **36**, 287–94.

Kawakami, Y., Natelson, B.H. and Dubois, A.B., 1967, Cardiovascular effects of face immersion and factors affecting the diving reflex in man. *Journal of Applied Physiology*, **23**, 964–70.

Kooyman, G.L., 1989, *Diverse Divers* (Berlin, Heidelberg: Springer-Verlag).

Kooyman, G.L., Wahranbrock, E.A., Castelline, M.A., Davies, R.W. and Sinnett, E.A.,

1980, Aerobic and anaerobic metabolism during voluntary diving in Weddell seals: evidence of preferred pathways from blood chemistry and behaviour. *Journal of Comparative Physiology*, **138**, 335–46.

Lin, Y.C., 1982, Breath-hold diving in terrestrial mammals. *Exercise and Sports Sciences Review*, **10**, 270–307.

Lin, Y.C., 1984, Circulatory functions during immersion and breath-hold dives in humans. *Undersea Biomedical Research*, **11**, 123–38.

Lin, Y.C., Carlson, E.L., McCutcheon, E.P. and Sandler, H., 1983, Cardiovascular functions during voluntary apnoea in dogs. *American Journal of Physiology*, **245**, 143–50.

Mathew, P.K., 1981, Diving reflex, another way of treating paroxysmal supra-ventricular tachycardia: clinical applications of therapeutic advances. *Archives of Internal Medicine*, **141**, 22–3.

Moore, T.O., Lin, Y.C., Lally, D.A. and Hong, S.K., 1972, Effects of temperature, immersion, and ambient pressure on human apneic bradycardia. *Journal of Applied Physiology*, **33** (1) (July), 36–41.

Morgan, E., 1982, *The Aquatic Ape* (London: Souvenir Press).

Schagatay, K.E. and Holm, B., The effects of water- and ambient air temperatures on human diving bradycardia. (To be published.)

Schuitema, K.E. and Holm, B., 1988, The role of different facial areas in eliciting human diving bradycardia. *Acta Physiologica Scandinavica*, **132**, 119–20.

Sterba, J.A. and Lundgren, C.E.G., 1988, Breath-hold duration in man and the diving response induced by face immersion. *Undersea Biomedical Research*, **15** (5), 361–75.

Strauss, M.B., 1970, Physiological aspects of mammalian breath-hold diving: a review. *Aerospace Medicine*, **41**, 1362–81.

Sutton, D., Taylor, E.M. and Lindeman, R.C., 1978, Prolonged apnea in infant monkeys resulting from stimulation of superior laryngeal nerve. *Pediatrics*, **61** (4), 519–27.

16 The Burden of Locomotion in Water: Could the Aquatic Ape Have Overcome It?

Joseph Ghesquiere and Helene Bunkens

SUMMARY

Special adaptations for buoyancy, locomotion, and thermoregulation are typical of any aquatic mammal. A hypothetical aquatic human ancestor must have lost such qualities in later stages of our phylogeny for present-day humans are poor survivors in water. Protagonists of the Aquatic Ape Theory assume the cradle of mankind to have been located in a warm climate on an African coast. The humans least subjected to ecological pressures, and hence most resembling those ancestors, would be those living nowadays in that area: black Africans. However, though their exercise capacity appears to equal that of other humans, their swimming performance is relatively poor. Their buoyancy is less, they are less streamlined and their thin subcutaneous adipose layer is less suitable for insulating the body. Of all the diverse present-day humans, black Africans seem the least well suited for an aquatic way of life.

INTRODUCTION

Among the factors on which survival in water depends, buoyancy and locomotion are undoubtedly of great importance, as would be thermoregulation in a colder environment.

All aquatic mammals have to emerge from the water to breathe. So buoyancy is one feature that would be advantageous to an ape adapting itself to an aqueous environment. Of all terrestrial mammals, humans are among the poorest survivors in water. If man did indeed descend from an aquatic ape, one must assume that at some later stage of human phylogeny our ancestors lost the ability, present in most animals, to survive longer in water than the average human does (Wind, 1976, and chapter 17 of this volume).

It is generally accepted that the cradle of mankind must have been situated in a warm, if not hot, climate: according to protagonists of the Aquatic Ape Theory, this would have been on the East African coast (Ellis, 1987; LaLumiere, this volume, chapter 3). Evolutionary pressure for change should have been stronger the farther our ancestors moved from this cradle. Of all the diverse humans running around on the earth's surface, which one resembles most the shape and body composition of an aquatic animal? Indeed, if the Aquatic Ape Theory is correct, the answer

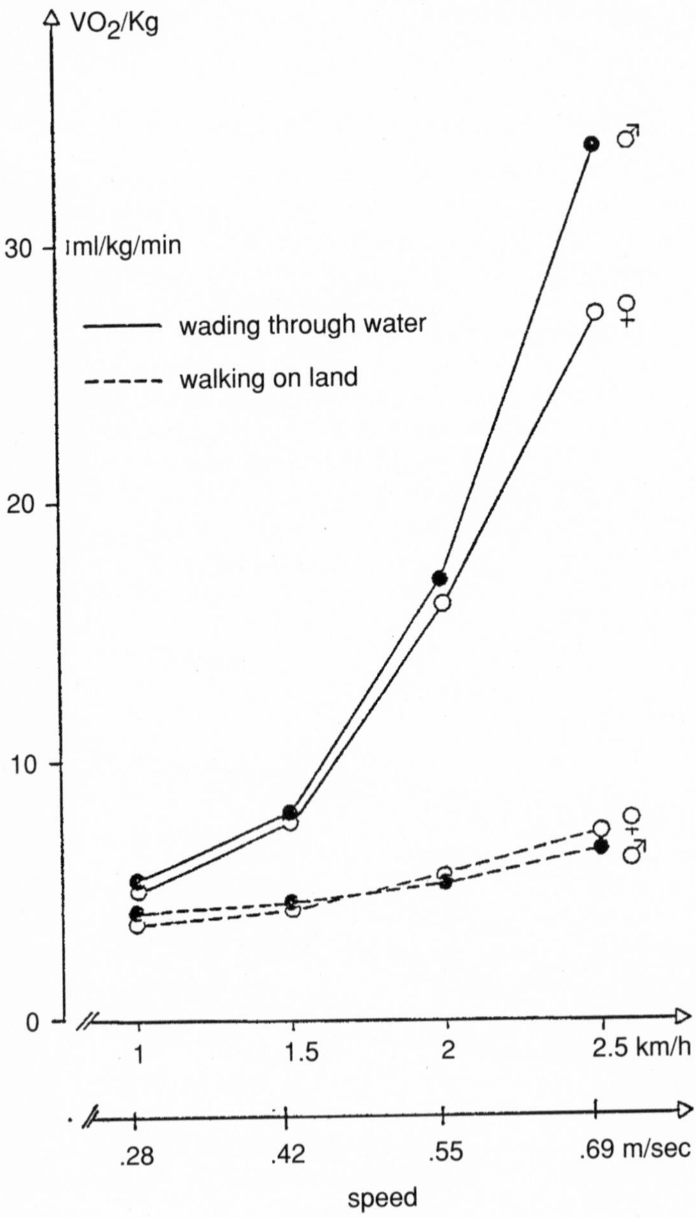

Figure 16.1 Net oxygen uptake in ml per kg body weight at speeds 1 to 2.5 km per hour in 6 women and 6 men (19 to 22 years old) on dry land and wading through water up to their armpits.

should be the humans living around the area where mankind originated, and where the selection pressure for evolutionary change was least. This leads straight to the black African.

WADING IN WATER

A successful hunter–gatherer has to move about to catch his prey. So locomotion is indeed very important. Aquatic mammals move mainly horizontally through the water. This is obviously the most economic solution, since wading in an upright position requires extremely thin legs to overcome the water resistance, as storks and kiwis demonstrate. Walking on sturdy legs in water will provoke such strong turbulence and drag that the energy requirements of displacement in the upright position, at even slightly increased speed, will become prohibitive.

Figure 16.1 shows the difference in net oxygen uptake in humans (six men and six women, about twenty years old) between walking on dry land and wading through water (submerged to the armpits) at speeds of 1 to 2.5 km per hour (unpublished data from our laboratory). It is obvious that wading through water can only be maintained at affordable levels of energy expenditure at a very low speed, at least for present-day man. Figure 16.2 shows that, at speeds of 0.8 m per second or more, wading through water becomes by far the most expensive mode of locomotion.

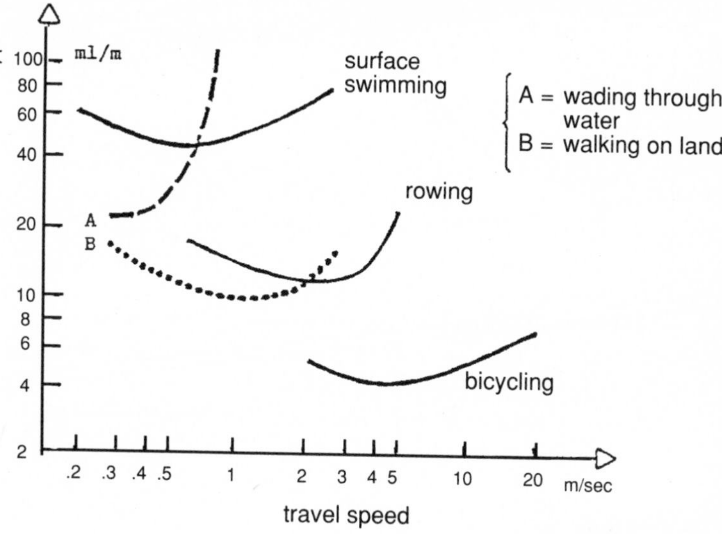

Figure 16.2 Oxygen consumption per unit travel range versus speed for various on-land and in-water activities (adapted from Baz, 1979; curves A and B are based on own data).

SWIMMING

We therefore can safely say that the vertical wading position was not the usual means of locomotion in the aquatic ape, and that it is more likely to have been horizontal locomotion by swimming. Obviously, the energy-yielding capability of the individual must have been very important. With regard to differences in energetic power between different human populations, there is no reason to doubt that the exercise capacity of blacks is as good as that of whites. This has been proved in many sporting events, where their achievements are equal, if not better – but with one exception: swimming. The absence of African swimmers, or swimmers of African origin, from the world sports elite is indeed conspicuous. To be sure, sociocultural background no doubt influences an individual's choice of sport; also (though it is no longer the case), for a long time access to some sports may have been denied to blacks. Hence, one could argue that biological predispostion is, at present, a more important determinant in the individual's choice of sport. Might it be that in swimming blacks have a certain handicap to start with? Are their body shape and composition less suited for swimming?

Leaving energy, motivation and culture aside, swimming, at least in the early learning stage, will be affected by:

(1) buoyancy in water;
(2) shape and morphology of the body; and
(3) the ability of the body to thermoregulate its core.

Buoyancy, if less of a problem to a top short-distance swimmer, is indeed an important feature with regard to locomotion in water over long distances or periods, and hence for the survival of aquatic species. As stated by Wind (1976), the survival time in water of man's air-breathing ancestors can be considered to have been positively correlated with buoyancy. Champion swimmers practise in heated pools, mainly to avoid the extra energy expenditure of keeping their bodies warm. Long distance swimmers and professional divers (Channel swimmers, for example, and Ama divers), who practise or work in cold water, do develop a subcutaneous fat layer which helps to protect them from the cold environment. This subcutaneous fat layer, it has to be stated, is to a large extent an acquired property (Clark and Edholm, 1985).

Patrick (this volume, chapter 14) points out that to stay at the surface, the density of the body has to be less than that of the surrounding water, and this difference has to be great enough to keep the airway-opening above the water surface, or at least to bring it there at regular intervals. If the density of the body is equal to or greater than that of the water, extra energy will be needed to keep the airway at the surface or to bring it above it. The colder and saltier the water, the greater its density – and hence the easier for a given subject to float. If early hominids went through an aquatic phase in tropical fresh waters, they would have required considerable buoyancy – greater than modern man's. But they would have required less buoyancy if they were living in tropical seas, and still less in cold sea water.

Buoyancy in water is determined by three main components:

(1) the lean body mass, which is heavier than water;
(2) the body fat, lighter than water; and
(3) the amount of air in the lungs.

Table 16.1 shows the average values for these components in the bodies of standard, 'constructed' black and white models. Of these three factors, the lean body mass is the site of most of the metabolic activity. A decrease in lean body mass, while increasing buoyancy, will at the same time reduce the energy-yielding capacity of the subject. Since we accept that the exercise capacities of blacks and whites are at par, in constructing our models in Table 16.1 we attribute an equally lean body mass to both.

Table 16.1 Buoyancy in 'constructed' black and white models

	Black	*White*
Lean body mass		
– weight (kg)	50	50
– density	1.08	1.08
– volume (l)	46.3	46.3
Adipose tissue		
– weight (kg)	5	10
– density	0.95	0.95
– volume (l)	5.26	10.53
Lung volume		
– FRC (l)	2.2	3.0
TOTAL		
– volume (l)	53.76	59.83
– weight (kg)	55.0	60.0
Buoyancy (kg)	- 1.24	- 0.17

FRC = functional residual capacity

An increase in the amount of body fat is obviously a handicap in terrestrial locomotion, where it behaves as dead weight. But in water it may offer advantages – by increasing buoyancy, by providing thermal insulation, and possibly by streamlining the body. Young blacks, particularly male Africans, tend to be slimmer than Europeans, or Americans of European origin (Tanner, 1964; Eveleth and Tanner, 1976). Their thin subcutaneous fat layer is obviously not simply due to the supposed prevalence of undernutrition. It is also observed among adequately fed Africans (Ghesquiere and Eeckels, 1984). One could hardly imagine that world cross-country champions are in an under-nourished state year after year. Yet the Ethiopian, Kenyan and Tanzanian athletes who perform these feats look very thin, as indeed they are.

Finally, a larger air volume in the lungs will increase buoyancy. On the other hand, a smaller lung volume leads to an increased respiratory frequency in order to provide the same effective ventilation. This, of course, adds to the work of breathing, which is less efficient and requires considerably more energy in water than in the air. On the other hand, lung volume is not in itself a limiting factor with regard to exercise capacity, as even at the highest rate of exercise a top athlete rarely uses more than 60 per cent of his ventilatory capacity.

That the lung volumes of Africans differ markedly from those of Europeans has been well documented (Damon, 1966; Johannsen and Erasmus, 1968; Dedoyard and Ghesquiere, 1980). The African has, in relation to his body size, a total lung capacity (TLC) and functional residual capacity (FRC) that is approximately 20 per cent smaller than the European's. FRC gives an approximate measure of the amount of air in the lung when swimming, and may thus influence buoyancy.

The effects of the differences in the amount of body fat and in the lung volumes can easily be calculated, as shown in Table 16.1, which shows a difference between black and white of 1.07 kg. The negative buoyancy of the white, -0.17 kg, can be overcome with little extra energy, while the -1.24 kg buoyancy of the black will require more. Again, this may be of little importance to the top swimmer, but it can be a handicap for black boys and girls learning to swim. Likewise, this inferior buoyancy will be an extra burden for any human having to spend long periods in water.

As for body shape, aquatic mammals, without exception, have superbly streamlined bodies. With top human swimmers, we should bear in mind that their performance lasts only one or more minutes, and that the ability to produce maximal pull with the relatively small muscle mass of the arms and shoulders is crucial. There has been a strong tendency towards greater stature among top swimmers in recent years: indeed, if body shape and composition are similar, the muscle power increases to the second power of stature, giving the taller individual an advantage.

That his body mass, and hence weight, will at the same time increase to the third power of his stature is irrelevant, since his body will float. (Compared to their land-dwelling cousins, aquatic mammals invariably have a large body mass – some extremely large.) Variety of body shape in modern man is rather limited. We can single out, though, the more angular and longer-lined body type of the black: the width of shoulders as compared to hips, and the ratio of arm or leg length to total body length, are both greater in the black than in the white (Hiernaux, 1985; Hauspie *et al.*, 1985). Comparatively broad shoulders, small hips, proportionally long legs and, in addition, a thin subcutaneous fat layer – all these factors will make the body less streamlined, and add drag and turbulence to a human frame moving through water (Clarys, 1978).

CONCLUSION

We must conclude that present-day humans are poorly suited for dwelling in water, be it for a short or for a long period. Of all humans, the one who has remained closest to the presumed cradle of mankind, where the aquatic hominid may have lived, and who has thus been least exposed to genetic pressure for change – the black African – seems to be the least suited for such an aquatic way of life.

REFERENCES

Baz, A., 1979, Optimization of man's energy during underwater paddle propulsion. *Ergonomics*, **22** (10), 1105–14.

Clarke, R.P. and Edholm, O.G., 1985, *Man and His Thermal Environment* (London: Edward Arnold), 165–6.

Clarys, J.P., 1978, Relationship of human body form to passive and active hydrodynamic drag. In *Biomechanics VI–B*, ed. E. Asmussen and K. Jorgensen (International series on biomechanics 2B) (Baltimore: University Park Press), 120–5.

Damon, A., 1966, Negro–white differences in pulmonary function, *Human Biology*, **38**, 380–93.

Dedoyard, E. and Ghesquiere, J., 1980, Evaluation of aerobic power and physical working capacity of female and male Zaïrians. In *Kinanthropometry II*, ed. M. Ostyn, G. Beunen and J. Simons (International series on sports sciences 9) (Baltimore: University Park Press), 129–41.

Ellis, D.V., 1987, Swimming monkeys and apes – know their biology. *Proceedings of the 1987 Western Region Conference, American Association of Zoological Parks and Aquaria*, 361–7.

Ellis, D.V., 1991, Is an aquatic ape viable in terms of marine ecology and primate behaviour? (This volume, chapter 4.)

Eveleth, P.B. and Tanner, J.M., 1976, *Worldwide Variation in Human Growth* (International Biological Programme 8) (Cambridge: Cambridge University Press).

Ghesquiere, J. and Eeckels, R., 1984, Health, physical development and fitness of primary school children in Kinshasa. In *Children and Sport*, ed. J. Ilmarinen and I. Välimäki (Berlin: Springer-Verlag).

Hauspie, R., Das, S.R., Preece, M.A., Tanner, J.M. and Susanne, C., 1985,

Decomposition of sexual dimorphism in adult size of height, sitting height, shoulder width and hip width in a British and West Bengal sample. In *Human Sexual Dimorphism*, ed. J. Ghesquiere, R.D. Martin and F. Newcombe (London: Taylor & Francis), 207–15.

Hiernaux, J., 1985, A comparison of the shoulder–hip-width sexual dimorphism in sub-Saharan Africa and Europe. In *Human Sexual Dimorphism*, ed. J. Ghesquiere, R.D. Martin and F. Newcombe (London: Taylor & Francis), 191–206.

Johannsen, Z.H. and Erasmus, L.D., 1968, Clinical spirometry in normal Bantu, *American Review of Respiratory Disease*, **97**, 585–97.

LaLumiere, L.P., 1991, Evolution of *genus Homo*: where it happened. (This volume, chapter 3.)

Patrick, J.M., 1991, Human respiratory adaptations for swimming and diving. (This volume, chapter 14.)

Tanner, J.M., 1964, *The Physique of the Olympic Athlete* (London: George Allen & Unwin).

Van Tilborgh, L., Daly, D. and Persyn, U., 1983, The influence of some somatic factors on passive drag, gravity and buoyancy forces in competitive swimmers. In *Biomechanics and Medicine in Swimming*, ed. A.P. Hollander, P.A. Huijinge, G. de Geest (International series on sport sciences) (Champaign, Ill.: Human Kinetics Publishers), 207–14.

Wind, J., 1976, Human drowning: phylogenetic origin, *Journal of Human Evolution*, **5**, 349–63.

17 The Non-Aquatic Ape: The Aquatic Ape Theory and the Evolution of Human Drowning and Swimming

Jan Wind

SUMMARY

From an analysis of the evolutionary processes that have led to the features that have diminished humans' adaptation for survival in the water, it appears that from a traditionally biological point of view we are indeed, like the apes, poorly adapted. However, the percentage of humans that actually die from drowning is relatively low – the result of other, counteracting, adaptations, namely, our cognitive and manual abilities. A central question of the Aquatic Ape Theory debate, not hitherto addressed, is therefore: did the aquatic ape already possess these abilities, including those of transferring to conspecifics, especially offspring, the necessary knowledge? Indications from comparative morphology, physiology and ethology, and from palaeoanthropology, appear to offer a negative answer to this question. The analysis, therefore, does not support the AAT.

INTRODUCTION

This chapter attempts to test the Aquatic Ape Theory (AAT) against a number of data (including personal observations) that permit us to roughly reconstruct the evolutionary background to swimming and drowning in modern humans. The data derive mainly from comparative zoology, palaeontology, evolutionary biology, anatomy, physiology and psychology (see Figure 17.1). Like other arguments for and against the AAT, mine, though based on quite hard data, may legitimately be considered as speculative. However, my general conclusion will be that there is little evidence in favour of the theory. This chapter will not discuss the adaptationist, the purely palaeontological or the methodological issues associated with the AAT (which are discussed elsewhere in this volume).

MAN AND WATER: THE PARADOX

Remarkably, most humans and all apes swim less well and drown much more readily than virtually all other animals, including monkeys. How has this come about? Before that question can be answered, drowning has to be defined. Somewhat simplified, it can be defined as a disturbance of the relations between the individual, water and air. Tracing the evolutionary background of human drowning may elucidate the intriguing comparative zoological observations mentioned above. Also, it may facilitate an assessment of the AAT and clarify our basic relations with water which are, at first sight, somewhat ambivalent.

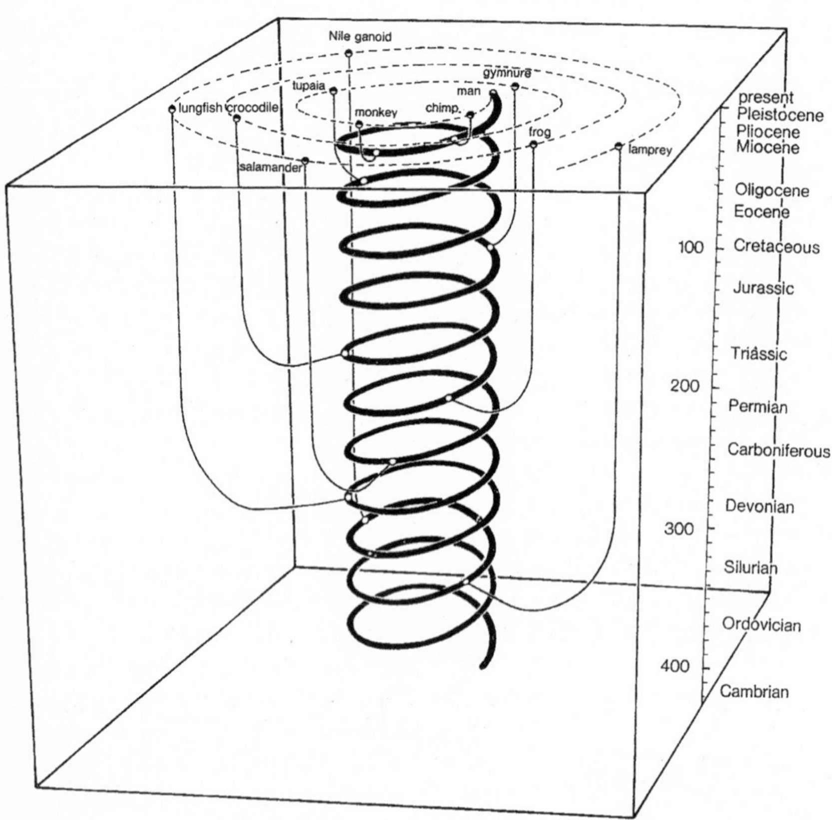

Figure 17.1 Schematic representation of the value of observing modern animals for elucidating the evolutionary history of humans. The upper face of the cube indicates the present, the lower parts of the cube the past, and the heavy spiral man's phylogeny. The species mentioned in the upper face have changed less than others and are taken to be indicative of conditions in our ancestors; yet they are also the end-result of an evolutionary process, as indicated by the lines leading from the heavy spiral to the upper surface. The series of modern species, therefore, merely provides a reflection of man's phylogeny as indicated by the broken-lined spiral in the upper face. The names mentioned here refer to species whose proneness to drowning is discussed in this chapter; the ancestral species are indicated by the white dots. The geological time scale is graded into millions of years.

On the one hand, humans can be considered to show *hydrophilia*: we all started life immersed in water for nine months, while for the rest of our lives we are hardly able to survive a few days without it. In addition, psychoanalysts, and poets in their wake, have stressed man's nostalgic longing for submersion in water, especially the sea, interpreting this as a symbol of our comfortable stay in the womb and as a deeply ingrained, biologically determined, ancient memory of the ocean in which life originated many millions of years ago (see e.g., Fliess, 1961; Ferenczi, 1968; and Richards, this volume, chapter 6). Indeed, it has been claimed that the composition of our blood still reflects that of the primeval ocean at the time when our aquatic ancestors evolved into terrestrial ones, some 300 million years ago (Grayson, 1988; for older references, see Wind, 1973). And are we not fond of playing with water and taking showers? Are we not able to conquer oceans by our advanced modern technology?

On the other hand, humans can be considered to show *hydrophobia*. Except in a warm bath, most humans when immersed feel rather threatened by the surrounding water. In fact, humans survive total or partial immersion in water for a much shorter period than most other organisms, including the majority of animals. Accidental human drowning occurs at least 160,000 times per year throughout the world.* And if the concept of drowning is broadened, many more people may be considered to die by 'drowning' – by their own body fluid, present in the lungs during the terminal stages of various diseases.

To put these somewhat puzzling and paradoxical phenomena into a proper perspective, we need to know their origins and evolution. These can crudely be reconstructed on the basis of Darwinian principles. In order to trace the evolutionary history of human drowning, the most probable reconstruction of the level and nature of our ancestors' adaptation to an aquatic environment will briefly be reviewed.

LIFE AND WATER

Water is present in all living organisms, and the more primitive ones usually live in an aquatic environment. Accordingly, it is generally assumed that life originated in water. Our vertebrate ancestors are likely to have remained largely aquatic until some 250 million years ago, and to have been good swimmers until some 50 million years ago. As far as the non-human primates are concerned, most modern prosimians and monkeys observed so far (and, for that matter, most terrestrial mammals) appear able to swim very well, mainly as a means of crossing small tracts of water (rarely exceeding a few hundred metres) or recovering food, or

* Based on Miles (1968), who estimated the number at that time to be 140,000. Extrapolating on the basis of the increase in world population, 160,000 is a low estimate.

just for playing.* These observations and similarities in morphology and ecology suggest that our monkey-like ancestors possessed the same swimming abilities. In contrast, the apes appear to be afraid when in water, and in fact (except, maybe, for some gibbons) they drown very readily, either sinking motionless or panicking.

Humans, assisted by sophisticated equipment, can dive deeper and for a longer time than any other mammal; and even without any equipment most humans are able to *learn* swimming and diving as well as the monkeys. However, without such technology and without having been taught to swim, humans drown about as readily as the apes do, and many humans are unable to swim. Therefore, considerable changes in the level of biological water adaptation must have occurred during human phylogeny.

Clearly, this level had already begun to decrease in Devonian times (some 300 million years ago) with the evolution of fish into amphibians, the most dramatic drop having been during primate evolution. Assuming that modern monkeys provide a model for our monkey-like ancestors, and apes for the hominids, this change must have occurred with the Oligocene splitting of the monkey and the ape–hominid lineages (Figure 17.1). From that time onwards our forebears' poor, ape-like water adaptation could only have been compensated for if they had possessed human-like technological and communication (that is teaching) abilities. Palaeoanthropology, however, suggests that these abilities evolved much later; for instance, rafts could hardly have been constructed prior to the invention of tool-making, 2 to 3 million years ago.

LOSS OF WATER ADAPTATION

What may have been the causes and the consequences of this 300-million-year-long decrease in water adaptation? In evolutionary–biological parlance, this question is formulated as: Did this loss have any selective advantage, or was there a relaxation of the selective pressures that favoured water adaptation? A satisfactory answer could only be given

* The extant tree-shrews and prosimians are terrestrial, but are generally able to swim; see Figure 17.4 (a) and Sprankel (1961) for tree-shrews; e.g., Eisenberg and Gould (1970) for some tenrec genera, and Walker (1967) for fossil lemurs. *Lemur fulvus* does swim, but *L. catta* probably does not (Tattersall, 1973); *Galago senegalensis* and *G. crassicaudatus* have never been seen in water (G.A. Doyle, personal communication, 1972). Many Old and New World monkeys, including immature individuals (Koford, 1963), although mainly arboreal, are frequently seen to take to the water and seem to enjoy swimming even in cold water (Coon, 1963). Though Kummer (1971) assumed that baboons do not swim, swimming was observed by van Lawick (1972). For swimming in Old World monkeys, see Kern (1964), Gartlan and Brain (1968), Frisch (1968), Schultz (1969), Gautier-Hion (1971), Stern and Oxnard (1973), Judge (1974); for New World monkeys, see Schultz (1969). Also see Table 4.3, this volume.

if we knew fully the morphology, physiology, behaviour and ecology of all our ancestors, as well as the complicated network of selective pressures that shaped them. Though this, unfortunately, is impossible, a number of probabilities can be formulated. The fact that the water adaptations of most vertebrates, even the terrestrial ones, are better than those of man and apes, suggests that the possession of these adaptations has a positive selective value for them, and that the same applies to most of our vertebrate ancestors.

The relatively minor reduction in water adaptation during the evolution from the first air-breathing vertebrates to our monkey-like ancestors was probably mainly the result of a relaxation of the selective pressures favouring a purely aquatic way of life. This was a consequence of ecological pressures – that is, the opening up of a new niche: the terrestrial one. Yet even this frequently involved contact with water and the need to cross it – for instance, to get to food or mates, to flee, or simply to reach the land after accidentally having got into the water. Monkeys, indeed, show the abilities needed to meet these requirements.

How, then, could the prehuman hominids like *Australopithecus* afford *not* to have such abilities? Compensation was probably offered by their intelligence and social behaviour, enabling them, even before the invention, for example, of any floating device, to learn to avoid deep water; to locate, communicate and remember the position of fords and intermingling tree-tops that permitted crossings; to look for branches and logs for floating on and for bridging smaller streams. The poor water adaptation of the modern apes may be explained by some of these mechanisms as well; in addition, its negative selective value would seem to be smaller in the apes' habitat, a tropical forest, than in a savannah habitat, which is generally considered to have been the cradle of the hominids.

Having thus delineated the general causes and consequences of the gradual decrease in water adaptation during evolution from the early vertebrates to man, I will now try to reconstruct the more specific ones – that is, the largely interacting anatomical, physiological, behavioural and environmental changes that have contributed to the process.

BUOYANCY

It is clear that, to prevent drowning, the individual in water must be able to continue breathing, which implies that the entrance of the airway should, at least occasionally, reach above the water level. The ability to breathe in water, then, depends on the individual's buoyancy and the position of the airway entrance. Buoyancy is determined by the density of the body relative to that of the surrounding water. Unfortunately, body density cannot be inferred from fossil remains, and so our ancestors' buoyancy is difficult to assess. Thus, we have recourse to comparative zoology; the density of modern mammals like cats, dogs, pigs, guinea-pigs and armadillos appears not to differ significantly from that of man – that is, ranging from about 1.02 to about 1.10 times that of water (Table 17.1). Buoyancy differences between mammalian species appear mainly to be determined by differences between the volumes of their bodies' air spaces. Unfortunately, this had not been taken into account in the measurements described in Table 17.1, which therefore possess limited value.

Table 17.1 A summary of animal and human density

Species	*Specification*	*Density (mean or ranges)*	*Reference*
Man *Homo*	27 adult females, maximal inspiration	0.9635–1.0614	Rork and Hellebrandt (1937)
Man *Homo*	14 adult males	1.043–1.086	Krzywicki and Chinn (1967)
Man *Homo*	99 adult males	1.021–1.097	Behnke *et al.* (1942)
Man *Homo*	1 infant 31 days old	1.031	Fomon *et al.* (1963)
Man *Homo*	1 infant 55 days old	1.061	Fomon *et al.* (1963)
Man *Homo*	1 infant of 5260 g	1.040–1.050	Falkner (1963)
Cat *Felis domestica*	10 adults, fur removed	1.031–1.080	Walser and Stein (1953)
Cat *Felis domestica*	1 adult	1.097	Noyons and Jongbloed (1935)
Guinea-pig *Cavia*	23 females	1.040–1.080	Liuzzo *et al.* (1958)
Sheep *Ovis*	14 adults	1.040–1.112	Beeston (1965)
Hog *Sus*	20 adults	1.018	Lynch and Wellington (1963)
Armadillo *Dasypus*	—	1.060	Bates (1964)
Dog *Canis*	4 adults	1.074	Kohlrausch (1930)

In all except one (Rork *et al.*, 1937), the air of the respiratory tract and of the fur was considered as not belonging to the body, thereby reducing their value for buoyancy determination. Angus (1971) reports chimpanzee specific gravity to average 1.025, but this figure is likely to be incorrect, because the observations of Hamlin *et al.* (1964) to which she refers concerned only chimpanzee urine. (References in Wind, 1976a.)

The relative volume of air present in the airways and lungs does not differ greatly in the various primates, with one exception: the laryngeal air-sacs present in the apes are of considerable size and could, when inflated, act as a lifebelt. Unfortunately, it is not known whether our ape- and monkey-like ancestors possessed such air-sacs. Anyway, when in water apes quickly sink despite possessing air-sacs, and the gibbon does not inflate his.

Air trapped in the fur does contribute to floating in many mammals. During evolution from the insectivores to man, this contribution must have gradually decreased because of the concomitant relative and perhaps absolute decrease in average hair length and fur density that accompanied the increase of body size (larger animals have a relatively smaller body surface and hence a relatively smaller heat loss). In addition, gas present in the digestive tract promotes buoyancy. The shift from a largely vegetarian to an omnivorous diet during evolution from our simian ancestors to the hominids suggests that concomitantly the average volume of such gas decreased somewhat, for the gut of vegetarian mammals usually contains more gas-producing bacteria than that of omnivores and carnivores. In conclusion, it seems that during primate evolution buoyancy has slightly decreased.

BREATHING

In fossilised prehominid mammalian and reptilian ancestors, as in virtually all modern vertebrates exemplifying them, the airway entrance appears positioned more superior and anterior than in man; that is to say, the muzzle could act as a snorkel-like organ. Their normal position allows most reptiles and mammals – and must have allowed our ancestors – to continue breathing while in water; only a slight neck extension is necessary.

In contrast, a human, unless he has learned to swim or is equipped with special devices, has much difficulty with inspiration when out of his depth in either fresh or sea water. This results from his poor buoyancy and the usual position of the body and that of the airway entrance. The human body position is likely to be upright because the centre of gravity lies caudally to the centre of the upward forces, the former being located in the upper abdomen and the latter in the lower thorax (Slijper, 1962). In addition, the stressful situation of being immersed tends to make the naïve individual assume a vertical position, rather than a supine or prone one by which the nose and mouth could more easily be brought above the surface. The individual's difficulty with inspiration relates to the fact that the buoyancy of the average human in a vertical position is not great enough to lift the nostrils, and *a fortiori* the mouth, above the water level. The familiarity of every swimmer with this inability can easily be illustrated quantitatively. Even in women, whose bodies contain relatively more (low-density) fat tissue than men's, and even during maximal inspiration, body density (including the air in the lungs) is no lower than 0.981 kg per litre. Assuming that the part of the head cranial to a horizontal plane through the nostrils weighs 2.5 kg, representing some 4 per cent of total body weight in adults and even more in children, a body density of at least 0.96 kg per litre would be required to keep the nostrils above the surface (Wind, 1976a).

ASPIRATION, HYPOTHERMIA AND OSMOLALITY

Accidental entry into deep water is more likely to cause *aspiration* of water – that is, inhalation of water into the larynx and lower airways – in humans than in our ancestors, for at least four reasons.

(1) Many people in water resort to mouth-breathing because of the exercise, the sudden cooling and their instinctive crying out; and, as just noted, the mouth is even less easily brought above the surface than the nostrils.
(2) Humans typically show a gap between the choanae and the laryngeal entrance (Negus, 1962; Wind, 1976b) (Figure 17.2).
(3) Human metabolic rate and ventilatory drive are higher than in our pre-mammalian ancestors who, being cold-blooded (or ectothermic), needed less oxygen than warm-blooded (or endothermic) mammals.
(4) Cooling of the body by the ambient water readily causes impairment of normal brain metabolism, leading to mental confusion, loss of memory and unconsciousness, and hence to aspiration (Keatinge, 1969).

During human phylogeny, immersion *hypothermia* has increasingly contributed to our drowning proneness, for the following reasons.

(1) *Homo sapiens* has spread out from his tropical cradle into colder parts of the earth.
(2) The mean sea and air temperatures have since Oligocene times steadily decreased (Newell, 1971).
(3) The dense, hairy coat of our earlier mammalian ancestors (see page 269) has disappeared, resulting in a decrease of insulation.
(4) Man, possibly like other endotherms, shows upon sudden immersion in cold water a reflex deep inspiration (Patrick, this volume, chapter 14) which, in combination with the gap in the airway (Figure 17.2), increased the risk of aspiration.
(5) During human phylogeny the brain, especially the cortex, has become more susceptible to lack of oxygen and more important for our survival in water, which is more dependent on learned behaviours. In fact, most animals survive total submersion for a much longer time than humans do.

After water has entered the lungs of a mammal, it is not only the decrease in pulmonary gas exchange that threatens the individual's life. In the alveoli (the tiny compartments of the lungs where this exchange takes place) there is very close contact between the blood and the contents of the alveolar space. Across the thin tissue layer that separates the blood from that space can occur an exchange not only of gases but also of water and substances dissolved in it. Therefore, when aspiration of fresh water occurs, some of it will enter the pulmonary blood vessels and some of the blood ions will pass into the alveolar space. This latter process results from the ion concentration (or osmolality) of human blood being higher than that of fresh water. By the former process, blood becomes diluted and increases in volume; subsequently, the red blood cells become overloaded with water and may rupture. As a result, many physiological functions become seriously impaired.

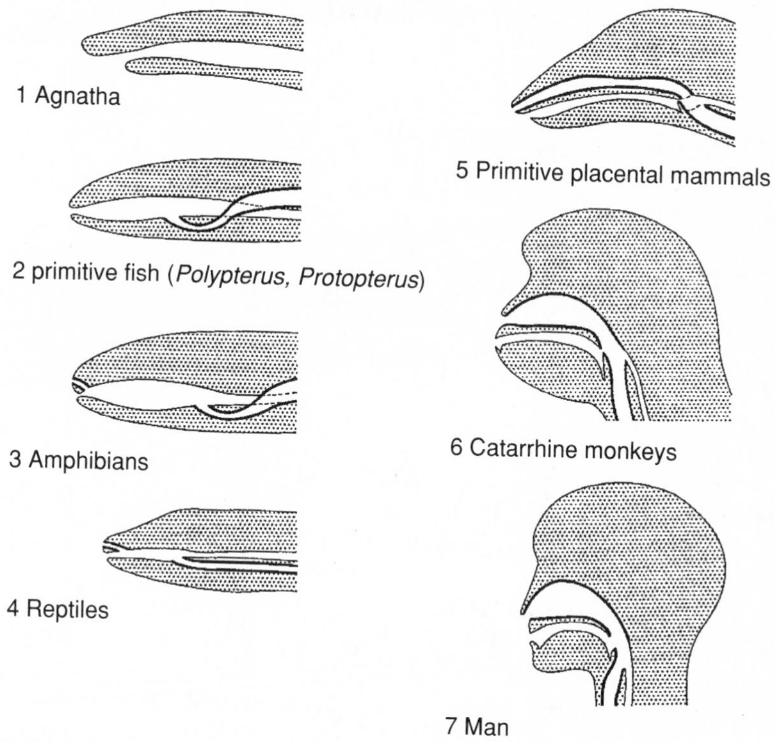

Figure 17.2 Evolution of the human airway as indicated by some representative modern species (from Wind, 1970).

Conversely, aspirated sea water – having an osmolality four times that of human blood – causes the passage of water from the pulmonary blood vessels into the alveolar space and the concomitant passage of the sea-water ions into the blood vessels. Thus, the aspiration of sea water also results in the impairment of physiological functions, though this is usually less serious than the aspiration of fresh water.

Comparative observations suggest that the concentration of the various types of ions in the blood, as well as the total blood osmolality, of our terrestrial ancestors – and hence the drowning mechanisms described above – were about the same as ours (Wind, 1973). But is our blood not similar to the ocean water of the Devonian, 300 million years ago, when the first terrestrial animals evolved – as suggested by the 'sea-within-us' theory mentioned earlier? The answer is no. The oceans have had their present composition for a much longer time, probably for a billion years (MacIntyre, 1970; Holland, 1984; Holland, Lazar and McCaffrey, 1986). Even if we assume that since the start of the water cycle (when evaporation and rain washed ions from the land into the seas) sea water has become four times saltier, the theory does not hold: the inorganic constituents of human blood are not similar to sea water diluted four times (see Figure 17.3). Therefore, in so far as drowning is caused by the osmotic differences described above, it must have been much the same in our terrestrial ancestors as it is in modern man.

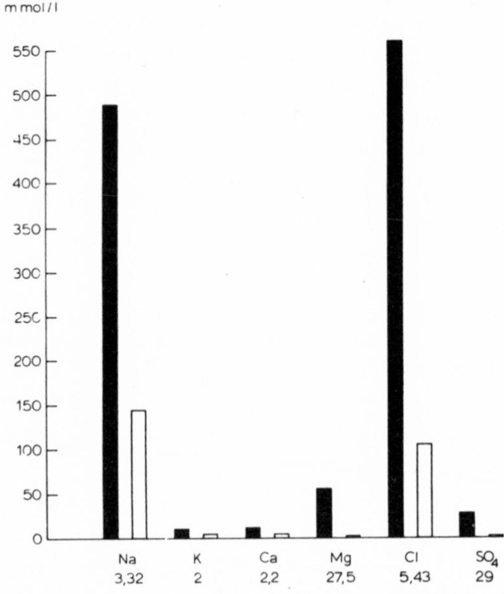

Figure 17.3 Comparison of the concentration of the most common ions present in sea water (black columns) and human blood plasma (white columns).

The sea water/blood ratios, as rendered below the bars, are significantly higher or lower than 4, illustrating that blood plasma cannot be considered as sea water simply diluted four times.

Dying as a result of pulmonary malfunctioning after the penetration of the lungs by water must, for three reasons, have been a more likely event for our mammalian than for our pre-mammalian ancestors.

(1) In our pre-synapsid (reptilian) ancestors, penetration of the lungs by water must have happened less frequently than in mammals, as already explained.
(2) The non-mammalian, more saccular, lungs have a much smaller gas-exchanging surface, and in amphibians and fish they function only as auxiliary respiratory organs.
(3) If our pre-synapsid ancestors had succeeded in removing the aspirated water – for instance, by (primitive) coughing – their lungs could probably have regained their function faster than mammalian lungs would. This can be understood by the fact that the function of the alveoli of mammalian lungs depends, among other things, on the presence of special substances – forming the 'surfactant – which, by lowering the surface tension, prevent the alveoli from collapsing, which they tend to do because of their very small size. So, once the surfactant has been washed out, as occurs with the aspiration of water, the alveoli collapse and gas exchange is severely hampered. This pathology – and especially the irreversible brain damage (resulting from a lack of oxygen lasting for more than a few minutes) and the serious lung infection that often accompany it – explains the bad prognosis of human drowning victims, in spite of all modern medical facilities.

LOCOMOTION

Survival in water depends not only on the anatomical and physiological properties described above, but also on the ability to move through and out of the water. Locomotion in water is achieved in most vertebrates mainly by undulatory body movements passing from head to tail, or by movements derived from these movements. The ubiquity, in aquatic species, of this mode of propulsion suggests that, in terms of energy cost, it is an extremely efficient one – as is illustrated by its presence in such remotely related organisms as bacteria, protozoans, spermatozoa, and a number of multicellular non-vertebrates. This indicates that the pattern evolved independently several times during evolution, by the mechanism of convergence: similar selective pressures led to this very (if not most) efficient means of locomotion in a liquid environment. In most quadrupedal terrestrial vertebrates, including the primates, this 400-million-year-old motor pattern is still recognisable in walking, in the simultaneous forward and backward moving of the two diagonally positioned limbs.

Comparative zoological and palaeontological data indicate that our pre-mammalian ancestors swam by means of these undulatory body movements, greatly assisted by their tails. As regards the modern animals that represent our mammalian ancestors, such as insectivores and non-human primates, when in the water all of them (except the apes) make their usual walking or hopping movements, which appear to result in effective propulsion.

In contrast, the stereotyped walking pattern of man has hardly any propulsive effect in the water. How has this come about? In order to answer this question, I made some observations of a few tree-shrews and a rhesus monkey which had never been in the water before, when they were swimming. They may exemplify, respectively, the condition of our earliest primates and of our monkey-like Oligocene ancestors. Because these animals were moving horizontally, it can be predicted that their forward limb movements encounter substantially less resistance from the water than their backward limb movements. How this happens can be understood by analysing the movements of their limbs during swimming (Figure 17.4).

What evolutionary processes, then, have made an equally naïve human, who suddenly finds himself in water higher than his head, barely able to achieve any horizontal displacement? First, this inability can be understood in terms of the loss of the strong muscular tail (which had probably already occurred with the transition from mammal-like reptiles to the first mammals) and the loss of the anatomical and physiological adaptations discussed earlier. Second, and more importantly, the acquisition of the erect posture can explain this inter-primate difference: for man's vertical posture in the water (see page 269) results in the body meeting considerable resistance during horizontal displacement – a resistance that is increased by the relatively flat human body.

An even more important factor in the human inability to swim effectively, however, is the limb adaptations associated with our erect posture: these have reduced the propulsive efficiency of stereotyped walking and, to a lesser extent, of crawling movements, in both the vertical and the horizontal positions. This can be explained by (1) the small ratio of the hands and feet to body size, as compared to the other hominoids; (2) the much reduced range of flexion and extension movements in hands, fingers, feet and toes; (3) the position of the axis of the elbow, with wrist and finger joints not being perpendicular to the walking direction and not being parallel, causing the contra-lateral propulsive forces (if any) to counteract.

My reason for assuming that this position of the joints is associated with the erect posture is that in virtually all vertebrates, including the synapsids (the mammal-like reptiles), the position of these axes in the limbs that support the body when walking is transverse – that is, perpendicular to

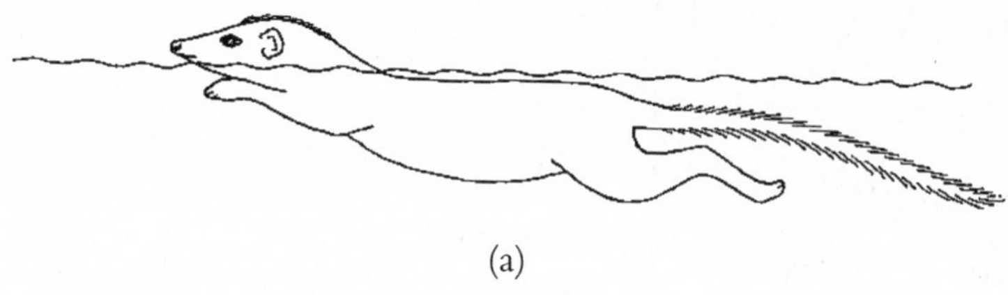

(a)

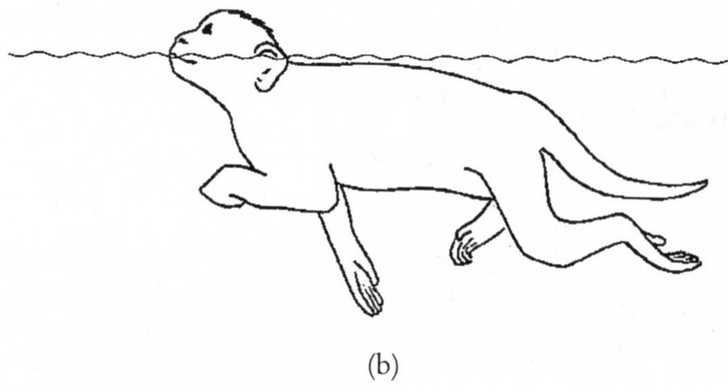

(b)

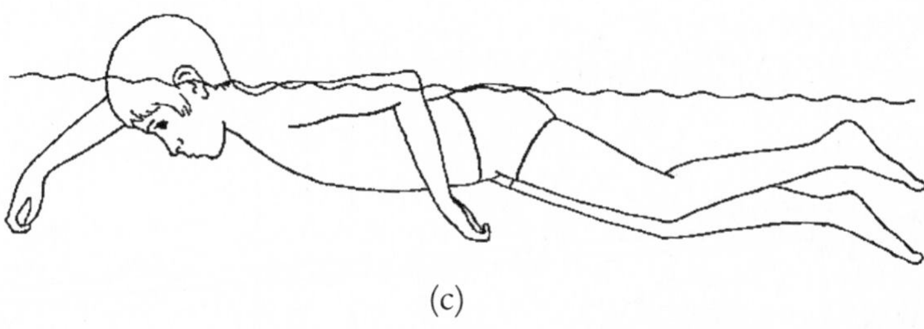

(c)

Figure 17.4 Swimming position in (a) the tree-shrew (*Tupaia glis*), (b) the rhesus monkey (*Macaca mulatta*), and (c) man, illustrating that breathing during swimming in pre-Miocene human ancestors must have been much less difficult than in man.

The normal walking movements of these ancestors are likely to have resulted in effective horizontal propulsion, whereas in man this is only possible by quite different locomotor patterns. (a) and (b) are based on original photographs of animals that had never been in the water before.

the longitudinal body axis, or nearly so. Indeed, from a mechanical point of view it is clear that if the axis of the limb joints used during walking was not transverse, the joints would be much more strained and locomotion would cost more energy. In species that have limbs not used for walking, however, there is a relaxation of the selective pressures favouring the transverse position of the axes within these limbs. In addition, during hominid evolution there have been selective pressures favouring this inclination, such as the use of tools, the carrying of infants, food and implements; and maybe also the earlier, suspensory, function of the front limbs, during the arboreal phase of our ancestry.

Humans, like many other mammals which accidentally and for the first time get into water, do not usually show the normal walking pattern, but rather a series of uncoordinated limb and body movements that can best be described as panic movements. These may, to be sure, include some normal locomotor patterns which other mammals soon discover to have a propulsive effect. But such behaviour in man actually adds to his drowning proneness, because it raises oxygen consumption; and it rarely leads him to discover the motor patterns that result in life-saving horizontal or vertical displacement – the swimming strokes. These are usually only acquired after much trial and error. On the other hand, their acquisition is facilitated by (1) the plasticity of human behaviour, usually greater than in animals, meaning that a new motor pattern can more readily be mastered; (2) the accumulation of knowledge and experience as a result of man's intellectual (including linguistic and social) capacities; (3) the extremely movable shoulder joints, which we owe to our arboreal ancestry and which enable humans to practise the breast, butterfly and crawl strokes, all of which considerably decrease the resistance met during the forward stroke. On the other hand, this arm-lifting ability, if utilised during the 'panic phase', may cause the rest of the body to go down.

HUMAN BEHAVIOUR

In addition to the anatomical, physiological, biochemical and environmental features noted above, other circumstances that contribute to humans' proneness to drowning have to be discussed. These are a series of species-specific behaviours which result, for instance, in alcohol abuse, panic, suicide, traffic accidents (such as shipping disasters), and competition between both individuals and groups. Competition permits people to boost their performances, but can lead to life-endangering behaviour. For instance, the anticipatory capacity of their brains leads many human divers to practise pre-diving hyperventilation. This not only raises the oxygen level of the blood, but it also lowers the carbon dioxide level. Now, it appears that a rise in the carbon dioxide level rather than a fall in the oxygen level stimulates the respiratory centres in the brain stem so as to cause an irresistible drive to breathe and to surface. However, the increased arterial oxygenation resulting from hyperventilation often insufficiently relieves the tissue (including the brain) hypoxia resulting from continued oxygen usage by the diver; consequently, the carbon dioxide level returns too slowly to the value that normally stimulates the respiratory centre of the brain. Hence, the hyperventilated diver may lose consciousness before noticing that his body needs a fresh supply of oxygen. This mechanism is one of the possible causes of unexplained fatal diving accidents.

EVIDENCE FROM THE APES?

The curious fact of apes' proneness to drowning, which is quite similar to humans' and, in fact, quite rare in the animal world, needs clarification. Unfortunately, the contribution that the observation of apes can make to the explanation of drowning in our hominid ancestors must, for the time being, remain limited; few experiments have been done because these animals are endangered and precious. It can merely be stated provisionally that the properties that explain apes' proneness to drowning largely coincide with the human ones. The main differences are that in apes (1) the body-covering hairs provide slightly more insulation and buoyancy; (2) hypothermia is less frequent because of the tropical habitat; (3) their behaviour usually involves taking fewer drowning risks than follow from the specifically human behaviours discussed above; and (4) their body density is possibly higher than ours, as suggested by their reportedly quick sinking and by an allometric relationship, in arboreal primates, between the size of the body and that of the limb bones. However, as long as exact data on their body density are lacking, this explanation remains hypothetical.

It may be that apes' usual locomotor movements in the water and, *a fortiori*, their panic movements are as poorly propulsive as man's because of a similar – that is, non-transverse – position of the axes of the front limb joints, due to their terrestrial (knuckle-walking) and arboreal (arm-swinging) locomotor habits.

'OCEANIC DESIRES'

As mentioned above (page 265), psychoanalysts and poets have adduced certain arguments in favour of humans' close or, in their terminology, ancient and deep-rooted, ties with water. Unfortunately, science is unable to account for the mental processes behind the back-to-the-ocean and back-to-the-womb associations underlying these arguments. However, one has to realise that (1) the frequency of these associations, even among those, educated in the Western world, upon whose thoughts the arguments are based, is unknown and therefore its ubiquity is questionable; (2) man is – and even the supposed aquatic ape was – separated from his aquatic, early vertebrate ancestors by millions of generations of non-aquatic species; (3) analogues to these associations have never been demonstrated in modern species representing the ancestral non-aquatic species, while comparative neurophysiology and ethology indicate that their presence is very unlikely indeed; and (4) whether there exists any memory of the intra-uterine submersion manifesting itself in such associations is doubtful.

Much more likely, these associations are the result of typically human mental processes based on a great variety of genes interacting with man's present environment, rather than on hereditary properties retained for millions of years and suddenly becoming apparent in modern humans. Moreover, the associations can more parsimoniously be explained on the basis of (1) an early memory of bathing, which the individual has experienced as pleasant because of the temperature, the relative weightlessness, the usually relaxed situation, and, in so far as the experience took place in childhood, the parental care; and (2) a combination of the typically human metaphorical associations and mental conditions underlying, for instance, escapism.

Finally, one of the alleged physical starting-points of the psychoanalysts and poets is false: as mentioned earlier (page 272), our blood is certainly not similar to the ocean water of the Devonian of 300 million years ago, when the first terrestrial animals evolved.

THE AAT AND THE SWIMMING BABIES

One of the arguments favouring the AAT has received little attention in the other chapters: the swimming abilities of human infants. The argument is based on two assumptions.

First, that the properties of human infants may be more indicative of those of our ancestors than are those of adults. This assumption derives from Haeckel's 'Biogenetic Law' (1866), postulating that each individual, during his development, 'recapitulates' the evolutionary history of the species. However, this 'Law' only rarely holds, as has been demonstrated by numerous observations and as can be predicted by theoretical evolutionary biology. The properties of living organisms are the result of the operation of genetic variation and natural selection in previous generations; and the selective pressures which have shaped modern developing vertebrates, embryonic and infant, are usually completely different from those that shaped adult ancestral ones. This has resulted in differences in morphology and physiology.

Second, the AAT argument assumes that human infants do indeed swim. To be sure, their usual crawling and kicking limb movements may have some propulsive effect in the water. But the immersed infant will only survive if supported so as to surface for breathing, for this is even more difficult than in adults because of the relatively large infant head. This is illustrated by the frequent reports of babies drowning in shallow water, including bathtubs, and by the extreme neck extension needed for breathing shown even by older children during swimming lessons. Therefore, a baby's 'swimming' should, rather, be understood as a combination of the infant's preference for a horizontal position and his relative weightlessness, which permits his generalised vertebrate motor patterns to be demonstrated. Some mysterious property indicating an aquatic habitat supposedly exploited by some of our hominid ancestors is a much less likely explanation of infant 'swimming'.

CONCLUSION

A systematic review of the evolutionary background of human proneness to drowning (as summarised in Figure 17.5) shows that the capacity to survive in the water must have gradually decreased during human phylogeny, in so far as it is interpreted in terms of the water adaptations that are usually labelled instinctive, genetic, innate or pre-programmed: in short, the adaptations that are the most obvious in animals and that can be called the biological ones. On the other hand, the capacity to survive can be considered to have increased in so far as it is measured by the adaptations that, in fact, usually prevent man from drowning. To these, environmentally dependent behaviour makes a greater contribution, that is, learning, communicating, applying technology, and so on – in short, the cultural adaptations. These have led humans to avoid water, to learn swimming strokes, to construct floating devices and bridges, and to provide medical care for people rescued from drowning.

Therefore, the paradox mentioned in the introduction to this chapter, already partly elucidated by the disproving of most of the 'hydrophilic' arguments, can now be reduced to the classic *nature–nurture dichotomy*. This too has, in recent decades, been shown to be false: all behaviour, animal as well as human, can be considered the result of an *interaction* of genetically determined (or innate) and environmental processes. It appears that the relative contribution to a specific behaviour of each of the two factors is difficult to quantify; and that at best, when comparing a similar behaviour in different species, it can sometimes be stated that in one species the relative contribution of one of the two factors is more obvious than in the other. (Consider, for instance, flying in insects and 'flying' in man.)

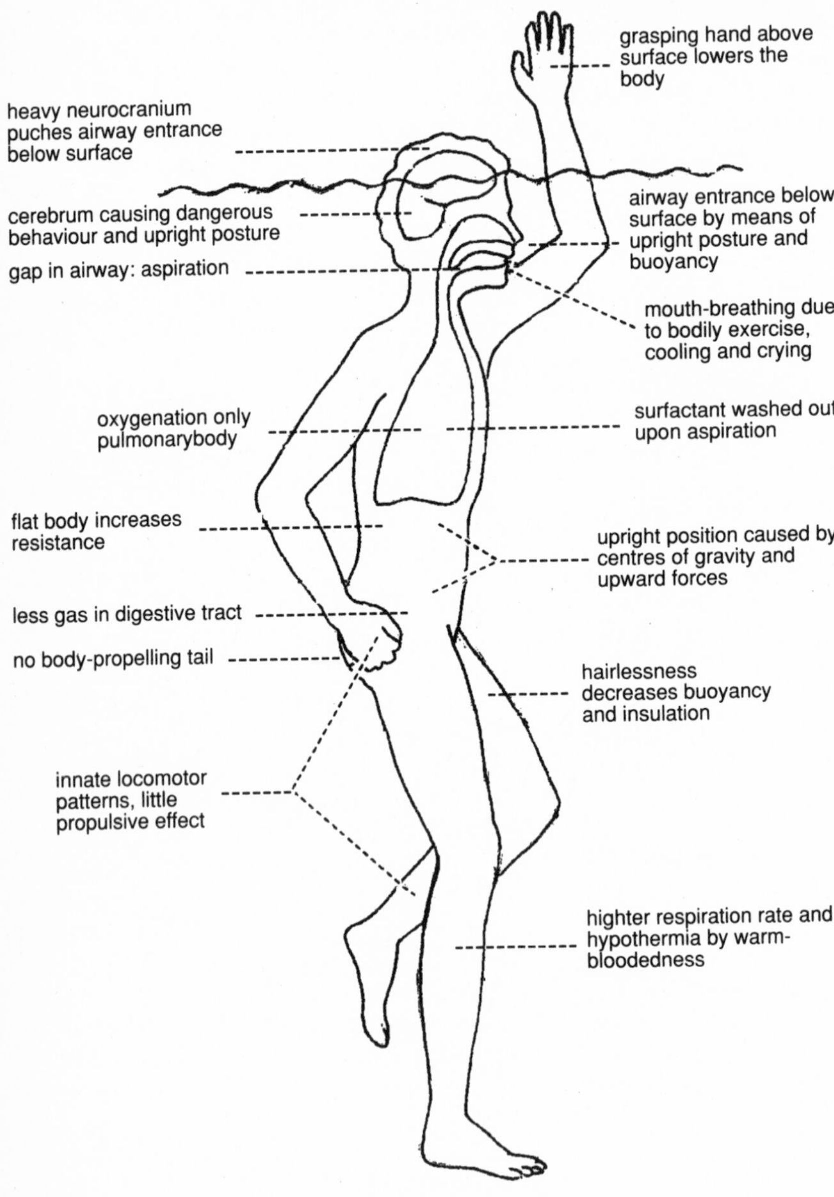

Figure 17.5 Summary of the causes of man's proneness to drowning as they have evolved during his descent from the first vertebrates.

Accordingly, when one tries to quantify the relative contributions of the 'biological' and the 'cultural' water adaptations, one can only say that during human phylogeny there has been a decrease of the former and an increase of the latter. Whether such a shift can be considered as actually having led to a change in the resulting water adaptation level depends on how the latter is defined. When measured by the proportion of the population actually drowning (drowning in one's own body fluids excluded), the human level may well be about the same as our mammalian ancestors' (except, maybe, for the prehuman hominids, where it may have been lower). So the decrease in biological adaptations has probably largely been compensated for by the increase in cultural ones.

Much of the discussion around the AAT can be resolved by taking the nature–nurture issue into account. The central question to be answered, then, by the AAT advocates is: *Could the presumed aquatic apes have learned and taught their offspring their supposed, primatologically extraordinary, swimming and other aquatic skills*? Obviously, a conclusive answer to this question will be rather difficult to find. After all, we do not know anything about the ape's intellectual (or, for that matter, any other) abilities; speculations on its morphology and physiology can only with great audacity be derived from comparative primatology, as long as the first fossil remnant of the aquatic ape is still waiting to be discovered. Therefore, my evolutionary considerations argue against rather than in favour of the theory. This is not to deny, however, that its proposals have had a beneficial – that is, a heuristic – value for palaeoanthropology, in forcing the palaeoanthropological establishment into the often necessary careful reconsideration and reformulation of its own assumptions and ideas. In that sense we should be grateful to Sir Alister Hardy and Elaine Morgan.

REFERENCES

Coon, C.S., 1963, *The Origin of Races* (London: Cape).

Doyle, G.A., 1972, personal communication.

Eisenberg, J.F. and Gould, E., 1970, *The Tenrecs: a study in Mammalian Behavior and Evolution* (Washington, DC: Smithsonian Institution Press).

Elsner, R. and Gooden, B., 1983, *Diving and Asphyxia. A Comparative Study of Animals and Man* (Cambridge: Cambridge University Press).

Ferenczi, S., 1968, *Thalassa. A Theory of Genitality* (New York: Norton).

Fliess, R., 1961, *Ego and Body Ego* (New York: Schulte).

Frisch, J.E., 1968, Individual behavior and intertroop variability in Japanese macaques. In *Primates: Studies in Adaptation and Variability*, ed. P.C. Jay (New York: Holt, Rinehart & Winston), 243–52.

Gartlan, J.S. and Brain, C.K., 1968, Ecology and social variability in *Cercopithecus aethiops* and *C. mitis*. In *Primates: Studies in Adaptation and Variability*, ed. P.C. Jay (New York: Holt, Rinehart & Winston), 253–92.

Gautier-Hion, A., 1971, Répertoire comportemental du talapoin (*Miopithecus talapoin*). *Biologica Gabonica*, **7**, 295–391.

Grayson, J., 1988, The environment and the perception of reality. A physiologist's point of view. *Ultimate Reality and Meaning*, **11**, 294–309.

Haeckel, E., 1866, *Generelle Morphologie der Organismen*. Vol. 2: *Allgemeine Entwicklungsgeschichte der Organismen* (Berlin: Reimer).

Hardy, A., 1960, Was man more aquatic in the past? *New Scientist*, **7**, 642.

Holland, H.D., 1984, *The Chemical Evolution of the Atmosphere and Oceans* (Princeton: Princeton University Press).

Holland, H.D., Lazar, B. and McCaffrey, M., 1986, Evolution of the atmosphere and oceans. *Nature*, **320**, 27.

Judge, J., 1974, Brunei. *Journal of the National Geographic Society*, **145**, 207–25.

Keatinge, W.R., 1969, *Survival in Cold Water* (Oxford: Blackwell).

Kern, J.A., 1964, Observations on the habits of the proboscis monkey, *Nasalis larvatus* (Wurmb), made in the Brunei Bay Area, Borneo. *Zoologica*, **49**, 183–92.

Koford, C.B., 1963, Group relations in an island colony of rhesus monkeys. In *Primate Social Behavior*, ed. C.H. Southwick (Princeton: Van Nostrand), 136–52.

Kummer, H., 1971, *Primate Societies* (Chicago-New York: Aldine Atherton).

MacIntyre, F., 1970, Why the sea is salt. *Scientific American*, **223** (5), 104–15.

Miles, S., 1968, Drowning. *British Medical Journal*, **3**, 597–600.

Morgan, E., 1982, *The Aquatic Ape* (London: Souvenir Press).

Mukhtar, M.R. and Patrick, J.M, 1986, Ventilatory drive during face immersion in man. *Journal of Physiology*, **370**, 13–24.

Newell, N.D., 1971, The evolution of reefs. *Scientific American*, **226** (6), 54–65.

Richards, G., 1991, The refutation that never was: the reception of the Aquatic Ape Theory, 1972–1986. (This volume, chapter 6.)

Schultz, A.H., 1969, *The Life of Primates* (London: Weidenfeld & Nicolson).

Slijper, E.J., 1962, *Whales* (London: Hutchinson).

Sprankel, H., 1961, Über Verhaltensweisen und Zucht von *Tupaia glis* (Diard (1820) in Gefangenschaft. *Zeitschrift für wissenschaftliche Zoologie*, **165**, 186–220.

Stern, J. and Oxnard, C.E., 1973, Primate locomotion: some links with evolution and morphology. *Primatologia*, **4** (11), 1–93.

Tattersall, I., 1973, personal communication.

Walker, A., 1967, Locomotion adaptations in recent and fossil Madagascan lemurs. (Unpublished dissertation, University of London.)

Wind, J., 1970, *On the Phylogeny and the Ontogeny of the Human Larynx* (Groningen: Wotters-Noordhoff).

Wind, J., 1973, De zee in de mens – de mens in de zee. *Nederlands Tijdschrift voor Geneeskunde*, **117**, 1779–82.

Wind, J., 1976a, Human drowning: phylogenetic origin. *Journal of Human Evolution*, **5**, 349–63.

Wind, J., 1976b, Phylogeny of the human vocal tract. *Annals of the New York Academy of Sciences*, **280**, 612–30.

18 Do Aquatic Mammals Provide Support for the Aquatic Ape Theory?

Machteld Roede

SUMMARY

Palaeontology and evolutionary biology suggest that sea mammals have needed many millions of years to become fully adapted to a marine environment. Compared to their long evolutionary history, the relatively short period of 1 to almost 2 million years for a supposed aquatic phase of pro-hominids suggests that only minor adjustments could have occurred in the latter. If there was a Miocene aquatic ape, it might have lived only partially in the water.

INTRODUCTION

In the AAT debate, both advocates and opponents of the theory refer to comparisons of man with aquatic mammals. Because general knowledge about the latter is not widespread, a short survey of their evolution and specific water adaptations may be useful. It may illustrate the various transitional stages between terrestrial life and an existence in the sea.

EVOLUTION AND THE WATER ADAPTATIONS OF AQUATIC MAMMALS

About 300 million years ago amphibians left the sea and became adapted to a permanently terrestrial life; and about 150 million years later various land animals started to return to a life near and in the sea. But the loss of gills was irreversible; they and all their descendants remained dependent on the use of lungs for breathing.

Whales Fifty-five to sixty-five million years ago a wolf-sized primitive ungulate lived along the shores of the Tethys Sea, located in the area of the present-day Mediterranean and Persian Gulf. The abundantly present fish and crustaceans may have caused selection pressures that led to its wading through the waters; slowly but persistently its descendants – the primeval whales (Archaeoceti) – adapted to a marine life. Around 30–40 million years ago – most probably as a reaction to extreme geological changes, including a drastic drop in sea level and the development of a cold gulf stream in the southern hemisphere – they evolved into the more modern baleen whales (Mysticeti) and the even more recent toothed whales (Odontoceti). Some species stopped evolving several millions of years ago. The smaller toothed whales, the dolphins, are known to have evolved about 12 million years ago.

Numerous findings of fossils, preserved in the sediments of former shallow seas, illustrate the long route that cetaceans have taken in adjusting to an increasingly permanent aquatic life. Their modern adaptations include a streamlined body shape: anterior extremities reduced to flippers and the disappearance of the hind legs; a specific pattern of locomotion including a highly developed diving capacity, facilitated by various strategies for super-efficient breathing and feeding; the adaptation of eyes and kidneys to the salinity level of the sea; loss of almost all fur; non-protruding penis and mammary glands; birth and suckling under water, during which the thick, concentrated milk spouts into the mouth of the young; dorsally shifted nostrils; an auditory apparatus able to hear under water, and echo-location systems. Cetaceans' increased body size has reached such extremes that larger species die after being stranded, because their own body mass squeezed their lungs (partly as a result of the absence of a sternum) (Slijper, 1958, 1979; van Bree, 1986; Fordyce, 1988).

The constancy of the body temperature is remarkable (35.5°–37°C), even though the thermal conduction of the surrounding water is 20 times higher and the thermal capacity 2000 times greater than that of air. In temperate regions surface sea-water temperature rarely exceeds 17°–18°C, and for many months it is just a few degrees above freezing point. For large parts of the year whales stay in much colder regions still. Also, they dive to great depths for prolonged periods; with increasing depth, the water temperature decreases rapidly to 5°C.

Certain adaptations are connected with their survival in (often cold) water. Increased body size effectively reduces the heat-losing body surface as compared to body mass. Yet the largest whales also have to keep moving most of the day in order to produce heat from muscle activity. However, the subcutaneous adipose tissue (or 'blubber') contributes to insulation – albeit to a lesser extent than previously suggested (see Pond, this volume, chapter 12) – but sufficient to endanger stranded animals by heat accumulation (Wheeler, this volume, chapter 13, page 229). For this reason even the smaller dolphins and porpoises have to be kept cool by keeping them wet when out of the water (during transport by man, for instance), though this is done partly to protect the sensitive skin against drying up. Overheating during normal activities, as well as loss of body heat from the extremities, is prevented by an efficient variant, present in numerous mammals, of the 'counterflow system' (that is, arteries to the limbs are surrounded by veins): in whales, a plexus of veins optimises the temperature exchange (Slijper, 1958, 1964, 1979; Harrison and Bryden, 1988; Wheeler, this volume, chapter 13, page 224).

The permanently aquatic Sirenia or sea-cows (that is, the naked dugong and the three almost naked manatee species) are slow-moving vegetarians. Their evolution started 50 million years ago, when an elephant-like mammal returned to the sea. Their adaptations include a massive, cigar-shaped body, fin-shaped front legs and the loss of hind legs.

The smallest sea mammal, the sea-otter (*Enhydra lutris*), is also permanently aquatic; neither mating nor birth happens on land. They have no isolating blubber, but float and keep warm by means of air trapped in their thick fur. During the day they wander out into open sea; during the night they rest in beds of the thick sea-weed, kelp. Like the freshwater otter (*Lutra lutra*), they are supplied with well-developed webbed feet.

Pinnipeds Their evolution started about 30 million years ago, with a coastally foraging dog-like carnivore. Nowadays they are almost permanently aquatic. They may rest and sunbathe on land or on ice-floes, and their young are born on land. They are smaller than cetaceans, and their body temperature is higher. Like the cetaceans, they produce an efficiently water-reduced milk for their young. They have thick fur and a streamlined body, and the legs have evolved fin-paws at the front and fins at the back. The oldest family, the true seals, has no external ears and cannot bend their hind legs forwards; as a consequence, they move on land in a caterpillar-like way; in water, the fins are mainly used for stabilisation. The later-evolved sea-lions (with external ears) and walruses (without external ears) can move their hind legs forwards and backwards, so their locomotion on land is fast.

It might be relevant to the AAT debate to consider the polar bear, *Thalarctos maritimus*. Less than one million years ago its ancestors were still purely terrestrial. They now stay on land or pack-ice, and spend a lot of their time swimming and diving, though they cannot stay under water for more than 1.5–2 minutes (Slijper, 1958; Bryden, 1988). Compared to the real aquatic mammals, their adaptations to water and fishing are minor: a smaller head, a longer neck and a more streamlined body than other bears. Mating, birth and suckling are land activities, but they rarely go further than 50 km inland.

Only a small number of the numerous terrestrial mammal species lives partially in or near fresh water. Mostly they live on land, but frequently go into the water to get food. Their fur is thick, the air among the hairs preventing the skin from getting wet. Apart from some freshwater dolphins, only the hippopotamus sleeps and rests practically all the time in or near the water. Normally, they stay under water four to five minutes; like the dolphins, they have lost their fur (see also Leyhausen, this volume, chapter 10).

DIVING

Among the spectacular adaptations of sea mammals to the aquatic environment are those for diving, such as a most efficient system of oxygen supply and locomotion – though relative to their size the lungs are not large, and in some species even rather small. The respiration rate and volume and the breathing interval is related to the diving depth and the frequency of dives. In whales, diving capacity is at its greatest, though there is a marked interspecific variability.

It has been recorded that the sperm whale (*Physeter catodon*) can dive for more than 90 minutes, down to a depth of 1000–2000 m, but usually sperm whales stay under the water for some 50 minutes. Fin-whales (Balaenopteridae) rarely dive for more than 40 minutes; true whales (*Balaenidae*), foraging on phytoplankton just under the surface, in normal circumstances (that is, when not endangered) dive for 4 to 20 minutes. Dolphins generally make frequent dives of only 3 minutes, going no further down than 30 m; the beloved bottle-nose (*Tursiops truncatus*) dives for 15 minutes at most. A special blood supply automatically keeps the pressure in the middle ear cavity similar to that of the immediate surroundings; whales do not suffer from earache as a result of diving. It is, however, still not fully understood how they cope with the other effects of diving that in humans cause caisson disease.

Of the pinnipeds, the true seals and sea-lions dive for periods of between 5 and 15 minutes; the Weddell seal, for instance, has been recorded as diving to 600 m. Fur seals do not dive as deep or as long; walruses can stay under water for only 12 minutes, and dive to 80 m. Sea-cows dive for periods of up to 16 minutes and sea-otters for 5 minutes.

In contrast, terrestrial mammals are not adapted for prolonged stays under water. For instance, dogs do not survive an immersion of more than 4 minutes; for cats and rabbits the limit is 3 minutes (Slijper, 1958). Normally, humans can stay under water about 1 minute. Yet, with training, diving time (without equipment) can be prolonged to up to 2.5 minutes, and in extreme cases, even up to 5 minutes (see also Patrick, chapter 14). Only professional human divers are able to dive to 20 m, even down to 30, without equipment (see Roede, this volume, chapter 20).

CONCLUSION

There is some point in Morgan's remark (1982) that, time after time during evolutionary history, mammals of divergent families have returned to the sea and adapted to an aquatic life. The possibility, in a primate species, of an initial impetus towards adaptation for a marine environment should therefore not, *a priori*, be rejected. However, the changes described above and other remarkable anatomical and physiological adaptations have taken many millions of years of aquatic life. In contrast, the Aquatic Ape Theory covers only the relatively brief Miocene period 5 to 3.5–4 million years ago, after the split between the apes' and the hominids' lineages and before the first appearance of Australopithecines. Even if it were true that ape-like creatures became isolated on land that was still emerging when large parts of Africa were temporarily submerged, there does not seem to have been enough time for complete water adaptation to have evolved. The alleged aquatic ape can only have been semi-aquatic – or, more probably, just coastally foraging.

REFERENCES

Bree, P.J.H. van, 1986, Over soortvorming bij walsvisachtigen (Cetacea). *Natuurkundige Voordrachten*, NR **64**.

Bryden, M.M., 1988, Adaptations to water. In *Whales – dolphins and porpoises*, ed. R. Harrison and M.M. Bryden (Sydney: Intercontinental Publishing Corporation), 110–21.

Fordyce, R.E., 1988, Evolution. In *Whales – dolphins and porpoises*, ed. R. Harrison and M.M. Bryden (Sydney: Intercontinental Publishing Corporation), 14–23.

Harrison, R. and Bryden, M.M., eds., 1988, *Whales – dolphins and porpoises* (Sydney: Intercontinental Publishing Corporation).

Leyhausen, P., 1991, What constitutes an aquatic mammal? (This volume, chapter 10.)

Morgan, E., 1982, *The Aquatic Ape* (London: Souvenir Press).

Patrick, J.M., 1991, Human respiratory adaptations for swimming and diving. (This volume, chapter 14.)

Roede, M., 1991, Aquatic man. (This volume, chapter 20.)

Slijper, E.J., 1958, *Walvissen* (Amsterdam: Centen).

Slijper, E.J., 1964, Reuzen en dwergen in het dierenrijk (Leiden: Sijthoff, Natuur en Cultuur).

Slijper, E.J., 1979, *Whales* (London: Hutchinson).

19 More Thoughts on the Aquatic Ape Theory

HOW THE AQUATIC ADAPTATIONS OF MAN DIFFER FROM THOSE OF THE GORILLA AND THE CHIMPANZEE

Karl-Erich Fichtelius

SUMMARY
Bipedalism and hairlessness have often been interpreted as aquatic adaptations. Other features distinguishing man from the apes – such as differences in erythrocytes, female genital organs and temperature regulation – can be similarly interpreted.

Introduction

In seeking to establish the validity of the Aquatic Ape Theory (AAT), Hardy (1960), Morgan (1972, 1982) and Morgan and Verhaegen (1986) have sought evidence of aquatic adaptations in man by making general comparisons with other mammalian species. The most relevant differences must be expected to be those found when comparing man with his closest relatives – the apes. This essay points to three features not discussed so far.

Physical and physiological properties of blood

As one of their physical adaptations to long periods of submersion, marine mammals have a reduced number of red blood cells per unit volume. They have large blood cells, with a higher haemoglobin content per unit volume per cell than is found in land mammals of comparable size (Lenfant, 1969). In this respect it is remarkable that chimpanzees have an average of 7.3 million red cells per cubic millimetre of blood, gorillas 6.3 and humans only 5.1 million; the average size of the cells is about the same. The percentages of haemoglobin per cell are about 12.2 for chimpanzees, 13.2 for gorillas, and 18.6 for humans (Eberl-Rothe, 1960).

Various other features, related to the effective utilisation of oxygen, distinguish deep-diving mammals from land mammals: the amount of oxygen per unit volume of blood, the dissociation curve for oxygen and haemoglobin, the blood's capacity to absorb carbon dioxide, lung volume, and the volume of air that is exchanged during each breath. From the point of view of the AAT, further comparative research on man versus apes on these features would be of interest.

The vagina

The vagina of toothed whales, seals and dugongs is long and winding, and has a better developed hymen than is found among land mammals. These arrangements presumably function as a barrier, preventing water from entering the vagina. Dugongs have, in addition, a gland-like structure covering the lower part of the vagina. Even the urethra is embedded in this tissue (Harrison, 1969). A comparison with African apes shows (Eckstein, 1960):

(1) In their embryonic state females of all three species have well developed labia majora. In our species they remain large and developed throughout life, but in the ape they become vestigial in adult life, and the labia minora are clearly visible.
(2) Human females have transverse folds in the vagina, while the apes have longitudinal ones. The gorilla has some transverse folds, but not nearly so well developed as in our own species. In apes the vagina is straight; in humans it is oblique, towards the ventral side. Also, it is considerably longer than that of the others, as judged by the length of the penis (Lindblad, 1987). On average, the erect penis of a gorilla is 3 cm long, of a chimpanzee 8 cm, and of man 15 cm.
(3) The hymen occurs in humans and prosimians, but not in monkeys or apes.

The primal function of the hymen bears a relation to the seasonality of sexual activity; in the guinea-pig and some other small mammals it reseals the vaginal opening after each reproductive period. In *Homo* it is unlikely to relate to this function, considering the all-the-year-round state of receptivity in the adult female. The presence of a well developed hymen in a number of large, unrelated aquatic mammals suggests that in an aquatic medium it serves a different function.

It would appear, therefore, that the labia and the vagina of the human female are in several respects better designed than those of the ape for keeping out water and water-borne impurities.

Prevention of heat loss

To minimise the heat loss from the peripheral parts of the body and yet retain an adequate circulation of blood to these parts, numerous terrestrial mammals (Bazett *et al.*, 1948) and marine mammals (Irving, 1960; Slijper, 1979) exploit a counter-current heat exchange, the limb arteries being surrounded by veins. Humans and apes have a similar effective arrangement. But in the gorilla the veins surrounding the femoral artery are thick-walled compared with corresponding human veins. They are almost as thick as the artery itself, and presumably less effective at taking up heat from it (Platzer, 1960). If the AAT is correct, there would certainly have been some selective pressure to diminish the degree to which surface heat loss affects the body's core temperature. Man's generic ability to do this should be compared with that of apes.

Conclusion

A comparison of relevant human anatomical and physiological features with those of gorilla and chimpanzee does not contradict the theory about the possible aquatic adaptations of *Homo*. Such systematic comparisons should be continued and extended.

REFERENCES

Bazett, H.C., Loe, L., Eisenberg, L., Day, R. and Forster, R., 1948, *Journal of Applied Physiology*, **1**, 169–83.

Eberl-Rothe, G., 1960, Blutzellen. In *Primatologia*, ed. Hofer et al. (Basel: Karger), vol. 3: 1, 1–21.

Eckstein, P., 1960, Reproductive organs. In *Primatologia*, ed. Hofer et al. (Basel: Karger), vol. 3: 1, 542–629.

Ellis, D.V., Is an aquatic ape viable in terms of marine ecology and primate behaviour? (This volume, chapter 4.)

Hardy, A., 1960, Was man more aquatic in the past? *New Scientist*, **7**, 642–5.

Harrison, R.J., 1969, Reproduction and reproductive organs. In *The Biology of Marine Mammals*, ed. H.T. Andersen (New York: Academic Press).

Irving, L., 1969, Temperature regulation in marine mammals. In *The Biology of Marine Mammals*, ed. H.T. Andersen (New York: Academic Press).

Lenfant, C., 1969, Physiological properties of the blood of marine mammals. In *The Biology of Marine Mammals*, ed. H.T. Andersen (New York: Academic Press).

Lindblad, J., 1987, *Människen, du, jug och den ursprungliga* (Stockholm: Bonniers).

Morgan, E., 1972, *The Descent of Woman* (London: Souvenir Press).

Morgan E., 1982, The aquatic hypothesis. *New Scientist*, **1405**, 17–18.

Morgan, E. and Verhaegen, M., 1986, In the beginning was the water. *New Scientist*, **1498**, 62–3.

Platzer, W., 1960, Das Arterien- und Venensystem. In *Primatologia*, ed. Hofer *et al.* (Basel: Karger), vol. 3: 2.

Slijper, E.J. 1979, *Whales* (London: Hutchinson).

★ ★ ★

SOME CARDIAC TOPOGRAPHIC AND MORPHO-PHYSIOLOGICAL OBSERVATIONS OF THE COMMON SEAL AND OF MAN

Cornelis J. van Nie and Machteld Roede

SUMMARY

Viewed in the light of the Aquatic Ape Theory, a comparison with sea mammals may assist our understanding of features in which humans differ from other terrestrial mammals. Reported here are some cardiac adaptations to diving in pinnipeds and some similarities between man and the common seal (*Phoca vitulina vitulina*), both in general morphology and in the congenital pathology of the heart.

Introduction

Pickford (this volume, chapter 7) is right, in that mere analogies are risky proofs of evidence. Yet some data on cardiac morphology may provide information relevant to the discussion of the AAT (Hardy, 1960; Morgan, 1982). They are based on observations made by the first author during numerous dissections of man and animals – mainly cattle and pigs, but also aquatic mammals. His special interest focused on the heart and its anomalies. The second author became involved with sea mammals when she was a student of Evert Slijper, a leading authority on whales.

Man is only remotely related to the aquatic mammals, which are more closely related to predators and ungulates (see Roede, this volume, chapter 18). Yet in view of the debate on the AAT, it may be useful to report some cardiac features of pinnipeds in connection with their diving capacities, and to describe some similarities between man and the common seal (*Phoca vitulina vitulina*).

The diving reflex

Patrick (see this volume, chapter 14) and Schagatay (this volume, chapter 15) have discussed the diving reflex (Hempleman and Lockwood, 1978), which implies a bradycardia in mammals, birds and amphibia. The reflex shows great interspecific variability; the degree of bradycardia is greatest in diving cetaceans and pinnipeds, where the pulse rate may decrease from 120 to 12 per minute. The increase of the interval between the heartbeats would seem to damage the brain and heart tissue, from oxygen depletion due to the expected sharp decreases in blood pressure. To maintain an adequate mean blood pressure, parts of the aorta ascendens function as an auxiliary heart or air chamber, by means of the widened bulbus aortae and the quantity and quality of the elastic fibres in its wall. Three examples are given to illustrate the relation between morphology and function with regard to the demands of diving.

(1) In 'professional' divers like the cetaceans and pinnipeds (see Roede, this volume, chapter 18), the whole aorta ascendens functions as an air chamber. In contrast, in occasional divers like humans and dogs, that function is restricted to the aorta's proximal part, the area of the semi-lunar valves (or sinus valsalvae).

(2) In seals the development of the bulbus aortae was found to differ in relation to habitat and behaviour. Pups of the common seal start swimming and diving within eight hours of birth. The elastic fibres in the wall of their bulbus aortae are well developed; the air chamber function starts right after birth. In contrast, pups of the Weddell seal have to learn swimming and diving after a post-partum period on the rocks of at least six weeks. The development of their elastic fibres is relatively retarded (van Nie, 1985).

(3) On dissection, the number of autonomous ganglial cells in the

> vicinity of the sinuatrial node in aquatic mammals (like the seal, the sea-lion and also the musk-rat) proves to be about three times higher than in terrestrial mammals, including man. The bradycardia during diving shown by aquatic mammals might be effected by the modification of sinuatrial node activity through the influence of the parasympathetic part of the autonomous nervous system (van Nie, 1986).

In these three respects, man differs from sea mammals.

Cardiac topography

Certain findings about man and the common seal are now summarised. First, there is a similarity in the spatial relationship between the heart and the great vessels, which is quite different from that in other mammals. Secondly, in both species we find the same shape and topography of the heart, its apex being directed caudally, not caudo-ventrally as in other mammals, and the cross-section of the thorax in both is dorso-ventrally flattened. In contrast, one finds latero-medial flattening in most quadrupedal species, including the fur seal (*Arctocephalus australis*). In the common seal there may be a functional relation between these specific morphological features and its typical caterpillar-like terrestrial locomotion (van Nie, 1982, 1983).

Coarctatio aortae

In humans and other mammals, many types and degrees of congenital anomalies of the heart occur. Some are predominant in one species, and others in other species. Here we focus on coarctatio aortae, a narrowing of the aortic arch near the ductus arteriosus; the stenosis may have the shape of a ring or a funnel. Coarctatio aortae – extremely rare in pigs and cattle – is rather common in seals; we found it in 4 out of 38 dissected seals. The incidence in man is 0.08 per cent of live births. In the seal, coarctation would seem to support the function of the bulbus during diving by ensuring a sufficient blood supply to the heart and brain. In man, the effect of coarctation might well be similar – that is, an increase in blood-flow to the brain. During embryonic life, coarctatio aortae is a necessary condition; accordingly, it is present in all humans before birth. It ensures the proper intra-uterine development of the brain. In adults one of the first symptoms is the presence of cold feet, due to the decreased circulation in the lower half of the body.

Lévi-Strauss has expressed the value of myths for modern science. This may be illustrated by reference to a Norwegian myth about sailors and seals. Sailors believe that seals are sinful sailors. Punished by the gods for their sinful life, they are condemned to become seals, in a hairy pelt and at the mercy of water, wind and tide. It may happen, though, that such a 'seal' saves the life of a sailor in the agony of near-death. Then the seal changes into a beautiful princess, and becomes the sailor's bride. These ladies are said to have lovely dark eyes and bodies, but their feet are always much colder than those of normal girls. This myth thus seems to tell the clinical history of coarctatio aortae in man.

Conclusion

We hypothesise that the initial aquatic functional adaptations acquired by Miocene ancestral hominids might have included some intrathoracic circulatory features.

REFERENCES

Hardy, A., 1960, Was man more aquatic in the past? *New Scientist*, **7**, 642–5.

Hempleman, H.V. and Lockwood, A.P.M., 1978, *The Physiology of Diving in Man and Other Animals* (London: Edward Arnold).

Lévi-Strauss, C., 1964–8, *Mythologique* (Paris: Plon).

Morgan, E., 1982, *The Aquatic Ape* (Souvenir Press: London).

Nie, C.J. van, 1974, Some reflections about the relation of the semilunar valvular rings of the heart and the transposition of the great vessels in animals. *Proceedings of the 9th Congress of the European Association of Veterinary Anatomists*, Toulouse.

Nie, C.J. van, 1982, De morfologie en de congenitale pathologie van het hart van de gewone zeehond (*Phoca vitulina vitulina*). Zeehonden Symposium. *Tijdschrift Diergeneeskunde*, **107**, 368–74.

Nie, C.J. van, 1983, A comparative study of the morphology and the topography of the heart of the *Arctocephalus australis* (Fur or Ursine seal) and the heart of the *Phoca vitulina vitulina* (Common or Harbour-seal) in their relation to the type of locomotion. *Aquatic Mammals*, **10**, 79–82.

Nie, C.J. van, 1985, The bulbus aortae (aorta ascendens) in the growing common seal (*Phoca vitulina vitulina*) (a morphological approach). *Aquatic Mammals*, **11**(3), 71–4.

Nie, C.J. van, 1986, The sinuatrial node and its adjacent autonomous ganglia cells in aquatic mammals (a morphological approach). *Aquatic Mammals*, **12** (3), 92–4.

Patrick, J.M., 1991, Human respiratory adaptations for swimming and diving. (This volume, chapter 14.)

Pickford, M., 1991, Does the geological evidence support the Aquatic Ape Theory? (This volume, chapter 7.)

Roede, M., 1991, Do aquatic mammals provide support for the Aquatic Ape Theory? (This volume, chapter 18.)

Schagatay, E., 1991, The significance of the human diving reflex. (This volume, chapter 15.)

★ ★ ★

THE ANSWER: THE AQUATIC APE THEORY AND THE SAVANNAH THEORY COMBINED

Sarah B.M. Kraak

SUMMARY

After brief comments on Wheeler's statements about cooling down in the sea and the loss of fur (this volume, chapter 13), it is proposed to consider the Aquatic Ape Theory and the Savannah Theory as complementary, and not mutually exclusive.

The answer

One of the interpretations of the Aquatic Ape Theory proposes that this ape lived on the shore and frequently went into the water to play, to swim and to collect food, as modern humans like to do when on holiday (Ellis, this volume, chapter 4; Richards, chapter 6). If we adopt this view of the aquatic ape, Wheeler's counter-evidence (chapter 13) – in support of the Savannah Theory – needs some re-evaluation.

First, some remarks about Wheeler's graphs (Figure 13.2) which show that humans cannot produce enough energy to maintain their body temperature in water. As many of us may know from experience, in the Mediterranean, when day temperatures in summer are between 25°C and 35°C and the water temperature is between 22°C and 26°C, it is perfectly possible to be in the water for several hours a day without danger from the point of view of survival. Of course, we cannot, as Wheeler shows, stay in the water for hours at a stretch, but we can alternate periods in and out of the water the whole day. Every time we go into the water we cool down, and use up some energy in trying to keep the body temperature up. When we leave the water we stay in the sun to get warm, and after a while we can go in again. It is not necessary to keep our body temperature constantly at 37°C; we can afford to cool down peripherally for a short time. The sun, which causes such a strong selection pressure for the savannah, according to Wheeler, will provide the heat to raise our body temperature again to the normal level. By eating enough food – we would need to eat more than when we do not go into the water at all – we will be able to replenish the calories lost during the periods in the water.

Furthermore, in his Savannah Theory Wheeler suggests that a selection pressure exerted by solar heat made our ancestors lose their fur and acquire eccrine sweat glands for keeping the body temperature low by transpiration. To compensate for the water loss by transpiration, he suggests, our ancestors drank water from freshwater sources that were always nearby on the savannah. If there was always water nearby, would it not be more likely that the sun's heat made our ancestors use that water to get wet, so that the evaporation of the water on the skin kept the body temperature low? They would not have needed to develop sweat glands and a furless skin if there was always water nearby in which to cool down.

I accept Wheeler's point that the loss of fur would not have been brought about during an aquatic phase in the evolution of our ancestors merely because they were too small. There exist modern mammals which spend some or much of their time in the water and still have fur. Hence, another explanation is needed for the loss of fur. However, there remain certain human features – such as the diving reflex, tears and perhaps the eccrine sweat glands – which seem to need to be explained by an aquatic phase in our early evolution. Therefore, I want to propose a combination of the Savannah Theory and the Aquatic Ape Theory.

The 'baboon marker', mentioned by Morgan (this volume, chapter 2), strongly suggests that for a while our ancestors were isolated from the African savannah animals. If a small group of African ape-like creatures became isolated – perhaps trapped on Danakil Island (LaLumiere, chapter 3) – it can be imagined that a rapid evolution of characteristics, quite different from those of the original species, took place. This often happens when a small group gets isolated in a small place: the result of a founder effect, no gene flow, genetic drift and slightly different selection pressures deriving from a slightly different environment. Imagine a small population of our ancestors who lived isolated on a small island, always very near to the sea. They would frequently go into the water, probably to escape not from predators but from the sun's heat, and to collect some easily available food. In the light of evidence showing that certain other primates like water, I do not think that there is any necessity to believe that our ancestors would have been hydrophobic. If they spent much time in the water it would have been advantageous for them to develop eccrine sweat glands and tears for salt excretion. If they had to dive for their food – urchins, molluscs, crustaceans, anemones and so on, which could be easily collected in shallow water near the shore – they would have benefited from a diving reflex. Perhaps if they spent much time swimming, the angle between their spine and their hind limbs would have become straighter – which later became a preadaptation for bipedal locomotion.

Then, when the island was joined to the mainland again, this group of 'different' apes spread on to the savannah. If they had been preadapted with eccrine sweat glands, which here happened to be useful for thermoregulation, and if another preadaptation had been a more upright posture, they could have become bipedal, furless, sweating creatures, as in Wheeler's Savannah Theory. They would probably not even have had to wait for the island to join the mainland: also on this island with a hot (savannah) climate it would have been advantageous, during the periods spent out of the water, to become bipedal and furless with eccrine glands.

Conclusion

In my opinion the Savannah Theory and the Aquatic Ape Theory are complementary, not mutually exclusive. We need the Aquatic Ape Theory to explain the diving reflex and, perhaps, tears. On the other hand, we probably need the Savannah Theory to explain the loss of fur. But here again we need the Aquatic Ape Theory to make the loss of fur possible as a result of the preadaptation represented by eccrine sweat glands. I would like to conclude that we need both theories to explain the first steps in our evolution.

REFERENCES
Ellis, LaLumiere, Morgan, Richards and Wheeler, chapters 4, 3, 2, 6 and 13 respectively, this volume.

★ ★ ★

THE SECOND CRISIS

Erika Schagatay

SUMMARY
When the Miocene drought changed into a moister climate, the increase in terrestrial productivity may have been paralleled by a decrease in reef productivity, as a result of greatly increased sediment transport to the reefs by run-off rainwater. Also, changes in sea level may have damaged the reefs. These alterations in the coastal habitat and decline in its edible marine life may have forced the apes to explore the terrestrial environment and finally to abandon the sea.

Figure 19.1 When food got scarce on the dying reefs the aquatic apes started to explore the river beds and finally left the sea.

The enigmatic question

The climatological changes in East Africa, having caused forests to retreat and savannahs and deserts to expand, may have led to a crisis for our arboreal ancestors. At the end of the Miocene East Africa was largely deforested but, because of ideal conditions for coral growth, its coasts were lined with rich reefs. It is plausible that a group of apes learned to utilise the marine resources, and over a long period of time became semi-aquatic. The diverse and easily accessible food resources might even have been partly known to some ape populations before the land became inhospitable to them. But once the apes had become adapted to the aquatic environment, what caused them ultimately to leave it?

Writers on the Aquatic Ape Theory conclude that, as soon as favourable changes permitted, the apes returned to a terrestrial life. But we need to go further, and try to explain why the hypothetical aquatic ape, highly dependent on the coral reef for food and shelter, returned to the land. Morgan (1982; this volume, chapter 2) suggested that the aquatic ape was well equipped to exploit the new conditions on land, as brought about by the end of the drought period. Indeed, it could be considered to have been preadapted to develop some of the qualities which would be of use to it later on land, though during the preceding phase the aquatic ape was equipped to utilise the reef habitat. At the end of the aquatic phase I picture a biped who could walk well but not yet run fast; a user of the first primitive tools, though not a skilled hunter.

LaLumiere (1981; this volume, chapter 3) suggests that the aquatic apes, after having been isolated on Danakil Island for at least 1.5 to 3 million years, walked back to spread out over Africa after the island had been reconnected to the mainland by the regression of the sea. It is indeed possible that selective pressures on a population of apes isolated on a geographical island caused them to start exploring marine resources; the geological history of the Danakil horst makes this an interesting proposal. But it provides no explanation of why the aquatic apes abandoned the sea. Morgan's suggestion that the sea may have abandoned the ape is interesting, but remains speculative when based on sea-level fluctuations alone. When the sea retreated, the apes could have followed the slowly retreating shore lines as deeper parts of the reef developed.

So what else could have contributed to the end of the aquatic period? There seems to be agreement that something happened at the end of the prolonged Miocene drought. To find an answer to this question, raised by Morgan as well as by some critics of the AAT as one of the most puzzling ones relating to this theory, one has to examine what can actually happen when a dry, tropical climate changes into a moister one.

A possible explanation

During a period of extremely limited rainfall, the soil loses most of its ability to absorb water, resulting in a massive surface run-off when precipitation increases. As a result, silt and sand are transported by the rainwater to the sea. A drastic increase in sediment outflow may suffocate the reef, since optimal conditions for reef-building corals are warm, saline, light, well aerated (oxygenated) water free of suspended sediment. More-over, immersion of coastal flora and transport by rainwater of organic material to the sea would have set off rotting processes and subsequent de-oxygenation of coastal waters (Stock, 1990). Finally, the supply of fresh water after a heavy downpour may have caused drastic local changes in salinity which could have affected the reef.

Machteld Roede suggests that sea-level fluctuations may also have contributed to reef destruction. The increased rainfall in the Miocene period and subsequently decreased evaporation at the surface of the sea due to cloud cover, may initially have led to a slight rise in sea level. If this rise exceeded the rate of coral growth, it could have had an inhibitory effect on reef development, as coral growth mainly takes place just below the water surface where light conditions are optimal. On the other hand, when the sea finally retreated it would have caused reef destruction above the new neap flood level. Corals are sensitive to air exposure longer than the usual inter-tidal period, and start dying after six hours of standing clear of water (Roos, 1971). The rise and fall of islands and reefs is well documented (Stock, 1990), and frequently used by geologists to reconstruct Ice Age cycli. Fossil reefs could possibly reveal whether such a scenario fits the AAT. It may be that massive reef destruction, due to the outflow of sediment (and so not correlated to Ice Age cycli), can also be detected in fossil reef series.

Thus, the changes brought about by the end of the Miocene drought period affected not only the environment on land, but also, to a large extent, the conditions in the marine ecosystem at its shores. The rapid increase in land productivity when seasonal rains returned was paralleled by the diminishing productivity of the coastal reefs. Such changes would have had a large influence on the habitat of the aquatic apes. When parts of the reef were damaged or destroyed, the apes could have started migrating in search of undamaged areas where drainage from the land was low. But when the productivity of the entire coastal habitat gradually diminished, the apes would have been forced to explore the increasingly rich river-beds and inland areas near the shore in search of alternative sources of food. Subsequently, they would have left the seashore, adopting a mainly terrestrial mode of life.

Conclusion

While drought was the first crisis for our ancestors, forcing them to adopt a semi-aquatic life, the return of the rains was their second crisis, forcing them once more to change their way of living in order to survive – and to return to the land.

REFERENCES

LaLumiere, L.P., 1981, Evolution of human bipedalism: a hypothesis about where it happened. *Philosophical Transactions of the Royal Society of London*, **B292**, 103–7.

LaLumiere, L.P., 1991, Evolution of genus *Homo*: where it happened. (This volume, chapter 3.)

Morgan, E., 1982, *The Aquatic Ape* (London: Souvenir Press).

Morgan, E., 1991, Why a new theory is needed. (This volume, chapter 2.)
Roos, P.J., 1971, The shallow-water stony corals of the Netherlands Antilles. *Studies Fauna Curaçao Caribbean Islands*, **37**, 1–108.
Stock, J.H., 1990, *Insular groundwater biotas – a biogeographic synthesis.* (Valedictory lecture, University of Amsterdam, 22 October.)

★ ★ ★

HUMAN SEXUAL DIMORPHISM: A SPECULATIVE APPROACH

Erika Schagatay

SUMMARY
In this essay a possible aquatic origin of sexual dimorphism in human fat distribution is discussed. It is proposed that the relatively large, fat-padded breast of the human female may primarily have evolved to facilitate nursing in the water. It is suggested that her protruding buttocks and hips, combined with a slim waist, may have evolved to enable the baby to cling on to the naked mother; and that the origin of the sexual dimorphism in overall fat insulation may be sexually determined behavioural differences deriving from an aquatic phase of hominid evolution.

Introduction

Features of sexual dimorphism, and sex differences in general, have often been a matter debate among human evolutionists. Some of these features have been discussed by Morgan (1972; this volume, page 15), Pond (this volume, page 209) and Fichtelius (1985) in the context of the AAT. I share their view that we have to concentrate on finding functional explanations for features which later may have been sexually selected for. In this essay, a personal speculation about the origin of sexual dimorphism in the distribution of human fat will be given.

Breasts

Morgan links this distinctively human attribute, the fat-padded breast, to the Aquatic Ape Theory by explaining how the aquatic mother – on land, with the baby on her lap – needed some arrangement for lowering the nipple to the baby's mouth. However, this is the way in which the mother chimpanzee often breast-feeds her baby, even though her breasts are of an entirely different shape. This gives rise to two questions:

(1) Does the usual shape of the nursing human mother's breast offer a firm grip to a baby's hands?
(2) Did our presumed aquatic mother have to leave the water to feed her baby?

The answer to the first question has to be a categorical no. Nursing mothers usually have round, firm breasts. Especially when full of milk, the taut breast does not offer any grip for tiny baby hands. I believe that holding on to a mother chimpanzee's slack nipple is easier for any baby than grabbing a human breast. The aquatic ape females may not have lived long enough to acquire the more tube-like, grippable swag-breasts required for the land-based theory.

When answering the second question, we have to bear in mind that a mother who carries her baby with her normally feeds it as soon as it gets hungry. This means feeding at least every two hours when the child is small (no matter what was recommended in the West during the first half of this century). This is the natural way still practised in many parts of the world; our aquatic mother probably fed her baby in the same way.

We now have to imagine the situation of a food-searching aquatic ape mother. She has come far from the place where she entered the water in her search for food. Suddenly the baby starts whining. Before she can reach the shore, the baby is howling, and sooner or later she will try to breast-feed it at sea.

This innovation must have spread through the population. Babies with mothers having slightly more fat padding around the nipples could drink more milk (and less sea water) than did other babies, and consequently grew faster and had a better chance of surviving. Mothers not succeeding in breast-feeding at sea lost valuable food-seeking time when they had to swim ashore, and were not able to feed their babies as efficiently as those feeding them at sea. After a great many generations, mothers usually fed their babies at sea, and males reproducing with large-bosomed females fathered more children. This led to sexual selection for this feature, which continued on land where the feature lost its original, functional value, and in extreme cases is even harmful to the owner. This answers my second question: the aquatic ape mother did not have to leave the sea to feed her baby, if there were other reasons for staying in the water. Of course, the aquatic mother fed her baby on land too. The child could feed comfortably from her type of breast there as well, when held by her or lying down beside her on the warm sand.

Now it is possible to explain the otherwise surprising fact that we have the same breast shape as sea-cows, but one different from the apes. It could be because our foremothers often fed their babies in the same way as sea-cows have been reported to do: floating vertically in the water while holding their babies in their arms. In both cases the breasts float, giving the baby good access to the nipple. The breasts also form a good seal against the baby's mouth, letting no water in, in spite of waves or accidental submersion. It is even possible to suckle a baby totally submerged (Tjarkowskij, 1982), although I do not think this was purposely practised among the aquatic apes.

By accepting an aquatic explanation instead of the land-based one, we also get an answer to why round, firm breasts, rather than tube-like ones, became ideal in the eyes of males.

Figure 19.2 Three positions which could be used by the aquatic ape mother when feeding her baby at sea.
In all situations the floating breast assured the baby easy access to the nipple, and the fat-padding made a watertight seal with the baby's mouth. The fat also kept the breasts well insulated and warm. It was the ideal solution for mother and child.

Buttocks

One of the most distinctive features of the human female's body is the buttocks, which are not nearly as well developed in the male or in any other primate. The fact that a woman needs a wide pelvis in order to give birth to large-headed babies is well known, and well developed muscles are needed to keep the body in an upright position. But why is this feature exaggerated by a deposit of fat in the female? For streamlining and insulation, this fat would serve a better purpose if distributed around the belly, as in the male.

In *The Descent of Woman* Morgan (1972) supposes that the buttocks were necessary to protect the female from getting sand and dirt into her genitals when sitting on the beach. But apes also often sit in this position on the ground (Goodall, 1971). Although such protection might have been one benefit of the feature, I think it had another origin.

When discussing the pros and cons of the aquatic adaptations on land, one of the most problematic innovations is that of nakedness – not only for adults, whose protection against the sun and hence their adaptation for heat control thereby decreased, but also for the babies who were used to clinging on to the mother by grabbing her fur. A formerly suggested solution to this problem is that the human female acquired long head-hair to give her baby a hold. But while the mother's hair would be very helpful to the child when both were in the water, it was not enough for babies clinging to their mothers on land. Another innovation was needed to keep the baby from falling off the mother. This is where the buttocks – protruding not only from the sides but also from the back – acquire their role.

Today this feature is particularly pronounced in some African populations, where the children are carried on the backs of their mothers. An extreme form exists in Bushwomen, where the buttocks form a flat, almost horizontal, 'shelf' serving this purpose very well (Figure 19.3 (b)). Even though most women are less extreme in this respect, when a pregnant woman puts on weight she puts it in large part on her hips and buttocks.

I think the mother's protruding buttocks, in combination with a slim waist and long head-hair, offered our water-baby the support needed for it to stay on its mother's back by itself when necessary. When climbing in and out of the water, the mother had to use both her hands and her feet to get through the waves and over the reef edge without losing balance, and she could not give the baby much assistance. On land the arrangement freed her hands for other tasks.

Again, there is a corresponding ideal image of a woman among modern men: a slim waist together with round hips give her the curved configuration desired in so many cultures. Stone Age paintings and carvings from various parts of the world often display women with enormously protruding, shelf-like buttocks (see Figures 12.1 and 19.3(a)).

In Western culture the importance of having a slim waist was so stressed at one time that to be considered attractive women had to wear corsets, often combined with built-up dresses, emphasising the buttocks or hips (Figure 19.3(c)).

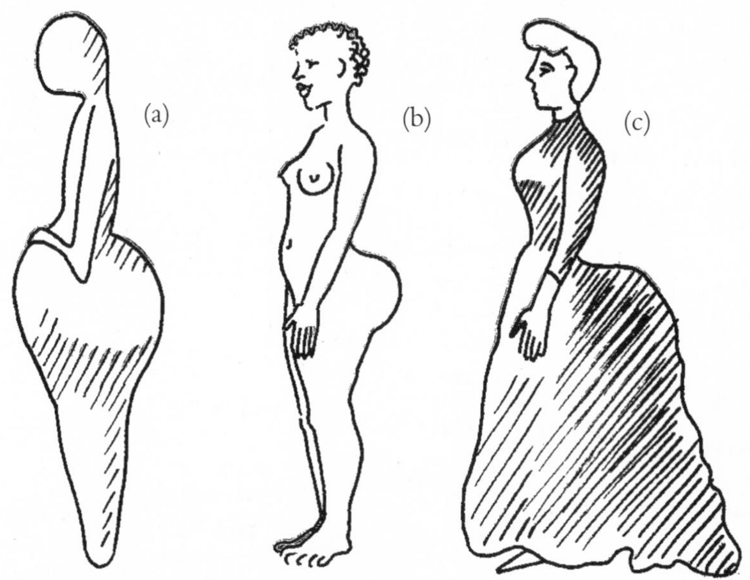

Figure 19.3 Stone Age torso, steatopygous Bushwoman and fashionable nineteenth-century lady.

'Blubber'

Why is it that men and women not only have their body fat distributed in different ways, but also have unequal amounts of it (Pond, this volume, chapter 12)? Women usually have a relatively thick layer covering the entire body surface – much like the blubber of marine mammals – while men have most of it in their belly area. Women consequently have a better insulation in water, which explains why they often survive boat accidents in which men die from the cold. This seems to suggest that women are better adapted to marine life than men are.

When discussing aquatic adaptations, Hardy (1960) emphasised the streamlining of the female body. But is not a somewhat plump man more streamlined? It has already been suggested that the females acquired their body curves not primarily in order to become better swimmers, but to give better support to their babies.

There is no evidence of sex differences in the diving reflex or in breath-holding time. Nevertheless, when occupied in the same activities as men, women can stay longer in the water without becoming hypothermic. This may be the reason for the tradition of sponge- and pearl-divers being mainly females (Ama and Haenyo peoples, in the cold seas between Korea and Japan). Women are also better at long-distance swimming than are men, while men are faster at short distances. I think the Aquatic Ape Theory can help us explain this difference. Again, it has to do with making the female a better mother.

Figure 19.4 At the end of the aquatic phase Ms Missing Link may have looked something like this.

While most aquatic ape females must have spent their days slowly swimming about at the pace of their children, collecting food on the reef, the males may have led much more mobile lives. Apart from collecting slow-moving seafood, the male might have been active in hunting turtles and other moderately fast swimmers. The muscle heat produced by fast swimming may have been sufficient to keep him warm in the relatively warm tropical waters; in contrast, the aquatic mother never swam fast enough for it to matter. The male could get into and out of the water much more easily than the baby-carrying female, and he may not have spent such long periods at a time in the water.

When there were predators on land the male could defend himself by approaching the threat in shallow water, throwing rocks, then quickly retreating into deeper water. For the aquatic mother this would have been out of the question, and in these situations she had to stay out of reach and spend extended periods of time in the water. As suggested, feeding the baby at sea offered her no problem. Of course, the baby would get cold before the mother, but when this happened the mother could move to a place where the water reached to her waist and the baby could warm up in her arms or on her back. The female could stay for extended periods in this position, thanks to the particularly well developed fat insulation in her lower body parts. This distribution of fat also gave her good buoyancy for floating vertically when breast-feeding in deeper water.

Conclusion

Thus, the blubber-like fat layer of the modern female does not necessarily indicate a difference in the degree to which the sexes were adapted to water, but a difference arising from different behaviour while in the water. Aquatic ape males and females might very well have spent the same amount of time per day in the water.

REFERENCES

Fichtelius, K. 1985, (*Hur apan miste pälsen och kom upp på två ben*) (Stockholm: Akademilitteratur).

Goodall, J., 1971, *In the Shadow of Man* (London: Collins).

Hardy, A., 1960, Was man more aquatic in the past? *New Scientist*, **7**, 642–5.

Morgan, E., 1972, *The Descent of Woman* (London: Souvenir Press).

Morgan, E., 1982, *The Aquatic Ape* (London: Souvenir Press).

Pond, C.M., 1991, Adipose tissue in human evolution. (This volume, chapter 12.)

Tjarkovskij, I., 1982. In *Vatten Barn*, E. Sidenbladh (Stockholm: Akademilitteratur).

20 Aquatic Man

Machteld Roede

SUMMARY

This chapter aims, by assessing the ability of modern humans to cope with the sea, to evaluate the plausibility of a temporarily (semi-)marine habitat in the early stages of hominid evolution. This is approached from two different angles: firstly, by discussing the physical nature of the marine environment, and secondly, by considering cultural reactions and adaptations. A short survey of oceanographic physics shows that the sea is no easy niche to invade; only a limited range of littoral areas would have been suitable dwelling places for the hypothetical aquatic apes.

As to human culture, some remarks are made about mastering the sea by floating devices, and about diving in the past and the present. Historical misinterpretations demonstrate how long it took before the physical and physiological consequences of underwater exploration were fully understood. Only in the last few decades have we acquired the technology which enables us to descend under the sea surface for more than a few minutes and at depths greater than a few metres.

References to the sea and its inhabitants in religious concepts, legends and myths indicate that, at least for the last few thousand years, mankind has been aware of the dual nature of the sea, which initially inspired mainly awe and dread of the destructive power of the sea and of its mysterious inhabitants.

INTRODUCTION

My interest in the Aquatic Ape Theory had a threefold origin. First, over a period of several years I led a semi-aquatic lifestyle, daily spending hours in the sea, partly on the surface, partly on the seabed at a depth of several metres, for the purpose of observing and collecting fish from coral reefs, and measuring and dissecting them on the beach. Secondly, my reversal from a marine to a human biologist meant that I became professionally involved in the subject of human evolution. In the third place, Elaine Morgan's *The Descent of Woman* (1972) attracted my attention because of her discussion of the role of women in evolution.

I was therefore immediately enthusiastic when Jan Wind suggested the Aquatic Ape Theory as a topic for a joint meeting of the Dutch Association of Physical Anthropology and the European Sociobiological Society, and readily agreed to act as host at the conference to be held at Valkenburg. During personal contacts with Elaine Morgan it became apparent that she was certainly no rigid defender of the original Aquatic Ape Theory. Rather she appeared to have an open mind, receptive of any information that might elucidate the environmental conditions of the hypothetical aquatic ape. All these circumstances led me to write this contribution.

Over geological time there have been extreme fluctuations of sea level; islands have been born and submerged again. Among the variety of scenarios that have been proposed, the hypothesis by LaLumiere (this volume, chapter 3) offers a plausible version – namely, that during the period of the Miocene drought some ex-arboreal pro-hominids became stranded on the then existing Danakil Island (now Danakil Alps). According to Hardy's Aquatic Ape Theory (AAT) (1960), aquatic features evolved as a consequence of seeking seafood. His concept has been propagated by Morgan (1982; see also 1990), and increasingly is taken seriously as an alternative scenario for the beginnings of hominid evolution (e.g. Calvin, 1986).

Most contributions to the AAT discussion focus on intrinsic physical features present in modern man, said to have been acquired during the proposed aquatic phase. The intention of this chapter is, however, to check how well-disposed the sea actually is towards us, and how easy to colonise (see Ehrlich, 1989). A short survey of current knowledge of the sea and its coasts may suggest where it would have been possible – and where impossible – for Miocene apes to turn to the sea. (Reasons for excluding freshwater wetlands are mentioned in chapters 3 and 4.)

In addition, man's methods of mastering the sea by floating devices, and hazards encountered during diving, will be discussed. Finally, religion, myth and legend may throw some light on the attitudes of (pre)historic humans towards the sea.

SEAS AND COASTS

It is not without symbolism that the symposium on the hypothetical aquatic ancestors was held in The Netherlands, the 'Low Countries', an area largely below sea level and reclaimed from the waves by the hand of man. For many centuries, Dutchmen have had to battle against the sea, which constantly threatened to reconquer the land levied a severe toll of the lives of its fishermen and coastal dwellers. How many heraldic arms show, as our province Zeeland does, a heroic lion struggling to keep its head above the waves?

This illustrates that a life in close relation to the sea is not without danger, although some marine ecosystems offer the advantage of rich food resources (see Ellis, chapter 4). Ellis briefly mentions (page 44) the risk of wave action on rocky shores, but there are other physical properties of the sea and coasts that would have tended to inhibit pro-hominids from adopting a semi-aquatic way of living.

The seas

More than three-quarters of our globe – that is, in the northern hemisphere 60.5 per cent of the surface, and in the southern half 80 per cent – is covered with water. The Pacific alone covers a larger surface than all the continents put together. The average depth of the oceans is 3,800 metres. Nowadays, all the oceans and seas are mapped. But, though its surfaces may have been recorded, the world beneath the sea level is still mainly unexplored; mankind's knowledge of the ocean is still largely limited to its upper levels.

Up to the nineteenth century, the waters of the world were regarded merely as a source of sea food and a barrier to be crossed. Scientific marine knowledge remained scanty until quite recently, whereas the exploration of high mountain areas, tropical jungles and deserts, had been accomplished much earlier. Even the level of actual knowledge of the stars, first acquired thousands of years ago by the Babylonians, contrasts sharply with knowledge of the sea. Ancient writings about such phenomena as the tides, salinity of the water and storms at sea were based on guesswork and were often wildly inaccurate. Few people ever attempted to plumb the ocean depths. The Vikings, though possessing genuinely scientific knowledge about sea lanes and navigation, were not at all concerned with what went on below the surface. Throughout the Middle Ages, the knowledge of marine matters that had been acquired suffered as a result of the general eclipse of scholarship and intellectual curiosity, and during the Renaissance, although men of learning evinced a passionate interest in the underwater world, their efforts failed to produce any new insights (De Latil and Rivoire, 1956).

The first scientific study of the sea started with the investigations of such men as Rumphius (1628–1702) (Ballintijn, 1944). An important later study was the voyage of the *Beagle* (1831–1836), which was mainly a mission to study ocean currents (Darwin, 1906; Moorehead, 1969). The first general knowledge about marine physics was obtained during the voyage of the *Challenger* (1872–1876) (Colman, 1951; Reader's Digest, 1974). Only during the last few decades, with the setting up of specialised oceanographic institutes, has a thorough knowledge been amassed of the oceans and their denizens and the physical laws which control them. Yet even today the depths are not easily probed; diving deeper than 10–20 metres is hardly possible without modern equipment, and most of the earth's oceans remain unexplored.

Various factors help to explain why humans have remained at a respectful distance from the oceans for so long—obvious as well as more obscure factors, explained by simple physical and chemical laws but of paramount importance.

1 First of all, the hazards of the open sea in the shape of high waves and storms. It is true that in some coastal areas waves tend to be longer but shallower. Nevertheless, breakers dashing against the coast can render

coastal areas totally inaccessible, at least during part of the year (see further p. 311).

2 The water pressure. This increases with the depth, viz., 0.1 atmosphere/metre. The effect of this pressure on the body need not be drastic, due to the high water content of most tissues, except for the risk of the lungs collapsing (see further Patrick, Wind and Roede; chapters 14, 17 and 18 respectively). Diving without properly designed equipment can be very dangerous (see pages 315–16).

3 The fact that in water mammals tend to cool down rapidly because the thermal conduction of water is 20 times higher than that of air (Roede, chapter 18).

4 Caisson disease. Ever since people started working under high pressure, such as in tunnel construction and deep diving, they have suffered from mysterious convulsions, nausea, paralyses, and even death. In 1878 Paul Bert explained most of the symptoms of this decompression sickness. When inhaled under higher pressure, as occurs during diving to 7 metres depth or more, oxygen becomes poisonous, and nitrogen starts to dissolve in blood and body tissues. This leads to problems when the diver returns to the surface too quickly and the nitrogen is given off at a faster rate than the lungs can discharge it, causing dangerous gas bubbles in the blood. In 1905 Haldane further analysed the problem; his experiments led to the recommendation of step-by-step decompression. Moreover, at *c.* 40–50 metres depth, a dangerous nitrogen-intoxication may occur, resulting in a serious mental disorganisation; nowadays this effect is prevented by adding helium to the inhaled gas mixture (Riffaud, 1976).

5 Visibility. The fact that the depths of the sea are hidden from view has certainly added to its being perceived as a mystery. Often vision is blurred due to the turbidity of the water. In clear, still water the human eye may be able to discern objects at a few metres distance, but even in clear, shallow water it is hard to distinguish the bottom from the surface. This is explained by the fact that holds good for all aquatic animals: sub-surface visibility is limited due to a multiple scattering of light rays in all directions. Also, there is a rapid extinction of colours in water: red disappears at a depth of only 6 metres, yellow penetrates down to 90 metres, green down to 106 metres; below 245 metres most wavelengths are absorbed and only dark blue to black remains.

The blurring of visibility under water also hinders detection of undersea hazards such as poisonous jelly fishes, snakes, sharks and barracudas. Divers are advised to acquire the habit of turning around regularly to check the surrounding area.

6 Vision. A further optical complication is the different *nature* of vision in air and in water; a functional aerial eye is rarely adapted to aquatic circumstances, and the reflection and refraction of light rays at the water line pose additional problems. (The fish *Anableps anableps* has resolved

this problem by a four-eyed system, one pair for aerial, one for aquatic vision (Brown, 1957).)

7 Oxygen uptake. In most aquatic animals the respiratory uptake of oxygen consists of oxygen dissolved in water, which can, for example, be achieved by means of gills. In contrast, vertebrates with lungs have to return to the surface for air-breathing. Various sea mammal species, adapted to a permanent aquatic life for many millions of years, can stay under water for prolonged periods, but humans can do so only for a much more limited period (Roede, chapter 18).

8 Apart from the real risk of sunburn of their naked skin when swimming at the surface, humans are faced with yet another, additional, handicap compared with other mammals. Generally, in mammals, the centre of gravity of the body (G) is found to be caudal to the point of action of the upward pressure (UP); in water, therefore, a mammal's body automatically sinks until G lies exactly under UP, resulting in an oblique posture with the nostrils above the water surface. In the bipedal human, however, G is already situated directly under UP on land; so that when in water the vertical position is maintained, the nose and mouth disappear under the surface (Slijper, 1958, 1979). This can admittedly be compensated for by treading water; but the short playing time of water polo (five minutes, alternating with two-minute breaks) illustrates the exhausting nature of bodily activities in water in a vertical position. Humans, however, can easily adopt a less exhausting horizontal position, either on the back (see Patrick, chapter 14), or prone (see Wind, chapter 17).

On the other hand, the sea undoubtedly offers certain advantages. For example, oceans provide a very stable environment. Marine geochemistry indicates that on average the chemical composition has seen no changes for hundreds of millions of years (Schuiling and Van der Weijden, 1970; Postma, 1970; see also Wind, this volume, chapter 17). Although differences in climate and seasons, in temperature and water movements, do occur over space and time, such fluctuations are never as extreme as on land; diurnal differences occur only in the most superficial layers. Therefore, marine creatures do not have to adapt to such extreme ranges of environmental circumstances as land animals do.

A second advantage is a plentiful food supply (albeit in restricted areas). Differences in temperature and in salinity induce continuous circulation of the water, which contributes to the richness of available nutrients. There are, however, wide local variations, due to the presence or absence of seasonal fluctuations in surface temperatures, which affect the zoning of planktonic plants and animals. (The primary food production of the sea is mainly limited to the photic zone of 200 m. sub-surface where sunlight can penetrate, with a clear maximum at some 10 m. depth.) About a third of the oceans is barren, fruitless biological desert, especially in the (sub)tropics, with an annual production of less than 100 mg dry organic material per m^3. Only a fifth of the world's oceans is highly productive, with an annual production of 500–1000 mg dry organic material per m^3 (Korringa, 1970).

A further advantage is the buoyancy in water, compared to the burden of gravity that land animals have to sustain.

However, these considerations appear to be outweighed by the manifold advantages of terrestrial life, as may be deduced from a survey of marine species as compared to terrestrial ones. In sharp contrast to the extent of global surface covered by water is the fact that, of the roughly two million plant and animal species in the world, only a small minority lives in water (albeit often in huge numbers). Along rocky coasts relatively large brown, green and red algae occur, but 99.9 per cent of the sea flora belongs to the microscopic phytoplankton (the first link in all oceanic food chains). Most sea fauna are invertebrates; except for the fishes and a few reptiles, sea birds and sea mammals, vertebrates are preponderantly terrestrial. The total number of aquatic mammal species is about 100, a small minority within the total of some 5,000 mammalian species in general.

The coasts

Generally the continents reach beyond the coast-line. The so-called continental shelf slopes gently downwards, and only beyond the edge of the shelf does the sea floor usually drop abruptly. The shelf is on average 70 km. wide and up to 135–200 m. under the surface. Consequently there is a large stretch of photic sub-surface zone, which is on the utmost ecological importance. Coastal belts, covering only one tenth of all water surface, are in general most densely populated, notwithstanding the extreme environmental demands.

Along the coast the power of battering waves can be enormous. Storm waves may reshape coastlines by displacing sand, often in huge quantities, and the forces of inrushing flood and outgoing tide may be immense. Tidal species show a variety of adaptations preventing them from being swept, drawn or whipped away. Sedentary invertebrate species may be attached firmly by a stalk or byssus filaments or by a secretion of limestone; other species brace themselves by means of a muscular foot, manifold suckers or sharp spines.

Due to the complex interactions of soil, currents, wave action and tide, there is great variety in coastal habitats. Rocky coasts may be too steep or too rough to be inhabitated at all by mammalian species. Pebble and shingle beaches are in general practically barren. Sand beaches pose a constant threat of being whipped or drawn away; many species live buried in the sand, or may dig in by means of all sorts of specialised movements of shell-foot, legs or fins. A sand beach might have offered a suitable habitat for the hypothetic aquatic apes, provided that there were places for shelter and nearby reefs as food resources.

Depending on geographical factors, tidal differences and ranges vary from less than 60 cm up to 15 m. With no fixed boundary between land and sea, the shoreline may move backwards and forwards daily over a distance of several kilometres. Species living in areas with a fairly large tidal range are exposed to extreme variations from hour to hour, from season to season. Specific adaptations are required to survive alternately total immersion and air exposure, extreme differences between cold and hot periods, large fluctuations in oxygen content and in salinity, all in combination with the often ferocious forces of the water. Numerous species resist these challenges by retiring, for example, into a protecting shell that can be closed with a horny plate. Another solution is shown by most flatfish and a number of crab and shrimp species: they draw back into gullies that do not dry up at low tide. Activity patterns of most species are synchronised to the rhythm of the tide; with low tide, activities slow down; with high tide, they restart.

The chief advantage of a littoral habitat is the large amount of water – be it salt, brackish, or fresh – of oxygen, and of nutrients. Like the open sea, tidal zones are inhabited by a relatively small number of species, but the individual numbers are large compared with those of land-dwelling species. The richness of the food supply may also attract foraging birds and mammals.

Wading mammals are confronted with insidious tidal currents and gullies; they risk being smashed against rocks by wave action, or on fringing reefs to be hurt by contact with stinging coral. Even when the seas are calm, weathered and eroded rocks may present knife-sharp edges, and be rendered abrasive by barnacles or slippery by algae.

Sea-urchins represent another worldwide hazard. Anyone who has ever stepped barefoot on their spines may agree with me that if there has been a Miocene semi-aquatic hominid phase, then echinoids – *Echinodermata* are millions of years old – would have been a serious impetus to bipedal locomotion to restrict this painful inconvenience.

Despite these aspects of various types of shoreline where primates could hardly be expected to flourish, there do exist some coastal regions that could have provided suitable habitats. For a detailed description of such highly productive coastal ecosystems, see Ellis (chapter 4).

HOMO SAPIENS AND THE SEA

Whether the Miocene hominids lived in and near the water remains an open question. Whether and how their descendant, *Homo sapiens*, in his more recent past exploited the sea is somewhat more readily traceable.

The evidence for this is found in engravings, sculptures, drawings and paintings, representations on vases, coins, fighting shields, temples and houses, supplemented in later times by written tradition, poems and writings, such as those of Homer and Aristotle, and of Herodotus, who recorded a good deal of marine history. (It is not surprising that there are so many Greek writings on the subject: few other countries are so exposed to the sea. Since the early Bronze Age, and most probably before, Greece and the sea enjoyed an intimate relationship.)

Shipping

It is a matter of conjecture how our early ancestors managed to populate so many islands. How, for example, did *Homo erectus* reach Java? There may formerly have been land-bridges that have now disappeared. Another possibility is suggested by the way small mammals are known to arrive on off-shore islands – namely, by clinging to floating tree trunks.

The use of specially constructed floating devices began some thousands of years later than the domestication of dogs and cattle and the invention of agriculture; yet water surfaces have been crossed by humans for thousands of years. There are indications that in the late Upper Pleistocene mankind was spreading to islands all over the world. The distribution over various locations in the Eastern Mediterranean of celts and chisels made of obsidian (volcanic glass) originating from the island Melos, gives evidence how widespread overseas shipping was in 7000 BC. At first, use was made of primitive papyrus rafts, animal skin boats and hollowed logs, such as the 3 m. long canoe found in the fenland of Drenthe (Netherlands), dating back to 6600 BC (Bloemers, Louwe Koooijmans and Sarfatij, 1981). They were most probably first used on rivers and lakes. An Egyptian drawing from 3400 BC shows a larger and more complex riverboat, provided with paddles. The first large boats with oars and sails were constructed in Egypt some 4,000 years BC.

In *Prometheus Bound* (452–454 BC) Aeschylus sang how 'one of the presents given by Prometheus to man, up to then living like ants in dark passages and caves, was a sailing boat'. His verses are more than just a poetic effusion; shipping was a relevant factor in the cultural development of the inhabitants of the region of the Aegean Sea (Themelis, 1987), and its importance rapidly increased. In flat earthenware from the early-Cycladic period from the third millennium BC various long ships with rows of oars are carved; the endless spirals are considered to be the first symbolic representations of the Aegean waves (Boulotis, 1987). Experts assume that these objects had a ritual meaning. Also, one of the first themes on early-Geometric vases is the ship (Andronilos, 1987).

Man first dared to venture onto the seas in search of food, next for purposes of trade, transport and migration, and later in pursuit of war and conquest as well; in Homer's day, ships were used only for transport, but fighting ships were developed not long afterwards.

The length of voyages increased, though the sailors rarely lost sight of the coast. At about 3000 BC Egyptians were already sailing to Crete, and by about 1700 BC even to the extreme east of Africa, to purchase incense, balsam, gold and ivory. Minos, from the island of Crete, is pictured as the first ruler of the seas; Crete became the central home-port for the first real maritime forces, and at some time between 2800–2600 BC their sailors were the first to venture out of the Mediterranean. The Mycenaean naval supremacy (from 1450 BC) was probably the inspiration for the heroic poems of Homer, including the story of the famous seafarer Odysseus, as well as the legendary voyage of Jason and the Argonauts who sailed from the Aegean Sea to the Black Sea, a masterly example of skilled seamanship. From 1200 BC the highly skilled Phoenician sailors embarked on their voyages, descending like locusts on all shores of Africa; in 600 BC they went on a three-year expedition from the Red Sea all round Africa ('seeing the sun rise first on their left and then on their right' (De Latil and Rivoire, 1956, p. 32). They also sailed from what is nowadays Lebanon to England to get tin, following the continental shorelines. The later Greeks and Romans, however, limited their sailing activities mostly to the '*mare nostrum*', having been forewarned about the horrors of the 'outer sea' beyond the Strait of Gibraltar, where even Hercules turned back (Pindar; in De Latil and Rivoire, p. 33).

At a time when the Western world generally feared that sailors who ventured too far across the high seas would tumble over the edge of the world, mass migrations were taking place elsewhere, across the Pacific. In those regions people dared to sail beyond the horizon on their long maritime voyages, with the stars and the flight of birds, and knowledge about wave patterns, as their sole navigational aids. These trips are sparsely documented and more difficult to trace; but there are indications that the casualty list was long. Overpopulation provides a ruthless motive for migration and, for islanders, that must entail crossing the sea. Some 10,000 to 8,000 years ago migrants knew how to reach Australia, and later New Guinea and the Philippines. At around 6000 BC pro-Malaysians sailed the Pacific; next came the Polynesians who 3,000 years ago populated Fiji and Tonga, and at 2,000 years ago the Marquesas and farther places, finally dispersing on their huge catamarans over an area covering 18 million square kilometres.

Later, the Norsemen frequently traversed the open seas, reaching Iceland, Greenland and even North America. Elsewhere in the world, Eskimos, and Arab, Indian and Chinese traders similarly defied the aquatic elements on daring sea voyages.

Diving

Human locomotion in water is not restricted to the surface; we can quite easily learn to swim under water and dive down a few metres to pick things up from the bottom. With practice, deeper dives can be attained, despite the handicap of not being able to stay under water longer than one minute, unless well trained. By contrast, few other terrestrial mammals practise actual dives.

Except from the supporters of AAT, this specific skill has received little attention in discussions of hominid evolution. We cannot be certain when humans first began diving. Most probably, the first motive for entering the alien waterworld was the desire to collect seafood; later came the wish to gain access to other sea resources. In an attempt to assess how well we can cope with these underwater activities, a short survey follows of the history of human diving and of the risks it may involve.

For well over three thousand years men and women have been diving to considerable depths while fishing for sponges. Even today there are commercial divers operating without any breathing tube or face mask; the length of time they stay under water is quite amazing (see also Schagatay, chapter 15). They usually descend to about 20 metres, but may go down to 30 metres, where the best sponges grow. Similar diving activities are described in the *Iliad* and the *Odyssey*. Also in classical times man was already venturing to dangerous depths to obtain other treasures of the sea, such as red (octo)corals, and the shells of *Murex brandaris* and *M. trunculus* which furnished the raw material for purple dye; 60,000 specimens produced about one pound of dye. The silk-like byssus threads of *Pinna nobilis* were harvested and used for ceremonial dresses, while pearl fishing was mainly confined to the Red Sea and the Indian Ocean.

Classical writers such as Oppian reveal that the dangers of venturing into the depths of the sea were never underestimated. The divers were subjected to rigorous training and told to abstain from drinking wine. Despite such preventive measures as having their ears filled with oil and covered by oil-soaked sponges, the divers' ear drums often became perforated by resurfacing too rapidly, and divers usually died at an early age (see, for example, De Latil and Rivoire, 1956; Riffaud, 1976). Many divers were females. Pausanius emphasised that although the pressure at great depths might cause ear drums to break, it did not affect a young woman's virginity (De Latil and Rivoire, 1956, p. 54).

In classical antiquity the underwater hunting of fish and shellfish was popular as a sport. But this must have occurred in calm, clear water, and not too far under the surface, so as to avoid the ordeals of the professional deep-sea divers.

War provided another incentive for diving. De Latil and Rivoire (1956) mention the various instances recorded by Greek and Roman historians of divers providing services in naval warfare. They penetrated the depths to bring supplies to besieged islanders (for example, at the end of the fifth century BC, during the Peloponnesian wars between Sparta and Athens); to sever anchor chains, as happened to the Persian fleet of Xerxes during the Median Wars; to pierce the hulls of enemy ships; to close a harbour's entrance, or to clear it of obstructions such as stones, or sometimes even vessels loaded with stones. Herodotus and others suspected that the tales of these exploits were often exaggerated, but the fact is that military writings of the time recommended the posting of sentries on deck armed with tridents to prevent such actions by the enemy's fighting divers. Centuries later, divers were also deployed in Moslem wars, while in the year 1000 the Swedish king Eric the Eloquent vanquished the almost unconquerable Vikings by employing unseen divers to drill holes in their ships' hulls.

Aquanauts in classical times may have used a kind of breathing tube, as described by Aristotle. There are also references to glass diving bells, like the huge one designed for Alexander the Great. Several historians relate how he was lowered into the sea because of his curiosity to observe the secrets and treasures of the underwater world. Since the air in the bell's upper part became compressed during lowering, breathing was possible for only a limited period without great risks. Special diving outfits were also used; in the fourth century Vegetius described in detail the outfit of fighting divers – the leather boots and masks, and the wine skins filled with air.

With the Renaissance, a revival of interest in classical times stimulated new explorations of the sea, and attention focused on equipment to make this possible. Leonardo da Vinci (1452–1519) designed various diving suits, including a mask, webbed gloves and flippers. His design for an underwater breathing apparatus reveals how little was really understood of the physical laws of the sea and its effects on humans during descent into an aquatic environment. His breathing tube would have worked well enough in shallow water, but in deeper water its user would have died from suffocation due to pressure on his chest.

In the eighteenth and nineteenth centuries diving equipment was increasingly based on a more realistic understanding of the physiology of diving. Attempts were made to take account of the laws of pressure, as formulated by Pascal in 1648, and the newly acquired knowledge about the chemical composition of air. But still too little was actually understood of the complex mechanisms involved, and casualties could not be prevented.

As underwater activities became increasingly popular, more effective equipment was introduced, including, in the first half of the nineteenth century, Siebe's diving helmet and dresses, and at the end of the century the Rouquayrol-Denayrouze apparatus. An 'improved' version of their *aérophore* became famous by being used by Captain Nemo and his crew in Jules Verne's *Twenty Thousand Leagues under the Sea*. De Latil and Rivoire (1956, pp. 166–8) have pointed out that Jules Verne's scientific accuracy failed him here, when he equipped Captain Nemo with 'a copper sphere to be worn over the head'. In combination with the rest of Nemo's outfit this was physiologically impossible: localised underpressure would have turned the helmet into a suction pump, resulting in fatal haemorrhages.

At the end of the nineteenth century safer diving became possible due to new outfits with a heavy brass helmet and heavy boots, necessitating slow and clumsy movements like those of a man on the moon, and severely limiting freedom of action. But the biologists were delighted with their new ability to study life on the sea bed at close quarters.

The final understanding of the phenomenon of decompression at the turn of the century opened the way for the modern approach to diving. When, during the Second World War, fighting divers were once more brought into action, the development of diving gear progressed by leaps and bounds. Jacques Cousteau and Emile Gagnan perfected the 'aqualung', a tank of air compressed to 120 atmospheres, combined with an ingenious regulator which ensures that at every depth the pressure of the inhaled air is similar to the prevailing water pressure. This scuba diving 'put the underwater world within the reach of everyone' (De Latil and Rivoire, 1956, p. 272); the divers were now as free and agile as fishes in their underwater explorations.

However, the aqualung is not really suitable for working at great depths: its user is still confronted with the problem of decompression, and usually does not dive deeper than 80–90 metres. For instance, one hour spent at a depth of 100 metres necessitates a decompression time of 7–8 hours.

On the other hand, a need is felt to explore the deep sea further in order to facilitate, for example, the exploitation of underwater oilfields and metal deposits. Oceanauts have been lowered in bathyspheres (introduced by Beebe and Barton in 1934), deep-diving (mini)submarines and bathyscaphes; experimental underwater laboratories are being designed. But large-scale underwater communities are not yet feasible, and for the time being we have to accept that humans in general have not succeeded in colonising the depths of the sea.

In recent decades, however, in addition to the use of air supply for descending to greater depths, the simple basis gear of mask, fins and snorkel for swimming at the surface and making short dives has become very popular, and the almost insuperable difficulties of former days are easily forgotten. But the modern snorkeller still needs to take account of temperature and radiation factors. In warmer regions, solar radiation received at the surface may keep the body sufficiently warm; some clothing is recommended to prevent sunburn of neck and shoulders. But for submergence over longer periods, even in shallow (sub)tropical waters, some protection against heat loss is needed, preferably by special 'wet suits'. The leather outfits of former days were hardly suitable; but the modern invention of new materials such as foam rubber – a cultural water adaptation which should not be underestimated – enables the human primate finally to cope satisfactorily with the problem of cooling-off.

Another physiological effect of diving has also come to be better understood. People with sensitive (allergic) mucous membranes and other airway complaints may suffer from pain, due to a relative underpressure in the paranasal sinuses and the middle ear known as 'squeeze' (Bennett and Elliott, 1982; Shilling, Carlston and Mathias, 1984). Even diving only a few metres for picking up shells or catching a fish may cause this temporary handicap. It is impossible to know whether the presumed aquatic apes from the Miocene suffered from rhinitis, but when diving they may well have been confronted with this complication.

LEGENDS AND MYTHS

> I must go down to the sea again, for the call of the running tide
> Is a wild call and a clear call that may not be denied.
>
> (*Sea Fever*, John Masefield)

Richards, in chapter 6, has commented on our necessity for water, not only to meet the daily needs of purely physiological requirements, but also for bathing, grooming, washing, rinsing and playing, as well as for mystic uses and rites. (In this respect the distinction between sea- and freshwater is not well defined.) Wind, in chapter 17, has relegated the so-called nostalgic, archaic longings for submersion mainly to the realm of fantasy. He remarks that 'science is unable to account for the mental processes behind the back-to-the-ocean associations' and that 'the frequency of these associations is unknown'. His reasoning seems logical. Specific remembrances of an ancestral aquatic past 300 million years ago, when terrestrial life started, and even of one some 5–4 million years ago, are indeed very unlikely to exist. Yet that is not the end of the affair. A better approach might be to look for indications about attitudes towards the sea from early historical times, in order to discover whether our apparent mental affinity for water is only recently acquired, and the popularity of bathing merely a trendy fashion (Preuschoft and Preuschoft, chapter 9), or whether these things are more deeply rooted in our species.

First, some remarks on bathing. Though for centuries bathing was indeed considered in Europe to be unhealthy, if we look beyond Western countries it becomes clear that the habit of bathing is deeply rooted in many longstanding traditions and rituals. Water is considered to possess magic healing power, to offer eternal youth, to act as a purifier from sins and to wash away evil spirits. Egyptian priests had to bathe twice a day, and both the ancient Greeks and modern Moslems perform ritual washing before devotions. For centuries Hindus have bathed in the river Ganges and the temple ponds, and Christian rituals include various forms of baptism, ranging from just a few drops to total immersion.

A possible evolutionary basis for such mores could be the tendency among birds and mammals to groom the skin, rather than a hypothetical and temporary hominid aquatic stage.

An opportunity to trace at least a reflection of innermost thoughts about the sea in the prehistorical past is offered by religion, legends and myths. According to Jung (1964), they originate in the period immediately prior to the establishment of civilisation. He introduced the concept of the collective unconscious, consisting of the mental inheritance of all mankind. Though his ideas are not generally accepted, there is a consensus among anthropologists that many folk tales contain a grain of truth. Nearly all religions owe a debt to previous beliefs by absorbing the superseded myths and legends, and thus may offer some clues to the 'archaic' ideas of earlier times (Cotterell, 1989, p. 7).

Humans cannot easily live with chaos. Inherent in the process of becoming human is a growing awareness of the cosmos and our earthly environment, and the consequent invention of theories to rationalise our individual and collective experiences, to come to terms with the complex world outside, and to suppress fears. In other words, the structure of religion is not arbitrary: it finds its origin in the need to explain and cope with a prevailing situation (Campbell, 1969; Cotterell, 1989). As a consequence, legends and myths may help us to trace how humans felt about the sea in earlier days, at a time when it was taken for granted that the world was flat and that the sea was its boundary river.

These sources as an indication of involvement in the sea among the peoples of the ancient Orient, Egypt and other parts of North Africa are well documented, as well as that of ancient Greece and Rome, and a wide range of places elsewhere. Here, only a limited selection will be given.

First, it may be asked if the relationship of Neolithic man with water can be traced. European rock paintings made 10,000 to 18,000 years ago rarely picture water; only the more recent ones depict some river fish. References to marine life are rare, though that is not surprising in inland caves. Yet, a rock drawing of 2200 BC on the island of Roddoy, Northern Norway, shows a man in a kayak chasing a seal and two porpoises (Slijper, 1979).

Little is known about the early history of human populations south of the Sahara; among the huge diversity of their present-day traditions and local beliefs, the sea hardly plays an important part. Thousands of cave drawings discovered in the Central Sahara (Hogger, Tassili-n-Ajjer) – dating back from 6000 to 2000 years BC – reveal that the area was then green and fertile. Various cave paintings picture sun-worshipping, but the (former) rivers were also the subject of rituals (for example, Lhote, 1977). In the Orange Free State, South Africa, 300 kilometres from the shore, there are 3000-year-old drawings by Bushmen of a stranded whale and dolphins; in those days their territory was much more extensive than nowadays, they may have migrated during winter to the coast for fishing (Slijper, 1979).

Upon surveying the vast multiplicity of religions, legends and rites of our more recent ancestors some general tendencies can be distinguished.

Creation of the world is a universal theme. During various epochs and among divergent cultures, such as that of the Egyptians, the myth is of a universe created as an empty bubble in an endless mass of waters, of a terrestrial landscape that had its origin in the boundless primeval ocean. The Babylonians believed that for a long period the world was entirely covered by oceans, until the level of the land was raised. Other versions conceived of the land as having been hooked out of the ocean (New Zealand), or that the primordially omnipotent ocean had to be conquered by one of his or her offspring before life on earth could start (for example, De Latil and Rivoire, 1956; Hyslop, 1986; Cotterell, 1989).

Deities. Throughout the world it has been believed that a diversity of gods, monsters, nymphs and other aquatic creatures inhabit the depths of the seas. In spite of an obvious diversity in the contents of the tales, on the basis of standard mythological analysis two worldwide *leitmotivs* can be recognised.

1 First, the one of a *profound duality*, reflecting how suddenly and unexpectedly serene waters can turn into stormy seas. The divine characters were pictured as unpredictable like the elements.

The duality was often represented in a single figure, such as Poseidon or Neptune, who was one of the three sons of primeval Kronos who divided the world between them. Poseidon became the ruler of the seas; when angry, he could use his magic trident to make the sea rough and threatening; in a different mood, he could use it to calm the waves. He could make islands emerge or submerge, and shake the earth. When in a cheerful mood, he rode the waters in his golden chariot – accompanied by dolphins and merry Nereids – magically transforming the boiling waves into a turquoise mirror. Like his brother Zeus, he fathered many offspring, but his children did not become deities or heroes. He only begat monsters, with the exception of his ravishing son, the horse Pegasus. But he was also worshipped in his role of revered benefactor (De Latil and Rivoire, 1956), a characteristic also found in the Babylonian amphibian god Ea, who nightly emerged from the Persian Gulf to educate humans, and in the Japanese fish-god Varuna (Hyslop, 1986).

The two opposing aspects of the sea may also be expressed by two closely related characters, as in the ancient myths about the two old men of the sea – Nereus, dispenser of universal benevolence, and the unstable and unpredictable Proteus. In Scandinavian mythology, the two contradictory aspects of Neptune are split into the noble Njord and the malevolent Aegir.

The negative side of the sea is not always portrayed as clearly as in the above examples. Some sea gods are purely benevolent, such as the primeval deity Varuna in Indian Vedic mythology, and Kompira, guardian of Japanese sailors. In Greenland it was believed that paradise was situated somewhere in warm, calm waters. Yet, these tales are a minority, and the concept of the ocean as two-faceted is much commoner throughout the world (De Latil and Rivoire, 1956, pp. 23–26).

2 Secondly, sometimes *geographic differences* are reflected in the mythic characters populating the seas. Greek sea gods, for instance, are as capricious as the Aegean sea, one moment dazzlingly azure, the next moment threatening, but rarely losing their charm. Deities that held sway in the cold, grim Atlantic, like Aegir, are fiercer and more malevolent.

Female sea deities are also depicted with a similar duality and a similar diversity, reflecting geographic differences. The most beautiful and whimsical of all goddesses, Aphrodite, was born out of the foam of the radiantly blue Mediterranean waves. Farther North, Aegir's fierce and cruel wife Ran found pleasure in capsizing ships in order to capture the drowning sailors in her nets; but those who succeeded in paying her tribute in gold became her lovers and banquet companions.

In many widely separated regions sailors have believed that the sea harboured ravishing and treacherous sirens, bringing both death and love – such as the nymphs in the tales of the Far East, or the European wave maidens, daughters of Aegir and Ran, the Nixen, the White Ladies, the Rousalki, and similar creatures under many different names (De Latil and Rivoire, 1956, p. 26; Hyslop, 1986, pp. 111–25). More than 3,000 years ago, Odysseus's crew resisted the Mediterranean sirens' songs by stopping their ears with wax, while the Argonauts were protected by Orpheus's music. Up to 1481 in Europe serious warnings about sirens were published. There are, no doubt, psychoanalytic explanations for these widespread fears of men concerning the deadly embraces of alluring female creatures. But the sirens also symbolise more plainly than any of the other myths and legends about the sea, how the glistening surface of the sea was mistrusted and the invisible depths feared.

Monsters. Here, the fear of the unknown is most outspoken. Supernatural powers were ascribed to numerous monsters and beasts of the sea, held responsible for causing shipwrecks by evoking wild waves, troughs and abysses, vortices that could draw ships down within seconds, or by raising unseen cliffs and reefs to just below sea level. Odysseus's journey is full of blood-curdling stories such as the choice he had to make between Scylla, with six screaming heads, and Charybdis, the neighbouring abyss. Up in the far North, near the Lofoten Archipelago, for centuries the fearful 'Maelstrom' was supposed to whirl ships around and at the end draw them into the maw of the sea.

The crooked serpent Leviathan produced vortices to engulf the ships, so did the fearful Tiburon, who devoured the carcases of the drowned. There were immense octopuses dragging ships down with mile-long tentacles, and giant lobsters pulling hapless sailors out of their ship, into the depths. Centuries later and elsewhere, equally frightening stories were told, such as the medieval legend about the biggest of all sea monsters the 'Kraken' (Pliny and Bishop Olaus Magnus, 1555; see De Latil and Rivoire, 1956; Hyslop, 1986). As Lord Tennyson (1849–1892) wrote:

> Below the thunders of the upper deep;
> Far, far beneath in the abysmal sea,
> His ancient, dreamless, uninvaded sleep
> The Kraken sleepeth.

In Europe up to the eighteenth century, the beasts of the sea were seriously feared. Some aspects of the dreadful encounters with fabulous animals of the deep, as described in various 'Bestiaries', may have been based on actual confrontations with the huge deep sea octopus (*Architheutis*), which can weigh up to 260 kilograms (yet according to Cousteau (1974) is basically a non-aggressive creature), or with whales. The nineteenth-century classic *Moby Dick* (1851), about Captain Ahab's vengeful hunt for the massive white whale, was inspired by Melville's personal experiences during a four-year journey on a whaling vessel, probably in combination with the sad tale of the wreck of the whaler *Essex* on November 20, 1820.

Holy fears. The widespread awe inspired by the ocean resulted in the solemn casting of propitiary offerings into the sea. Seafarers had to pay tribute with bread and salt to the waves; warships would sacrifice boxes full of golden coins. How the sea was personified is illustrated by the Persian royal prince Xerxes, who had the sea punished with strokes of the lash for having destroyed his ships in the naval battle of Salamis, 484 BC (Herodotus, VII, 35; De Latil and Rivoire, p. 43). It was a daring act, since the boldest of seafarers dreaded the power of the sea. Even the notorious Norsemen paid homage to the sea god Aegir and his wife Ran.

Aquatic creatures. Surveys of legends and sea myths seem to indicate that the traditional reaction to the sea was chiefly one of fear. Indications of any deep-seated longing for the sea are harder to find.

There are countless fables about relatively harmless inhabitants of the sea, such as mermen and mermaids. Yet they are often said to nurse a craving to come out onto the land and stay there. There are, for instance, various Mussulman stories about half-human beings inhabiting the sea near Rosetta and Alexandria, and frequently coming to promenade along the shore. Until a few centuries ago, similar creatures were said to frequent the seaside in the north of the Netherlands.

There are some tales about human beings descending into the waves, such as the story told by Ovid about the legendary fisherman Glaucus, who was so intent upon entering the marine world that the deities turned him into a marine immortal; his body became covered with seaweed and shells, and his beard acquired the glaucous colours of the waves (Kingsley, 1855; De Latil and Rivoire, pp. 26–28) (see Figure 20.1). There is a similar legend about a Japanese fisherman transformed into a sea god by the favours of Otokimi, the goddess of the sea (De Latil and Rivoire, pp. 26–28). Bushmen believe that the dead come to rest in the sea (Allan, 1986), and ancient tribes of good fairies are said to have fled into the depths of the sea because of their fear of human beings (Phillips, 1986). Yet incidental folk tales such as these can hardly be said to add up to a general 'collective unconscious' or a folk memory of a remote aquatic phase.

More recent fairy tales, like Andersen's 'Little Mermaid' and Charles Kingsley's *The Waterbabies* (1863) can hardly be included in an analysis of traditional water stories, although the latter tale may be inspired by Kingsley's earlier work on Glaucus (1855). And advocates of the folk-memory theory may argue that the popularity of the two stories is due to the fact that they echo such primeval images.

Myths about the sea include many stories about the souls of drowned sailors, embodied in seagulls or seals, often rather hostile towards living men; another common theme features drowned cities. It was said that near Sicily, the Strait of Messina, the submerged palaces of Fata Morgana could be seen; in Sweden there is a legend about the island Gummer's

Figure 20.1 The fisherman Glaucus (after a seventeenth-century Dutch engraving).

Ore, which appears only to disappear again. Scottish people tell of Heather Bleather, near the Orkney Islands, ruled by sea people, while off the Irish west coast the old sea god Manannan Mac Lir rides on the foaming billows among fairy-like islands with glass palaces and strange monsters. Various tales tell about an engulfed town from which occasionally the sound of the church bells can still be heard. Nowadays various explanations have been formulated, such as the eruption of the former Greek island Thera around 1500 BC, which may have inspired the stories about Atlantis.

DISCUSSION AND CONCLUSIONS

In this chapter two lines of reasoning have been followed, one focusing on the physical properties of sea and coasts, and the other on our technological and cultural relationship with the sea as evidenced by shipping and diving, and by legends and myths.

The physical properties of the sea

Do the above data support the belief in the existence of an aquatic ape three million years ago? It was emphasised that, in approaching this question, it is important not to underestimate the substantial number of difficulties and impediments that would have to be overcome in embarking on an aquatic existence.

These include storms, turbulence, high waves and dangerous currents as well as the loss of body heat, hampered vision, and the need to return frequently to the surface to breathe. Deeper diving would incur further difficulties arising from water pressure, decompression sickness and the possibility of nitrogen-intoxication. It is not known how upright Miocene apes might have been, but a bipedal animal in a vertical position would also need to counteract the natural tendency to sink in the water until the nostrils were below the surface.

It is true that other mammals have successfully adapted to a permanent aquatic life, but it took them many millions of years to achieve this (Roede, chapter 18). In the period of 1-2 million years covered by the AAT, a complete adaptation to an aquatic existence cannot have occurred. Had there been any hominid ancestors who returned to a life in the sea, they could at most have been semi-aquatic coast dwellers.

However, coastal areas present divergent disadvantages, such as dangerous breakers and streams, sharp or slippery rocks, and sea urchins; tidal beaches demand special adaptations for coping with the sweeping forces of tidal streams, and wide ranges in temperature, humidity and salinity.

If a Miocene aquatic ape ever existed, it could only have survived in a very narrow range of littoral habitats, such as productive fringing reefs with enough (mangrove) cover for protection and sleeping places (see Ellis, chapter 4).

Cultural relationship between humans and the sea

Mankind was relatively late in developing the skills of making rafts, boats and, later, sailing ships. Thereafter, due to the need for expansion, trade and wars, these techniques improved rapidly, but for many centuries Western sailors, confronted with the dangerous outer waters of the North Sea and the Bay of Biscay, preferred to sail close to the shore, and even among seafaring nations there was little knowledge of the world below the sea surface.

Nevertheless, since time immemorial, humans have attempted diving for both commercial and military reasons. They had to contend with the universal fears of sea monsters, and the known physical hazards such as perforated ear drums, collapsing lungs, and drowning fatalities. Fighting divers may have suffered less than sponge, coral and pearl divers, since the naval divers did not descend as deep as the commercial ones.

They also had to cope with the problem of heat loss. Various methods were tried, but only the recent introduction of new technology has enabled humans to overcome this handicap. Without such protection we are still vulnerable, as shown during shipping disasters where, even today, most of the casualties are the result of hypothermia.

In the eighteenth and nineteenth centuries, an increasing number of instruments and equipment for diving were designed; but frequent casualties could not be prevented: divers died, or became crippled. 'Blunders' made by men like Da Vinci and Jules Verne indicate how difficult it was to understand the physical and physiological risks of diving. Only in this century has our understanding of the marine environment increased significantly, and even today the investigation of outer space seems to progress more rapidly than the investigation of those parts of our own planet which lie at the bottom of the ocean.

Legends and myths are said to reflect past attitudes towards the surrounding outer world. Thus tales about the fabulous inhabitants of the sea may well reflect the fears of our ancestors about the unknown, mysterious borders of their territory. Worldwide, legends, myths and fables reveal a general feeling that the sea is much more unpredictable and treacherous than the terrestrial world. In fact, there seems to be common awareness of the paradoxical, dual nature of the sea, resulting in conflicting feelings – namely, fear of its power combined with appreciation of its serenity. On balance, evidence of any genuine folk-memory of a remote aquatic past is hard to find. The stories about submerged towns and continents seem rather to relate to actual (pre)historical catastrophes.

To summarise, the physical properties of the seas and coasts, and the thousands of years it took modern man to become somewhat better culturally adapted to the marine world by using special equipment and clothing, suggest that our Miocene progenitors can hardly have lived permanently in the water. Only a few types of littoral areas would have qualified as possible new niches for them.

The sea has played an important part among seafaring and coastal populations. It has been seen as a cradle and a grave, both origin of life and bringer of death, benefactor and enemy. But even today human invasion into the world of the deep is still in a pioneering phase, due to physical barriers which are very hard to surmount. It can hardly be accidental that man has set foot on the moon before he has penetrated the oceans' depths. However, due to overpopulation and our demand for oil and metals, we may be forced to revise our priorities. If we seek for aquatic man, we are more likely to find him in the future than in the past.

ACKNOWLEDGEMENTS

I am grateful for Jan Wind's critical corrections and comments.

REFERENCES

Allan, T., 1986, *Seekers and Saviors*. New York: Time-Life Books.

Allan, T. and Steel, D.A., 1986, *Water Spirits*. New York: Time-Life Books.

Andronikos, M., 1987, Antieke kunst en de zee. In *Griekenland en de Zee*, ed. A. Delivorrias. Athens: Cosmopress, 61–2.

Ballintijn, G., 1944, *Rumphius, de Blinde Ziener van Ambon*. Utrecht: De Haan.

Bennett, P.B. and Elliott, D.H., 1982, *The Physiology and Medicine of Diving*. London: Baillière Tindall.

Bloemers, J.H.F., Louwe Kooijmans, L.P. and Sarfatij, H., 1981, *Verleden Land*. Amsterdam: Meulenhoff Informatief.

Brown, M., 1957, *The Physiology of Fishes*. New York: Academic Press

Boulotis, Christos, 1987, Het Egeïsche gebied in de prehistorie: cultus en religie. In : *Griekenland en de Zee*, ed. A. Delivorrias. Athens: Cosmopress, 20–35.

Calvin, W., 1986, *The River that Flows Uphill*. New York: Macmillan.

Campbell, J., 1969, *The Masks of God: Occidental Mythology*. New York: Penguin Books.

Colman, J.S., 1951, *De Zee en haar Geheimen*. Amsterdam: Kosmos.

Cotterell, A., 1989, *Myths and Legends*. London: Guild Publishing.

Cousteau, J.Y., 1974, *Inktvissen, schrander en schroomvallig*. Utrecht: Bruna.

Darwin, C., 1906, *The Voyage of the 'Beagle'*. London.

Deacon, G.E.R., 1962, *Oceans*. London: Paul Hamlyn.

De Latil, P. and Rivoire, J., 1956, *Man and the Underwater World*. London: Jarrold.

Ehrlich, P.R., 1989, Attributes of invaders and the invading processes: vertebrates. In: *Biological Invasions*, ed. J.A. Drake, *et al.* John Wiley, 315–28.

Hardy, A., 1960, Was man more aquatic in the past? *New Scientist*, **7**, 642–5.

Hyslop, S.G., 1986, *Water Spirits*, ed. T. Allan, and D.A. Steele, New York: Time-Life Books.

Jung, C., 1964, *Man and his Symbols*. London.

Kingsley, Charles, 1855, *Glaucus, or The Wonders of the Shore*.

Kingsley, Charles, 1863, *The Water Babies* (London: Macmillan).

Korringa, P., 1970, De zee als voedingsbodem. *Chemisch Weekblad*, **66** (36), 23–30.

LaLumiere, L.P., 1991, Evolution of genus *Homo*: where it happened. (This volume chapter 3.)

Lhote, H., 1977, Toen de Sahara nog groen was. In: *De grootste mysteries aller tijden*. Amsterdam: *Reader's Digest*, 205–19.

Melville, H., 1851, *Moby Dick or The Whale*. New York: Harper and Brothers.

Morgan, E., 1982, *The Aquatic Ape. A theory of human evolution*. London: Souvenir Press.

Morgan, E., 1990, *The Scars of Evolution. What our bodies tell us about human origins*. London: Souvenir Press.

Moorehead, A., 1969, *Darwin and the Beagle*. London: Hamish Hamilton.

Ovidius Naso, *Metamorphoses*. See e.g. translation by Humphries, R., 1955. Bloomington, Indiana: Indiana University Press.

Patrick, J.M., 1991, Human respiratory adaptations for swimming and diving. (This volume, chapter 14.)

Postma, H., 1970, Het chemisch onderzoek de oceanen. *Chemisch Weekblad* **66** (36), 37–41.

Preuschoft, H. and Preuschoft, S. 1991, The Aquatic Ape Theory, seen from epistemological and palaeoanthropological viewpoints. (This volume, chapter 9.)

Reader's Digest, 1974, *Merveilles et Mystères du Monde sous-marin*. Paris: Sélection du Reader's Digest.

Riffaud, C., 1976, 2000 jaren geschiedenis van het duiken. In *Wonderwereld onder de zeespiegel*. Amsterdam: Readers Digest, 12–29..

Roede, M., 1991, Do aquatic mammals provide support for the Aquatic Ape Theory? (This volume, chapter 18.)

Schagatay, Erika, 1991, The significance of the human diving reflex. (This volume, chapter 15.)

Schuiling, R.D. and Van der Weijden, C.H., 1970, De zee: opvangcentrum en doorgangshuis van opgeloste stoffen. *Chemisch Weekblad*, **66** (36), 31–6.

Shilling, C.W., Carlston, C.B. and Mathias, R.A. (eds.), 1984, *The Physician's Guide to Diving Medicine*. New York: Plenum Press.

Slijper, E.J., 1958, *Walvissen*. Amsterdam: de Boer.

Slijper, E.J., 1979, *Whales*. London: Hutchinson and Co.

Themelis, P., 1987, Griekenland en de zee: mythologische aspecten. In: *Griekenland en de Zee*, ed. A. Delivorrias, Athens: Cosmopress, 58–60.

Wind, J. 1991, The non-aquatic ape: the aquatic ape theory and the evolution of human drowning and swimming. (This volume, chapter 17.)

Part III

GENERAL CONCLUSIONS

21 Cold and Watery? Hot and Dusty? Our Ancestral Environment and Our Ancestors Themselves: An Overview

Vernon Reynolds

SUMMARY
The chapter begins with a discussion of the nature of scientific arguments generally, and the matter of consensus in scientific progress. Next, a number of substantive topics bearing on the Aquatic Ape Theory are reviewed, including bipedalism, body hair, sweating, subcutaneous fat and the 'diving response'. The conclusion is reached that while human ancestors were never truly aquatic, the evidence suggests that they may have been selected for their ability to make occasional use of rivers and lakes in the ancestral African habitat.

INTRODUCTION

This overview will be brief and, inevitably, incomplete. The details of the arguments for and against an aquatic phase in hominid evolution have been presented in earlier chapters. What I shall do here is, first, make a general point about the nature of this particular kind of scientific inquiry; and, second, take a look at the key issues raised, and come down on one side or the other. For the most part, I shall favour the arguments for savannah evolution, but in some respects the evidence for adaptation to water is convincing. These are, of course, personal decisions rather than definitive judgements.

PROLOGUE: ON ADVOCACY

The question of whether we went through an ancestral aquatic phase cannot, by its nature, be subjected to an empirical test. Behaviour leaves no trace in the fossil record. We thus are obliged to use secondary, circumstantial evidence for our arguments. The kind of work that results from this necessity is commonly called 'advocacy'.

Perhaps the best known work of advocacy is Richard Dawkins' *The Blind Watchmaker* (1986) (Dawkins himself labels it a work of advocacy – it is not I who do so). What he means is that he presents lines of evidence that lead to one conclusion rather than to another. In the case of *The Blind Watchmaker*, the conclusion is that life, including human life, has evolved in all its complexity as a result of the process of natural selection and not as a result of the process of divine creation. Would it be possible for Dawkins to 'prove' his argument by means of an experiment? It would not. Dawkins is not dealing with the field of falsifiability, with a Popperian world of hypothesis-testing by experiment. He is, rather, dealing with systems of argument, characterised by canons of epistemology, and those canons are validated by consensus among communities of like-thinking people.

We thus have to remind ourselves that, in the field of evolutionary theory, the best we can hope for is to deploy the evidence about any given problem in such a way as to mount a convincing argument – that is, one that would convince any rational person. Clearly, this is asking more than can actually be done. Assuming that all authors in this book are rational, we can conclude that the evidence has not yet been assembled in such a way as to convince one and all.

Science is a very human enterprise, but it is also a very moral one. In *Varieties of Realism*, Rom Harré (1986) declares that science is among the most moral of human enterprises. What he means by this is that scientists are forced to adhere to the principle that they should be as honest and truthful as possible in their work by the constant scrutiny of other scientists. If a scientist selectively uses facts or data to push a pet theory, it does not matter too much because in the long run other scientists will put matters straight. This may seem to some to be too optimistic. It can be argued that all treatment of data by scientists is selective. That is true as well, but it remains a fact that in an open society all the different selections of data compete with each other; and over a period of time, as the scientific community forms a consensus, some issues are resolved. For instance, in modern anthropology there is an emerging consensus that man had an African ancestry. This consensus is arising as more and more anthropologists become aware of the findings of palaeontology and molecular population genetics, both of which point to an African origin. The Asianists are gradually being defeated.

The details of just *how* man evolved in the African continent are still unclear. From Laetoli in Tanzania we have the evidence for bipedalism some three million years ago, in the form of fossilised footprints. Lucy, far off in Hadar in Ethiopia, had a pelvis more human- than ape-like at the same time horizon. These ancestors of ours, *Australopithecus afarensis*, were remarkable, with their ape-sized brains and ape-like heads but human-like bodies. Had this early hominid passed through an aquatic phase? We have no direct evidence either way. The circumstantial evidence is reviewed in this book.

THE EVIDENCE AND THE ARGUMENTS

Some substantive topics are reviewed below. These are not the only discussion points, by any means, but cover the main ground. Each is reviewed rather summarily to avoid repetition of what has gone before. The views expressed are entirely personal, as is the inevitable selectivity with which each topic is approached.

Bipedalism

As mentioned above, we know that our earliest hominid ancestors were already bipedal. There is some evidence from the bones of the foot of *Australopithecus afarensis* that tree-climbing may have been practised as well, and we would not expect to find bipedalism in its full-blown form in the earliest hominids, since evolution of radical new morphology and function takes time. Clearly, in order to establish this novel characteristic, a strong selection pressure has been at work in the period from 5 to 3 million years ago. There is no indication of bipedalism in the Miocene–Pliocene apes from which *Australopithecus* evolved. What, then, was this selection pressure? Those who favour the AAT find an explanation in the survival value of being able to stand upright in water, with feet on the bottom and only head exposed, thus enabling the early hominids to get into deeper water than their predatory pursuers. Also, locomotion in water is easier with an angle of 180° between legs and spine. Elaine Morgan has pointed out that amongst the birds it is the penguins, which have been selected for aquatic life, that stand most upright on land. AA theroists also point out that bipedalism, in its early stages, would be selected against, as inevitably there would be stumbling. Other savannah mammals all move quadrupedally, including savannah primates such as baboons, so clearly bipedalism is not an inevitable savannah adaptation – indeed, it is extraordinary.

What, then, were bipedalism's advantages? C. Owen Lovejoy (1981, 1988) has argued that bipedalism arose because it gave reproductive advantages to those hominids (*males* especially) who could travel widely from a home base and return carrying, using their hands, high protein foods (meat) for their own particular offspring. He envisages bipedalism evolving as part of a set of coevolving properties of early hominids, including social processes such as monogamy and home-base living. Nancy Tanner (1981) discounts the details of Lovejoy's scenario, which she claims is sexist anyway. She favours the idea that freeing of the hands was advantageous because it enabled individuals (especially *women*) to carry vegetable foodstuffs to a processing place, rather than just foraging as they moved around in the way that apes do. She considers that the invention of the basket was a crucial step forward for the hominids.

Quite apart from the freeing of the hands, Peter Wheeler (chapter 13) points out that there is an advantage to standing and moving bipedally in terms of reduction of heat loss and protection of the skin from sunburn during the heat of the day, because at midday the erect bipedalist exposes the minimum of his or her body to the sun (that is, to intense ultraviolet radiation). He points out that other African savannah species such as the ungulates deal with heat loss in two ways. First, they absorb heat in their bodies; and second, they have evolved a carotid rete – a cooling mechanism beneath the brain – absent in primates. We therefore cool our bodies in other ways, one of which is the exposure of minimal surface area to the direct rays of the sun. This idea is supported by the existence of copious hair on the top of the head – in the case of Africans, woolly hair – and this acts as a buffer both between the brain and the sun's heat, and between the skin of the scalp and the ultraviolet radiation.

Finally, mention should be made of the improvement in visual field that results from bipedalism. I have observed both chimpanzees and vervet monkeys standing bipedally to get a better view of distant objects in open conditions in Africa, and others have reported the same for many species of primates. We can well imagine that our early hominid ancestors might have gained considerable survival advantages to being able to see predators a long way away and take evasive action. Potts (1987) has indicated that the early Australopithecines were in all probability afraid of the savannah-adapted animals around them, of wild dogs, jackals and hyenas as well as the predatory cats. To this day some African prey species such as topi use hillocks to gain a better view of predators.

On balance, I would conclude that the arguments that bipedalism evolved on the savannah are stronger than those that it evolved in water.

Body hair

We do not know when our ancestors began to change the pattern of body-hair cover from its original ape-like form to the modern one. Apes have a lower density of body hair than humans, and their hair is longer than ours. If you look at an orang-utan, you will see that the hair is really quite sparse, but very long and orange–brown in colour. The hair of gorillas and chimpanzees is black, intermediate in density, and intermediate also in length. In man, hair colour varies from pale to dark, and it varies from one part of the body to another. It is characterised by very high density, especially on the head, and is of course extremely short over most of the body, although this varies from place to place, the Ainu of Japan being well known for their long body hair, and the well covered Europeans coming, in many cases, a close second. Africans and other Asians are the least hairy of humans today.

Elaine Morgan points out that there are several disadvantages to the substantial loss of body hair found in modern man. Life without body hair in a sunny climate gives rise to a high incidence of skin cancer, as Australians are currently finding out, and as expatriates living in the tropics have known for a long time. The explanation for this may, however, be in terms of light skin pigmentation rather than hair cover.

One of the best known correlations in anthropology is that which exists between skin colour and intensity of ultraviolet radiation. Quite possibly a covering of dark hair would give humans of any skin colour protection from the sun. But instead, skin pigment has been selected for. The argument that hair loss has led to skin cancers thus overlooks the question of skin pigmentation, for Africans have very little body hair and very low rates of skin cancer.

Two other arguments of Elaine Morgan's concern skin-scratching and slipperiness. She argues that hair cover protects the skin against the tearing action of thorns and other obstacles encountered on the savannah. Second, bare skin is poorly adapted to carrying babies, as, especially when sweaty, it becomes slippery and can lead to difficulties. She may be right about both of these points. Hair does have many advantages. Following Sir Alister Hardy, she stresses the fact that hair loss is of particular advantage in the water, so that all aquatic mammals have either very short hair or no hair. This point seems valid although, as Paul Leyhausen (chapter 10) points out, only *fully* aquatic mammals have become hairless, while a number of hairless mammals – for instance, rhinoceros and elephant – have become hairless without being in the least aquatic.

Peter Wheeler in fact reverses the argument, claiming that water mammals do in fact have body hair, which they use to reduce body heat loss by trapping a layer of warm water around the body, thus insulating themselves from the cold environment in which they live. Certainly it is true that some fully aquatic mammals such as sea-lions do have plentiful body hair. In humans the length and distribution of body hair is insufficient to achieve effective insulation in cold water. What, then, is the function of the small body hairs that cover the human body? Wheeler finds the explanation in increased efficiency of heat loss. When a human being is standing upright body heat is emitted by radiation and warm air then flows upwards around the body surface and disappears above the head. The small hair tracts around the body point downwards, and act to trap this air and slow down its vertical movement, which prolongs the time it takes for the sweat to evaporate, thus giving the body more prolonged cooling per unit of water used up as sweat. This is thus an argument for understanding body hair as a savannah cooling device. It would presumably be possible also to argue that body hair traps warm air around the body in cold conditions, so that it serves a dual function.

The arguments for seeing the fine covering of hair on the human body as a savannah adaptation rather than an aquatic one seem convincing.

Sweat

The human skin is characterised by a high density of sweat glands, higher than in any other primate species. These glands produce two kinds of sweat, apocrine and eccrine. Apocrine glands are activated by emotional stimulation, whereas eccrine glands are activated by body temperature. The latter are by far the most frequent, and testify to the intensity of natural selection during human evolution for the ability to produce copious amounts of sweat.

Elaine Morgan points out that sweating is not a wholly efficient way of losing heat. Sweating is slow to start, and a body can become seriously overheated before sweating has had time to get under way. Because sweating uses a large amount of body water, it is dehydrating just at the time when the body needs to conserve its moisture, because at times of dry heat water in general is in short supply. Other species such as camels and hamsters that are adapted for dry, hot conditions have evolved physiological mechanisms to retain body moisture; man, by contrast, is profligate with body moisture and as a result needs to drink large amounts of water each day in hot conditions. This must amount to a serious disadvantage in conditions of water shortage, such as are characteristic of large parts of Africa during the dry season. Sweating additionally excretes a large amount of body salts, which also need replenishing. It is known that humans who become seriously dehydrated are at risk from death as a result of thickening of the blood leading to failure of the circulation, and this could be expected to be a grave disadvantage to copious sweating.

Yet sweat we do. As always, advantages and disadvantages are weighed in the evolutionary balance. If the benefits of sweating outweigh the costs, then natural selection will enhance sweat mechanisms. Perhaps the most convincing positive argument of the AA theorists is that the salty component of sweat, which seems to have no advantage on the savannah, does provide a means of salt excretion for a sea-living primate, or a primate ingesting a lot of salt as a result of eating a diet of seafood.

For their part, the Savannah theorists point to the long-held 'bare-skin-and-sweat' hypothesis, whereby body heat is efficiently lost in the hominids by covering the body with a thin film of moisture which then evaporates, taking heat from the body surface and putting it into the atmosphere. We have already mentioned the role of small body hairs in achieving an economy of water loss. Sweating is a particularly efficient adaptation in two conditions: where there is a plentiful supply of water, and where the air is dry rather than moist. We know from findings of *Australopithecus*, *Homo habilis* and *Homo erectus* at sites such as East and West Turkana in northern Kenya that these early hominids lived in a lake-shore environment, where drinking water would not have been a scarce resource. We also know that the climate of East Africa was everywhere, except in the rain-forests themselves, inclined to be dry and hot. In such circumstances sweating can be readily understood as a primary adaptation to a savannah environment rather than an aquatic one.

Subcutaneous fat

One of the initial insights of Sir Alister Hardy, himself a marine biologist, which led him to formulate the Aquatic Ape Theory, was the observation that man, like the sea mammals he knew so well, has a distinct layer of subcutaneous fat. It is a fact that this layer is not found in any other primate species in the wild (though captive apes, deprived of exercise and wrongly fed, develop one). Wheeler points out, however, that the amount of subcutaneous fat found in humans is insufficient to keep the body warm for long in cold water. By comparison, aquatic mammals of human weight or greater have vastly more subcutaneous fat, enough in fact to round off their bodies, whereas the human body remains angular with long extremities, and is covered in a porous skin which is permeable by water and unsuitable for prolonged immersion, quite unlike the skin of aquatic mammals. These seem rather serious objections to the AAT.

Caroline Pond (chapter 12) has made a detailed study of the anatomy and distribution of fat in mammals, and has dissected numerous species, including primates. She finds that all primates, even those that look skinny and are disinclined to store subcutaneous fat, do in fact have fat depots in particular locations around the body. These adipose sites are essentially the same in primates as in other mammals. In some species, such as hedgehogs that hibernate in winter, fat storage is enormously increased in the pre-hibernation period. In other species this variation does not occur. The subcutaneous fat of humans is very largely a simple extension from the normal fat depots, which are located anatomically in the typical mammalian locations. This is in contrast with the situation in aquatic mammals, in which subcutaneous fat is not extended from local depots but exists as a continuously thick layer over the whole body.

There is another characteristic of human body fat, which is the sex difference in fat deposition. Women have, at least since the Willendorf Venus and doubtless well before that, accumulated fat around the buttocks and thighs, and on the breasts, to an extent matched neither by other primate species nor by male humans. This fat is of the same kind as other body fat. What is responsible for the extra deposits in particular peripheral locations in women? Caroline Pond suggests that sexual selection may be responsible, as well as natural selection. In other words, selection would favour not only fatter women at times of pregnancy and lactation, but also selective mating by males with women with these extra reserves. The buttocks, thighs and breasts may have been the most convenient or least costly places for such storage to occur.

Besides its function as a nutritional reserve, a subcutaneously distributed layer of fat must inevitably increase body temperature. We have been at some pains to explain how the bare-skin-and-sweat adaptation functions to keep the body cool; are we now going to have to explain the need for fat to keep the body warm? The answer is yes. There is no contradiction involved here. Hominids or humans on the open savannahs of Africa would find themselves experiencing very hot days, but night-time temperatures would be cool or even at times cold. Adaptations have to cope with all conditions, not just some of them. In the discussion of body hair, above, we concluded that such hair had both cooling and warming functions. The same is true here. While the bare-skin-and-sweat adaptative complex excels during the daytime it is not at all useful at night, when the fine body hairs become inadequate to the task of keeping the body warm, even though they make a contribution. Subcutaneous fat is much more effective as an insulator, and the thickness of the fat layer is optimally that thickness which keeps the body just warm enough at night while not interfering with heat loss during the day. As a result, adequately nourished humans have a thin layer of body fat; but as we know from experience, this can easily become a thick layer in conditions of idle prosperity, where almost none of the checks and balances of a natural way of life apply.

Overall, the arguments for an aquatic origin for human body fat seem weak or untenable, while the savannah arguments seem more convincing.

The 'diving response'

John Patrick (chapter 14) has shown that human beings have a set of rather specific respiratory adaptations for swimming and diving. First of all we have voluntary control of respiratory function: although our respiration is controlled automatically by the nervous system, we have a limited amount of control over it and can inhibit breathing for a short time, which can be increased by training. This enables us to hold our breath when diving. Further, the body's natural buoyancy while we are holding our breath ensures that we surface again. Breath control is also useful in swimming. The fastest method of swimming, known as the crawl, involves holding the breath for longish periods while the head is held face down in the water and the legs and arms propel the body forwards, and then breathing out and in again rapidly before beginning the next cycle.

What is perhaps most remarkable is the *reflex* closure of the human airway in water. It is not known whether this occurs in other primates, but the evidence suggests that it does not. In humans, experimentation by John Patrick has shown that it is the contact of the face with water that brings about this reflex. A person can be treading water up to his or her neck and the reflex does not occur. But if a person is wholly out of the water, with just the face placed in a shallow dish containing water, then the reflex occurs. It appears that there are receptors on the surface of the face that trigger the response. Nor is it just the closure of the airway that occurs: constriction of the bronchioles of the lungs occurs simultaneously. Finally, when the head emerges from the water, humans have a clear-cut gasp response, rapidly making up the oxygen deficiency. But Patrick concludes that these reactions in humans are 'slow in onset, small in extent, and not triggered by immersion in warmer water'; he therefore emphasises cortical control of breathing as the best evidence of aquatic ancestry.

These certainly do look like aquatic adaptations. It is unclear how any of the above would increase the fitness of a hominid for life on land. How do these human adaptations compare with those of aquatic mammals? The answer is that they have gone a good deal further than we have. Seals actually reduce their respiratory drive while diving. In this way they are able to stay under water for many minutes, far longer than any human can do. Nevertheless, we can see the human level of adaptation as a step on the way to aquatic adaptedness.

What conclusion should we draw from this? We know that some of our ancestors were living by the lake-shore at what is now Lake Turkana, from 3 million years ago. The fossil fauna there indicates that there may have been rich pickings in the lake itself. For instance, the carapace of a giant turtle has been found in hominid deposits at Lake Turkana. Such benefits, and others such as the availability of shellfish, crabs, slow-moving fish and maybe even young crocodiles (which live in this lake), could well have led to selection for individuals who were able to move efficiently in the lake waters, perhaps for an hour or two every now and then.

For a largely savannah-dwelling hominid, however, the water would inevitably have been a dangerous environment. Jan Wind (chapter 17) has pointed out that drowning remains a common cause of death at the present time; we have to learn to swim, it is not innate, and not all humans are able to learn it. Would we not expect swimming to be innate if it had been selected for as suggested above? As for the voluntary control of breathing, this might have been selected for in other contexts – for instance, in stalking prey or in connection with the evolution of speech. And it has been pointed out that holding the breath is essential in picking up heavy loads, as well as in diving.

All in all, however, the evidence here points to the presence of an aquatic element in the environment, and one which was important enough to bring about some selection for agility in the water. There are things here that the Savannah Theory cannot properly explain.

Marsh-wading

Derek Ellis (chapter 4) lays emphasis on the details of the ecology of the early hominids. He stresses that a marine shore environment can be one of the richest of all. There is plenty of good nutrition in such wetlands:

oysters, mussels, the eggs of marshland birds, and the possibility of capturing animals by driving them into the marshes from which they have no escape. He thus shows that there is an environment that is neither 'aquatic' nor 'savannah', but somewhere in between. A hominid exploiting this niche would not have to be a fine swimmer, nor a diver, and would have ample opportunity to keep cool in the heat of the day. Certainly this environment does need close consideration, but could it be a lake-shore marshland rather than a sea-shore one? That would seem to accord more with the facts. And the swimming and cooling adaptations that we see indicate a greater degree of adaptability of the hominids than a marshland habitat alone would produce, so that marshes may well have been a contributing habitat, and one that we should remember, but are unlikely to be more than this.

Location

Leon LaLumiere (chapter 3), an acoustic physicist with the US Navy, has mounted a clear argument concerning the whereabouts of the evolution of aquatic life in the early (pre-*Australopithecus afarensis*) pongid–hominid period. He posits a decline in the sea level some 5–4 million years ago in what is now the Danakil Depression in north-east Ethiopia, leaving exposed a large tract of land surrounded by water, which he calls Danakil Island. A relic group of pongid–hominids, isolated on that island, rapidly evolved a set of aquatic adaptations as they adapted to the new conditions, which included saltwater/freshwater marshland and the sea itself. Later, with further decline in the sea level, these water-adapted hominids spread south into the Afar triangle, where Lucy (*A. afarensis*) was found, and further still into the rest of East and South Africa. This scenario is appealing as an explanation of aquatic adaptations, if such an explanation is really needed. But in the absence of any fossil pongid–hominid evidence from the Danakil area it has no real substance, and further evidence would be needed before it could be taken seriously.

CONCLUSION

A number of other arguments exist on either side, but I shall not discuss them all; in any case, they are fully dealt with in the chapters of this book. All I have tried to do here is to pick out a number of key arguments, present them as fairly as possible, and then make a personal choice. Overall, it will be clear that I do not think it would be correct to designate our early hominid ancestors as 'aquatic'. But at the same time there does seem to be evidence that not only did they take to water from time to time but that the water (and by this I mean inland lakes and rivers) was a habitat that provided enough extra food to count as an agency for selection. As a result, we humans today have the ability to learn to swim without too much difficulty, to dive, and to enjoy occasional recourse to the water.

REFERENCES

Dawkins, R., 1986, *The Blind Watchmaker* (Harlow: Longman Scientific and Technical).

Harré, R., 1986, *Varieties of Realism* (Oxford: Basil Blackwell.)

Lovejoy, C.O., 1981, The origin of man. *Science*, **211**, 341–50.

Lovejoy, C.O., 1988, Evolution of human walking. *Scientific American*, November, 82–9.

Potts, R., 1987, Reconstruction of early hominid socioecology: a critique of primate models. In *The Evolution of Human Behavior: Primate Models*, ed. W.G. Kinsey (New York: SUNY Press).

Tanner, N.M., 1981, *On Becoming Human* (Cambridge: Cambridge University Press).

22 Epilogue: Is There a Future for the Aquatic Ape Theory?

This volume presents the first thorough published analysis of Sir Alister Hardy's Aquatic Ape Theory. The organisers of the AAT meeting in Valkenburg in 1987 feel that they assembled a representative sample of the broad array of existing opinions: both the advocates and the adversaries, as well as a number of uncommitted contributors in the middle. Readers are now invited to make up their own minds.

As editors, however, we feel obliged to give our own judgement on the theory, on the basis of the various contributions to this book. These are drawn from the standpoints of geology, palaeontology, palaeoanthropology, comparative zoology, primatology, evolutionary biology, morphology, physiology and methodology. We have attempted to remain as neutral and objective as possible, as none of us has previously dealt in any depth with the AAT, coming to it from our different disciplines but each with an interest in human evolution.

First, it is clearly impossible to provide a conclusive answer to the question of whether there was an aquatic ape. Second, the arguments for and against the theory are difficult to weigh against each other. We will not rehearse them all; they are summarised at the start of each chapter. Our general conclusion is that, while there are a number of arguments favouring the AAT, they are not sufficiently convincing to counteract the arguments against it.

Let us add three final points. First, all the participants appreciated the open attitude and the fair and friendly atmosphere that characterised the Valkenburg conference. All lent a willing ear to their adversaries. Second, it may well be rewarding to reconsider the issue once further evidence – for instance, from palaeontology – becomes available. Third, we are convinced that the whole undertaking – both the conference itself and the preparation of this book – has been well worthwhile. And it has certainly not been merely a rebuttal of the theory. We feel that its advocates, reproaching the anthropological establishment either for having refused to listen or for laughing it away, had the right to be heard and in turn to hear the counter-arguments. An important epistemological function of the introduction and defence of a somewhat far-fetched idea is the moral obligation imposed upon the scientific establishment to listen and not to shy away from reformulating its own position, and so to improve its own quality. This at least has been one positive outcome of the Aquatic Ape Theory debate.

Machteld Roede, Jan Wind,
John M. Patrick and Vernon Reynolds.

Index of Authors

Index of Subjects